Electrons, Waves and Messages

Electrons,
Waves and
Messages

By JOHN R. PIERCE

Drawings by Felix Cooper

HANOVER HOUSE, *Garden City, New York*

To Jeremy

Preface

CHAPTER I of this book tells what the book is about. I believe that it gives any introduction and guidance that the reader really needs. In retrospect there is, however, a little more, not strictly essential, to be added.

The title *Electrons, Waves and Messages* describes the chief content of the book: the science of electronics and the electronics of communication. The book also discusses scientifically related material, such as the heat of the sun, and communication theory and the arts; these digressions show the intimate relation of science and technology to the common world about us.

Within this general range, various topics were selected or rejected in an effort to produce a book with some reasonable degree of coherence and development. No doubt some things with which I am not very familiar could well have replaced some of the things which are in the book, but then it would have been a compilation from unfamiliar sources rather than a firsthand account; it would have been a different sort of book.

Among the things which are covered, the reader will find some more difficult to understand than others. This is partly a matter of familiarity; one can't grasp an idea until the concepts and terms used in expressing it have to some degree stuck in his mind. Perhaps re-reading will clear up some difficulties in understanding. It must be admitted, however, that some things appear really to be harder to understand than others. One can't very well omit all of the hard things without giving a very false view of electronics, and so I have included some of them.

Technically trained people may wonder about the choice of

material in particular chapters. Some points are explained in detail and others, equally important, are merely mentioned. This was done because it seemed impossible to give detailed explanations of more things, and yet I felt that important related matters should be called to the attention of the reader. When a matter is mentioned briefly, I have striven to give the reader a clear and generally correct impression rather than to produce an unambiguous and rigorous statement at the risk of being unintelligible. Some things, of course, have been omitted entirely—sometimes to limit the size of the book, and sometimes (as in the case of explicit mention of the concept of electric potential) for what I considered to be very good reasons.

Besides its technical content, the book sometimes cites names, dates, and stories about scientists or scientific discoveries. I have not knowingly erred concerning these, but I may nonetheless have erred. I don't think that any such errors could be important. The real content of the book is technical; other material is used chiefly either to locate discoveries in approximately the right era or by way of precept or parable.

The reasons for writing this book are given in Chapter I; briefly, they are enthusiasm for science, concern about current ignorance of science, and alarm about books which try to give an understanding of science without conveying anything of its content. This last seems to me like writing about the understanding and appreciation of music in some world in which most people have never heard a tune.

Of course it takes more than enthusiasm, concern, and alarm to produce a book. This book would never have been written had not Clarkson N. Potter of Hanover House asked me to write it and talked with me so sympathetically, intelligently, and constructively that the task seemed and was easy. But I would have been in no position to write a book if John W. Campbell, Jr., editor of *Astounding Science Fiction*, and, to a lesser extent, Anthony Boucher, editor of *Fantasy and Science Fiction*, had not encouraged me to practice writing by buying articles and stories from me over a period of years. Finally, this book would certainly have been less clear and less accurate without the help of friends and associates who read and commented on the manuscript.

My mentor and friend, Harald T. Friis, for whose knowledge of and contributions to microwaves I have unbounded respect and admiration, helped me to clarify and improve a number of sections. A. J. Torsiglieri, whose field (patents) is different from mine, pointed out many instances in which explanations which had satisfied me were actually obscure or difficult. He also found a number of numerical errors in my calculations. R. Bown, R. Kompfner, C. F. Quate, C. E. Shannon, and H. W. Lewis all made valuable comments and suggestions, and J. P. Molnar rendered an invaluable service in checking the figures when I was unable to.

CONTENTS

Electrons, Waves and Messages

CHAPTER I

Electronics and the World

WHEN I used to commute to New York by train, I passed a surprising number of technical enterprises: a pump company, an electrical-instrument company, a computing-machine company, and a lot of others. Now, as I occasionally drive to the city, I see more: a company making furnace controls, a tractor company, a company making potentiometers, a host of companies engaged in various sorts of engineering or scientific work. This makes me feel very ignorant and humble. After seven years of undergraduate and graduate study, followed by twenty years of research in an industrial laboratory, I know a good deal about a segment of one field, electronics. I have no detailed and expert knowledge about even most of the other work done in the company which employs me. Outside of that company, all sorts of things go on about which I have only the vaguest sort of information. With so much to know, is it not hopeless even for an expert to try to understand our science and technology? Is it not even more hopeless for an outsider to try to understand these matters? Should he try?

Literate and curious men of every age have thought and read and learned about matters outside of their immediate physical needs and experience. What they have thought and read and learned about has varied from age to age, as both the tasks of everyday life and the aspirations that go beyond these tasks have changed. Sometimes men have been concerned with religion, sometimes with mathematics and philosophy, sometimes with exploration, trade and conquest, sometimes with the theory and practice of government, sometimes with ancient learning, sometimes with the arts.

In different times, in different cultures, these matters have engaged the attention of the unusually able and intelligent men. When some of the best thought and best effort of a culture is spent in political philosophy, or in classical learning, or in art, the cultured man is the man who is acquainted with, and whose thought reflects, political philosophy, or classical learning, or art.

One can scarcely deny that the most effective thinking of our age, and a great deal of its energy and enterprise, go into science, and especially into the sort of science which guides an immensely complicated technology in doing new things and in doing old things cheaper and better. This prodigious technology in turn supports science with a lavishness unprecedented in any former age.

It is not only true that the world about us would astound a man of a much earlier age. It would astound a man of fifty years ago almost as much. He could not help being astounded by electric power, washing machines, dishwashers, freezers, highways, automobiles, radio, television, airplanes, rockets, nuclear energy. The widespread good living, the rarity of servants, the diminution of great luxury would astound him as much. If he looked more deeply, the growth of science—both in knowledge, in magnitude of effort, and in monetary reward and public recognition as well—would astound him.

The world of fifty years ago had writers, poets, painters, musicians, philosophers, politicians, and governments. No doubt all of these have changed of recent years. It is clear, however, that the great, the characteristic, the significant changes have been in science and technology and in the way the world is divided into countries and governed. We might even argue that the tremendous political upheavals of our age are primarily a consequence of a revolution in science and technology. Whether or not we go this far, it is clear that science and technology, together with political change and turmoil, are the outstanding features of our culture. Many would put science and technology first.

One cannot be in tune with his age without understanding some·thing of science, and yet this does not seem to have dawned on many people who consider themselves educated or, indeed, on professional educators.

The very things that enable a man to understand something of our culture—mathematics, physics, chemistry—are pared away from the curricula of grade schools, high schools, and colleges, to be replaced by generalizations and surveys. Men who profess to be educated flee frantically from the most significant feature of their culture and seek culture in almost any place but where it is to be found. It sometimes seems to me that writing, painting, and music have become weak, ineffective, and discouraged by seeking nourishment in the decaying remains of the past and ignoring the vigorous thought and achievement of the present.

Suppose we do grant that our science and technology are the great and important contributions of our era, the first things that men should know about when they look beyond the tasks and problems of the day and want to partake in some measure of the spirit and achievement of the times. Is it not hopeless to try to understand a science and technology so multifarious that no scientist can grasp all the details of more than a tiny fraction of it? I believe the answer to be no.

In the past there was less technology to understand. However, in the past technology was empirical art. The understanding of those who had mastered its skills and rules did not go beyond those skills and rules themselves. It seems to me that the outstanding feature of modern technology is that skill, rule of thumb, art, are rapidly being replaced or explained by science, by understanding. Engineering education, which waxes brilliantly while much of education flourishes dubiously, is continually being freed from detailed art and special knowledge to make way for more physics and mathematics, for more and wider fundamental understanding. The engineers who are graduated today are far better educated than I was twenty years ago. Their education is tougher, they learn more that is fundamental and broadly important, and they spend less time on special rules and tedious art. Engineering by handbook is not enough in the modern world. Handbooks last scarcely long enough to become familiar before they are outmoded. An engineer must understand and think to keep up with his art.

My specialty is vacuum tubes, and particularly microwave vacuum tubes. It is true that I have special knowledge, but this alone will not suffice. I find that in contemplating new problems in old tubes, and new tubes themselves, I am continually led into considering related and analogous problems in other branches of science and technology.

When I study the electromagnetic waves in a traveling-wave amplifier, I can easily go on and trace them out through the wave guide of a radar, to the antenna, and from the antenna into space, perhaps as far as a planet and back again. Understanding these waves, I can understand the sound waves in the air, the waves in the ocean, and waves of light. I can understand how small an object a biologist can see through his microscope, and how fine detail an astronomer can hope to see on the planet Mars. Through understanding the motions of electrons in a vacuum tube, I can understand the motion of the planets in their orbits and the paths that rockets may someday take through space.

No longer can any effective part of our science and technology be an island unto itself. Actual content overlaps the boundaries, and mathematical methods and physical concepts are shared widely. To know a part of science or technology well is to know something of the whole.

Thus, while I am astonished and dismayed at the total scope of the enterprises past which I ride or drive, I know that should I inquire concerning them I would find something familiar about them. I would find connected with them men who talk the language of science. The details of what they would say would be unfamiliar, but what they explained I could in some measure understand and appreciate.

This makes me want to tell these colleagues of mine something about my particular field of work. I am sure that what I have to say will be clear and interesting to communication and electronics engineers who have worked on problems somewhat different from mine. Beyond this, I am sure that I can speak intelligibly to scientific and technical men in fields very much farther from mine. But can I make myself understood to those whose backgrounds are not scientific, not technical? Can I convey to them also what seems to me to be important about science and technology, and especially about the particular field in which I work?

I think that this is possible, but only by being very clear and simple in what one says. I do not think that technical men are bothered by such simplicity, but I have a feeling that others sometimes are. Occasionally, when I have taken great pains to explain an important point to someone unfamiliar with science and have succceded, I am made to feel that I have failed in some way through my very success. The reaction to understanding finally achieved is sometimes "Oh, that is simple," with an implication that because it can be understood it can't be very important or profound. Such an attitude disregards the fact that brilliant men have failed for centuries to understand just such simple matters, and that only very brilliant men were finally able to make them clear and simple to us, the heirs to their insight.

There is of course another approach to the popularization of science. People sometimes learn from popular books how to string complicated scientific terms together in plausible sequences. None of us is entirely immune to a desire to astound others by a display of this sort. A friend of mine, a very good physicist himself, says that he can talk to "physicists" for as long as half an hour without being found out. By "physicists" he means those who work in newer and more recondite fields than his own. To get away with this sort of thing one must choose his phrases to suit the company. Pat phrases about relativity and the uncertainty principle may impress a lay audience. You had best leave them alone in the presence of physicists. If you are clever with your timing, you can stop a solid-state physicist in his tracks by saying, at the appropriate moment, "It all comes out in the Hamiltonian," or "Of course, it depends on the density of energy levels." With other physicists you must use other phrases.

While this approach may make one the life of the party, it is just as apt to mark him as a Mrs. Malaprop or a M. Jourdain. And, indeed, it may lead him to take for a luminary of science someone analogous to the Grank Turk of Molière's comedy.

There is no royal road to science. Those with little or no background can get only a talking knowledge of science by starting first with the most advanced, generalized and difficult aspects of modern physics.

Science has great generalizations. These are highly important and very moving to scientists, for in them the scientist sees summed up many particular phenomena with which he is familiar. Some scientists delight in treating a well-organized subject by presenting it first in its most generalized form and then deducing special instances. This, however, is not the way that things are discovered or the way that things can be learned.

Really to learn anything about science, one must start with simple things which can be easily grasped and understand these thoroughly in the terms of science. In this way the terms acquire precise meaning and become familiar. They come to call up real objects and experiences. For the professional scientist, the experiences may be experiences he has had in the laboratory. For those who have not and will not work in the laboratory, they must be experiences from his life and from his general reading. Once one has mastered some scientific terms and ideas and associated them with the world about him, he can go farther afield and study less familiar things and phenomena. As he learns, he will find all about him examples of what he already knows. He will, I think, really come to understand a part of science, though he will not, of course, equip himself to practice it professionally in competition with those who have spent more time in learning.

Many simple phenomena were understood by science centuries ago. Will one not be out of date in starting with this early science? I can reply only that among the scientific tools I use every day in doing research in electronics are Greek mathematics, eighteenth-century mechanics, nineteenth-century electricity and magnetism and twentieth-century relativity. I have even ventured a little into quantum mechanics.

Valid science is never old or out of date. It is only speculation about science, the "application" of science to philosophy, and false analogies between science and other matters that become old almost as soon as they are new. To understand the most recent advances in science without a background of the sound science on which they are built is as ridiculous as it is impossible.

This book is about electronics in a very broad sense of the term. It is not just about electrons in vacuum tubes, although there is a strong emphasis on this narrower aspect of electronics, which happens to be my field of work. Rather, it is about electronics in the sense of radio, of television, of sending messages across the continent or of detecting planes by radar. The aim of the book is not to present vivid pictures of the size, the cost, the complexity or the wonder of electronic devices or systems, but to give some idea of how they work. To achieve such an understanding, one must understand a variety of things.

Fundamentally, electronics is based upon an understanding of the physical world which gives us some control over it, that is, upon physics. Thus, the reader of this book will find a good deal of physics in it. Much of this will be old, because that is a part of the new. He will find Newton's laws of motion illustrated by the very problems Newton himself solved, but he will also see these laws used in explaining vacuum tubes which are scarcely in commercial use. He will find Faraday's lines of force in the latest electron devices. Ideas concerning waves which go back to Huygens will be found fundamental to the understanding of microwave antennas, but the propagation of such microwaves will be explained in terms of Maxwell's equations, which belong to the last century. Relativity is needed to understand linear accelerators and cyclotrons, and quantum mechanics to understand electron microscopes, electron-diffraction cameras, and transistors. The old and the new of physics mingle together in the newest electron devices.

Electronics in a broad sense includes more than devices, and more than physics. It includes putting devices together into systems to accomplish definite purposes. It would be hopeless to try in one book to explain all the things that electronics can do; this includes electronic computing and control devices of enormous variety and complexity as well as communication systems of many sorts. Because it is closest to my background, I have chosen to illustrate electronics at work chiefly in long-distance communication and in radar, though examples such as the electron microscope are given where they occur naturally.

Historically, men at first put complicated devices or systems together through a sort of intuitive insight, guided by experience. It is only later that they wonder why they did things in a certain way, and whether they might have done better. *Communication theory*, or *information theory* (the terms are synonymous) is the fruit of such pondering, and it occurs in this book in its due place; after the reader has gained through specific examples some insight into the sort of problems information theory tries to treat in a unified manner.

One thing about science is notorious; it often fails to solve the problem that one wishes to solve and solves some other problem easily. We will see that a microwave link to the moon, which we have no need or even opportunity to build, is much simpler than the microwave system which has been built to transmit television from coast to coast. It would be narrow and foolish to concentrate entirely on the bread and butter of electronics and to pass by interesting and sometimes romantic things which the principles we grasp bring within our understanding. Hence it is that some of the things I will discuss constitute a sort of visit to the relatives and something of a vacation.

In our survey of a part of the field of electronics, together with certain side tours, how much can one expect to learn about science and technology in general? Certainly, one will acquire no direct knowledge of biology or chemistry, for instance. He will learn very little directly about solid-state physics, which explains the electrical properties of solids (as in the case of transistors) and the mechanical properties of metals and alloys. He will learn nothing directly about nuclear physics. In the wonderful world of devices, he will find no discussions of aerodynamics, of heat engines, of rockets.

Yet, I think that the reader can get more from this book than merely the understanding of something of one part of science and technology. I think he can learn the sorts of problems that science tries to solve, what sort of things science can learn about such problems, and how such knowledge can be organized and applied to solve some of the problems of the world. The reader can, I hope, learn something of a way of looking at things, something of a frame of mind in which clear understanding even of small and particular problems is valued far above sweeping and appealing statements concerning unclear situations. It is only by approaching the problems of other parts of science and technology with such a background, such a frame of mind, that the reader can make sense of the science and technology of which there is nothing specific in this book.

There remains, then, only to go on to the following chapters. Here, perhaps some specific warnings are necessary. I think an expert in some other field of science or technology will have no trouble with any part of the book. I have tried to make the book intelligible also to the intelligent person whose background in science is almost negligibly small, either because he never learned much mathematics and science or because he didn't like what he learned and has long since forgotten it. Largely for such readers, I have included in the first few chapters material which the expert in another field may well want to skip over.

This material is certain basic, pre-quantum and pre-relativity physics; Newton's laws; electric and magnetic fields; and waves. With the chapter on Maxwell's equations, and perhaps even before, I hope even the expert in another field will find material that is new to him. The expert reader will have to judge for himself what he should read and what he should skip.

The person without scientific background should, however, make every effort to get through the first chapters first. The unpleasant part of swimming is getting into the cold water. The unpleasant part of skiing is the first few awkward tumbles. I am afraid that the chapters immediately following this one may be the least interesting ones in this book. It is essential to be familiar with their contents, however. One simply can't talk about electronics without knowing a few words and understanding a few concepts. Getting these may be painful, but it is necessary. I hope that the initial difficulty will not be too great.

There is another hurdle for the non-expert reader. Mathematics is in some degree essential to science. I have tried to explain things largely in words and pictures. However, I have written some things down in the form of equations. In many cases, the equations can be skipped with little loss, although they do enable anyone who might care to, to work out examples for himself. In some cases, as in the case of Maxwell's wonderful equations, the equations are the heart of the matter. In the chapter on radiation, the equations are very simple, and they enable one to make interesting calculations.

I have tried, whenever mathematics is necessary, to explain everything in the most elementary terms. Nonetheless, the notation is that of algebra, and this seems an appropriate place to say a few words about it to those who have forgotten some simple matters through years of disuse.

Letters are used to represent various quantities. I will illustrate this by the simple example of the area, A, of a rectangle of height h and width W.

We can say that the area, A, of a rectangle is the product of the height, h, and the width, W. This is the same as saying that A is h times W. Written out as an equation, the statement becomes:

$$A = hW$$

or

$$A = Wh$$

No multiplication sign is used. When one letter follows another, this means to multiply the two quantities.

If the rectangle is 2 feet wide and 4 feet high, we write:

$$A = (2)(4) = 8 \text{ square feet}$$

We use the parentheses as a sort of punctuation; we cannot write 2 times 4 as 24—that means twenty-four.

We sometimes say that a quantity, A, for example, varies *directly* as some other quantity, say, h. This means that the quantity A is something times h. In the case we have been considering, A is W times h, so that A varies directly as h. It also varies directly as W.

Division is always written as a fraction. Thus, the statement that h is A divided by W is written:

$$h = \frac{A}{W}$$

We would read this, "h equals A over W." In a relation like this, we say that h varies *inversely* as W. This merely means h is equal to something divided by W.

If the rectangle is a square, and the length of each side is l, then

$$A = (l)(l) = l^2$$

The symbol l^2 (l squared) is simply the product, l and l.

Sometimes we say that a quantity varies *inversely as the square* of another quantity. In the equation

$$F = \frac{g}{r^2}$$

the quantity F varies inversely as the square of r. In this case, if we double r, F is one fourth as great.

In the case of a square whose sides have a length l and whose area is A, we can write:

$$l = \sqrt{A}$$

This says that l is the square root of A. $\sqrt{A}$ multiplied by $\sqrt{A}$, that is, the square of the square root of A, is equal to A.

$$(\sqrt{A})(\sqrt{A}) = (\sqrt{A})^2 = A$$

In a numerical example,

$$(\sqrt{2})(\sqrt{2}) = (\sqrt{2})^2 = 2$$

The square root of 2 is approximately 1.414.

In using letters to represent quantities we sometimes use the same letter with subscripts to denote different quantities. Thus, if we had three circles of different radii, we might use

$$r_1, \quad r_2, \quad r_3$$

to denote the different radii. r_1 might be the radius of the first of the three circles, r_2 of the second, and r_3 of the third. Sometimes the subscripts are letters, as:

$$f_n, \quad f_p$$

Here n in connection with f_n may mean the component of the force f *normal* (perpendicular) to some direction, and f_p may be the component of force *parallel* to that direction. The meaning of these particular terms will be made clearer in Chapter II.

In the equations of mathematics and physics, certain numbers recur over and over again. The most common and the most venerable of these is represented by the Greek letter π (pi). It is the ratio of the circumference of a circle to the diameter of the circle. More often, we shall talk about the radius of a circle, or of a sphere, which we may call r.

If r is the radius of a circle, the circumference, S, of the circle is

$$S = 2\pi r$$

If r is the radius of a circle, the area, A, of the circle is given by

$$A = \pi r^2$$

If r is the radius of a sphere, the area, A, of the surface of the sphere is given by

$$A = 4\pi r^2$$

The number π is represented symbolically by a letter because it cannot be expressed in numbers with perfect accuracy, no matter how many digits we use. When we come to make calculations, we use an approximate value which is accurate enough. To three significant figures we can use for π either 3.14, or the old schoolboy approximation, 22/7.

Engineers and physicists make use of negative numbers such as -2 (minus 2) as well as positive numbers such as $+2$ (plus 2); $+2$ is also written simply 2. Negative numbers are used because negative numbers make it more convenient to describe physical quantities; height, for example. Instead of having to say 2 feet *above* or 2 feet *below*, we need use only one word, height. We can let a height of $+2$ feet mean 2 feet above and a height of -2 feet mean 2 feet below.

Suppose, for instance, we reckon height above the surface of the ocean. Suppose that we raise an object a feet and then b feet more; we increase its height, h, by $a + b$ feet, so we write:

$$h = a + b$$

Suppose as an example that we raise the object 10 feet and lower it 5 feet. We can use the same formula for its final height if we represent the raising and lowering by:

$$a = 10,$$
$$b = -5,$$
$$h = 10 + (-5) = 5$$

When we add a negative number to a positive number we take the difference and use the sign of the larger number.

What if we raise the object 5 feet and lower it 10 feet? We then say:

$$a = 5,$$

$$b = -10,$$

$$h = 5 - 10 = -5$$

This indicates that the object ends up 5 feet below the surface, which is just right.

The reader will have to take my word for the fact that, in order to get consistent results using negative numbers, we must say that the product of two negative numbers is a positive number, while multiplying a negative number and a positive number gives a negative number.

The use of negative numbers is a convenience. When we use them we don't have to use several terms, as, both *height* and *depth*, nor write the equations several ways for several cases.

In expressing large numbers, I have often said "a billion billion" or some such thing. Physicists write large numbers in the following way:

$$10^9 \text{ (ten to the ninth)}$$
(that is, 1,000,000,000, or one billion)

$$10^{-4} \text{ (ten to the minus fourth)}$$
(that is, .0001 or one ten-thousandth)

In the upper example, the exponent 9 means that 10 has been multiplied by itself nine times.

$$10^9 = 10 \times 10 \times 10 \times 10 \times 10 \times 10 \times 10 \times 10 \times 10$$
$$= 1,000,000,000$$

We see that the exponent 9 is also the number of zeroes. In the case of the negative exponent, the meaning is

$$10^{-4} = \frac{1}{10 \times 10 \times 10 \times 10} = .0001$$

The negative exponent tells how many times we divide by 10.

A particular number will be written as follows, using the $\times$ sign for multiplication:

$$2.38 \times 10^5 \qquad (\text{meaning } 238,000)$$

$$9.0 \times 10^{-2} \qquad (\text{meaning } .090)$$

We write 9.0 to show that the quantity is accurate to two significant figures. That is, we guarantee only that the value is nearer to 9.0 than it is to 8.9 or to 9.1; it might be 8.98 or 9.04, for instance.

There is one more matter connected with the equations in the text. Some rare reader may wish to use the equations to make calculations. While I mention a variety of units, such as feet, pounds, and centimeters, the equations are all valid in the M.K.S. (meter-kilogram-second) system of units. In an appendix at the end of the book these are related to feet, pounds, and other familiar units, and numerical values are given for various constants which are represented by letters in the equations quoted in the text.

CHAPTER II

The Laws of Motion

Two great universal phenomena which must be understood in order to understand electronics are the motions of particles—that is, very small bodies—and the motion of waves. Waves we shall consider in Chapter V. The particles with which electronics deals are chiefly electrons. These are tiny particles with a negative charge. Sometimes in electronics we deal with positive or negative ions. These are atoms or molecules which have lost an electron from their make-up, leaving a net positive charge (positive ions), or to which an extra electron has become attached (negative ions). In electronics, ions may be produced when electrons strike atoms or molecules. They may also be produced when short electromagnetic waves, such as ultraviolet light or X rays, strike the molecules of a gas.

In order to understand the motion of electrons or ions through the emptiness of a vacuum tube, we must have some understanding of the laws of motion, laws which govern not only the motion of electrons and of ions in vacuum tubes but all motions in the world about us and the motions of heavenly bodies as well: the motions of baseballs and automobiles, the motions of satellites and planets in their orbits, and the motions of the stars in their courses.

To one familiar with the laws of motion, they come to seem simple and obvious. Certainly they are not obvious, for they eluded thoughtful and intelligent men for many centuries. Indeed, recently, during a trip by air, the man in the seat next to mine marveled that when he dropped a pencil in the plane it did not fall behind on its way to the floor. I explained to him that in the seventeenth century Newton stated that a body continues at rest or in uniform motion in a straight line unless it is acted on by a force, and that this explained the behavior of the dropped pencil.

The laws of motion do not seem obvious except to those who are familiar with them, and, while they are simple, motion as we see it in the world about us certainly is not. This is because the objects we see about us are complicated and the forces which act on them are many and varied. The objects themselves are complicated in shape and structure, and they exhibit rotations and distortions in form as well as motion as a whole from place to place. Of the forces acting on them, some, like the gusty wind, vary with time; some, like the drag of water on a boat, vary in a complicated way with velocity; some, like the friction on a box dragged along the ground, vary from place to place. Thus, the most competent mathematician or physicist would be sorely puzzled to analyze in detail almost any everyday example of motion. It is for this reason that the laws of motion eluded natural philosophers for so long.

Even in relatively simple cases, motion proved difficult to understand. Our common experience is that all motion naturally tends to cease unless some mover maintains it. The motions of the heavens seem eternal. This led early philosophers rather to look for a prime mover as the cause of this motion than to regard the unceasing motion of the heavens as a clue to the understanding of sublunar phenomena.

There are, however, a few common examples of motion which can be understood in detail as well as in principle. Most of these examples are to be found in man-made machines; in automobiles, in airplanes, or in vacuum tubes. Perhaps the simplest and most beautiful are the motions of planets and stars, which wheel through the vacuum of space free of friction that would slow their progress and are acted on only by their mutual gravitational attractions. Among the most fruitful examples of motion which we can analyze are the motions of electrons in vacuum tubes, and we will talk about these in due time.

It is best, however, to proceed from the familiar to the unfamiliar. Henri Poincaré, who was perhaps the greatest mathematician of the latter part of the nineteenth century and the early part of the twentieth, pointed out that even in as abstract a science as mathematics one should cultivate an intuitive appreciation of concepts such as straightness, although one must check and guide intuition by formal proofs. It is even more important to have an intuitive feel for the laws of physics, so that they do not remain abstract patterns of words but rather call up a host of familiar instances of the actual observable behavior of physical systems.

To the professional scientist, many of these instances which make the laws of physics real are things with which he is familiar in the laboratory. To one who does not have a background of laboratory work they must come from the observable world about us. Hence, in introducing the laws of motion it is much better at first to consider familiar objects rather than such a tiny, unfamiliar, unseeable, and almost unbelievable particle as the electron.

Among the rare examples of simple and easily understood motions which we encounter in everyday life is skating. Skating offers a fine example of the laws of motion, for the friction which slows our progress is small, and we are willing to accept the pressure of the wind as a force to be accounted for separately. Too, the ice is level, so that the force of gravity does not enter into consideration. In fact, you slide on straight ahead, just as Newton asserted two centuries ago, unless some easily identified force changes your speed or the direction of your motion. When this happens, you can feel the force very clearly. Someone may push you from behind: you can feel him pushing; you observe that you go faster. You may run into someone. You feel the pressure that slows you down as you come to an abrupt stop.

If you are a little more skillful, you may suddenly turn your skates sideways, edge on. As you lean against the force of the ice on the skates, they shave the surface, and the sideways force of the surface against them brings you to a stop. If, however, the skates are turned less abruptly, you go around a smooth curve with undiminished speed; the force which you feel, and which causes you to lean lest it topple you over, changes the direction rather than the speed of your motion. If, while skating along past a smooth upright pole, you grab it and swing around it so as to reverse your direction, you feel even more strongly the force that changes your motion from that motion of constant speed in a straight line which, as Newton assured us, will persist unless a force acts.

When a body moves, at any instant it is moving in a particular direction, even if it is moving in a curved path. Fig. 2.1 shows the

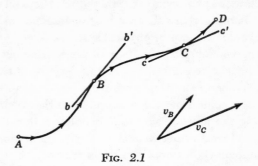

FIG. 2.1

path of a body moving from A to D. The arrowheads indicate which way the body is moving along the curve. Just as the body is passing some intermediate point, B, its direction of motion is the direction of b–b', the tangent to the path at the point B. The tangent is a line which just touches the curved path at one point, point B in this case. As the body passes some other point, C, the velocity will be in the direction of the tangent to the path at that point, c–c'.

At every point such as B or C the body has a speed of motion as well as a direction of motion. The speed of motion may be measured in feet per second, miles per hour, or some other units. We get this speed by dividing a small distance that the body moves by the time it takes to traverse that small distance.

When physicists speak of the velocity of a body, they refer not only to its speed at a point in its path but to its direction of motion as well. Physicists represent the velocity of a body, whether it be a human body, a planet or an electron, by an arrow. Two such arrows, v_B and v_C, corresponding to the velocities at points B and C, are shown in Fig. 2.1. The length of such an arrow is proportional to the speed, in feet per second, miles per hour, meters per second, or other units. The arrow points in the direction of motion. If the speed is doubled, the arrow is made twice as long. If the direction of motion changes, the direction of the arrow is changed. The motion represented by the arrow, and the arrow itself which represents the motion, are called *vectors*. Because the arrow represents the velocity of, say, a man or an electron, we are tempted to draw it with its head or its tail at the position of the man or of the electron. We can do so if we like, but usually, as in Fig. *2.1*, we do not. The arrow represents the *speed* and *direction* of motion, and *not* the *position* of the moving body. We can if we wish draw the arrow representing the velocity in a fixed place as the body moves about. In Fig. *2.1* the arrows or vectors v_B and v_C, representing the velocities at points B and C, have been drawn from a single point. This is just as reasonable as it would be to have (by remote radio control) a speedometer always in one place which would indicate the speed of a car as it traveled away across the country.

When the direction or speed of motion changes, the arrow or vector representing it will change in length or in direction. It cannot be said to change in position, for we can draw the tail of the arrow wherever we wish. In the left part of Fig. *2.2*, the arrow 1

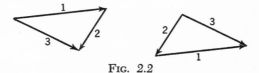

FIG. *2.2*

represents the original velocity of a skater. The arrow 3 represents the skater's velocity after he has slowed down a little and turned to the right. A third arrow or vector, numbered 2, has been drawn in Fig. *2.2*; its tail proceeds from the head of vector 1, and its head is at the head of vector 3. This vector 2 represents the change in velocity, both in speed and in direction, as the skater turns and slows down. The final velocity, 3, is called the *vector sum* of the original velocity, 1, and the change in velocity, 2. The vector sum of two vectors is always obtained by connecting the vectors, tail to head. The vector sum is then a vector with its tail at the free tail and its head at the free head, just as in the left part of Fig. *2.2*.

Suppose we added vectors 1 and 2 in the other order, placing the head of 2 to the tail of 1, as in the right of Fɪɢ. 2.2. Remembering that it is only the magnitude and direction of a vector and not its position that is important, we see that we get the same vector sum, 3, as in the left of Fɪɢ. 2.2. The vector sum does not depend on the order in which vectors are added.

Sometimes, one adds many vectors together to obtain a vector sum, as shown in Fɪɢ. 2.3. Here the vectors 1, 2, 3, 4 are shown

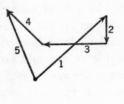
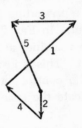

Fɪɢ. 2.3

added together in two different orders to obtain the same vector sum, vector 5. By one of the most elementary rules of geometry, two joined vectors always lie in a plane, or flat surface. When we have three or more vectors to add, they will not in general lie in the same plane, as they have been drawn in the simple sketch of Fɪɢ. 2.3.

The first of Newton's laws says that motion proceeds at a constant speed in a straight line unless a force acts. His second law says that when the velocity does change, the force that changes it acts in the direction of the change in velocity (in the direction of vector 2 in Fɪɢs. 2.2 and 2.3) and that the force times the interval of time during which it acts is proportional to the magnitude of the change in velocity, that is, to the length of the vector 2. Thus, a given force acting for a given time might cause the skater to turn without speeding up. In this case, the vectors representing the initial and final velocities and the change in velocity would look as shown to the left in Fɪɢ. 2.4. Or, the same force acting for the same time might cause the skater to speed up without turning, as shown in the right of Fɪɢ. 2.4. In each case, the change in velocity—that is, the arrow or vector 2—has the same length, which is proportional to the strength or magnitude of the force times the time during which it acts.

We can easily think of common examples in which a force changes only the direction of the velocity. For instance, when we swing a weight around and around at the end of a string, the string

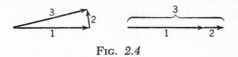

FIG. 2.4

must pull inward on the weight to keep it going in a circle. If the string broke, the weight would continue in a straight line (except that gravity would cause it to fall). If we want the weight to turn continually, and so to change direction continually, as it must in going around in a circle, we must apply a force normal (at right angles) to its direction of motion, and that is just what the string does.

We could, if we wished, fasten the string to a spring scale and measure the force needed to keep the weight circling. This is called the centrifugal force of the weight in its circular path.

The effect we see in whirling a weight about on a string is the same effect which we experience in a car going around a corner. Our body tends to continue on in a straight line, and it is only because the seat or door presses sidewise against us that we are able to turn with the car. The bicycle rider, the runner, the skater, lean when they turn so that the ground may not only support them but push them toward the center of the circle in which they turn. In the huge spinning bowl used as an amusement device, the walls push in against the people so that their velocities may be changed continually as they travel in a circular path.

We can also think of common examples in which a force acts to change the magnitude of the velocity without changing its direction. When a car accelerates on a straightaway, the wheels push against the road. In turn, the back of the seat presses against the driver's back in order that he may gain speed as rapidly as the car. In diving from the edge of a pool a swimmer gains speed by pushing back with his legs.

In all of these cases, the change of velocity is in the direction of the applied force and the magnitude of the change in velocity is proportional to the force times the time during which it acts. The change in velocity per second is called the *acceleration,* and Newton's second law states that the force required to produce a given acceleration of a body is the *mass* times the acceleration. This may be written as an equation:

$$f = ma$$

Here f is force, m is mass, and a is acceleration. If velocity is measured in feet per second, acceleration will be measured in feet per second per second.

The force of gravity, which causes a falling body to gain speed, offers another example of a force which can act in the direction of motion to increase the speed of a body. If we hang a body on a scale, we can measure the force of gravity; this is called the weight of the body, and it is proportional to the body's mass.

If we release the body, this force of weight causes the body to fall downward. As both the weight (which is the force accelerating the body) and the force required to give a body a given acceleration are proportional to the mass of the body, the acceleration of a freely falling body is independent of its mass. This is what Galileo may or may not have demonstrated at the Leaning Tower of Pisa. Disregarding air resistance, any falling body gains velocity at a rate of 32.2 feet per second for each second of fall. This acceleration of 32.2 feet per second per second is called the acceleration of gravity at the earth's surface.

The force of gravity, which causes a dropped body to fall, can also cause a body to curve in its path. When we throw a ball, it rises for a while and then begins to fall downward; the curve it follows is called a *parabola.* If an object were thrown upward fast enough it would rise forever and escape from the gravitational attraction of the earth. The velocity required is about 7 miles a second. Our rocketeers hope to demonstrate this some day. And the moon circles the earth, perpetually drawn from the straight path it would otherwise follow by the gravitational attraction of the earth.

It was, in fact, by means of the motion of the moon around the earth that Newton checked his idea of a universal law of gravitation. At first he was doubtful about his proposed law because the moon's distance was not known correctly, and the proposed law appeared to be wrong. Some twenty years later, the moon's distance was measured more accurately, and calculations based on these new data fitted Newton's law.

Because this example illustrates so beautifully both the laws of motion and the law of gravitation, it seems worth while to go through it in detail.

In order to understand the motion of the moon, we must state Newton's law of gravitation. Newton's way of stating this was to say that two particles of matter attract one another with a force which lies in the direction of the line connecting the particles and whose magnitude is proportional to the product of the masses of the particles and inversely proportional to the square of the distance between them.

A particle is a body so tiny that we can disregard its size and shape. The earth and moon are not particles, but Newton was able to show that a spherical body attracts another spherical body as if the mass of each sphere were located at its center. Thus, Newton's law applies to the earth and the moon, which are nearly spherical, if we measure distance center to center. We can state Newton's law of gravitation as an equation if we wish:

$$f = g \, \frac{m_1 m_2}{r^2}$$

Here f is force, g is a constant, m_1 and m_2 are the two masses, and r is the distance between them.

At the surface of the earth, the acceleration of gravity is 32.2 feet per second per second. According to Newton's law, twice as far away from the earth's center the acceleration would be 32.2 divided by 2 squared (which is 4), or 8.05 feet per second per second. The mean radius of the moon's orbit is 238,000 miles, while the earth's radius is 3,960 miles. At 238,000 miles from the earth's center the acceleration of gravity will be, according to Newton,

$$32.2 \left(\frac{3,960}{238,000} \right)^2 = .00892 \text{ feet per second per second}$$

Newton asked, does this actually correspond to the observed acceleration of the moon in its orbit?

The actual path of the moon is slightly elliptical, but we will consider it to be a circle with the mean radius of the ellipse, that is, 238 thousand miles or 1,257 million feet. The circumference of the orbit is 2π times this, that is, 7,900 million feet. The moon travels around this orbit in a period of 27.2 days or 2.35 million seconds. Thus, its orbital velocity is 3,360 feet per second.

As the moon moves around the earth, its velocity continually changes in direction. At full moon the moon is outside of the earth's orbit and is moving parallel to the earth in its orbit, and in the same direction. Seven days later, at the waning half-moon, the moon is moving toward the sun. Seven days later still, at the dark of the moon, the moon is between the earth and the sun and it is moving contrary to the direction of the earth in its orbit. Seven

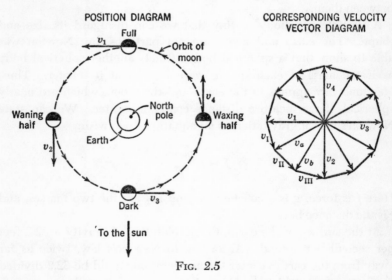

FIG. 2.5

days later still, at waxing half-moon, the moon is moving away from the sun. These successive positions of the moon with respect to the earth and the sun are shown at the left in FIG. 2.5. The diagram is drawn looking down on the plane of the moon's orbit from above the earth's north pole, that is, looking south. Arrowheads show the

direction of motion of the moon in its orbit, and a circular segment
with an arrowhead shows the direction of rotation of the earth.

I have also shown in the left-hand part of FIG. 2.5 vectors representing the velocity of the moon at each of four phases. These
vectors have their tails at the position of the moon at each phase.
This is allowable because the position of a vector may be chosen
as one wishes. Vector v_1 represents the velocity of the moon in its
orbit at full moon. Vector v_2 represents the velocity of the moon
at the waning half. Vector v_3 represents the velocity of the moon
at the dark of the moon. Vector v_4 represents the velocity of the
moon at the waxing half.

As the position of these vectors is purely arbitrary, in the right
of FIG. 2.5 I have redrawn the vectors v_1 through v_4 as radiating
from a common center. The diagram in the right of FIG. 2.5 is a
vector diagram representing *velocities*. The arrows do not show
the positions of the moon; these are shown in the corresponding
diagram of *positions*, in the left of FIG. 2.5. For each position of
the moon in the left of FIG. 2.5 the moon will have some particular
velocity, represented by an arrow radiating from the center of the
velocity diagram at the right of FIG. 2.5.

I have shown in the right of FIG. 2.5 vectors representing the
velocities of the moon at a number of intermediate phases as well
as at full, waning half, dark, and waxing half. Thus, as the moon
moves in the position diagram successively from the position at full
moon through two successive intermediate positions to waning half,
the corresponding velocities at successive positions are v_1 (at full),
v_a, v_b, and v_2 (at waning half), as shown to the right in FIG. 2.5.
The velocity v_a is the vector sum of the velocity v_1 at full and a
change in velocity shown as v_I in the right of FIG. 2.5.

At a later position, further toward that at waning half, the
velocity is the velocity v_a, plus a change in velocity, v_{II}, and so on.
Thus, the short vectors forming the twelve-sided polygon in the
velocity diagram at the right of FIG. 2.5 represent successive changes
in velocity as the moon moves between twelve successive positions
about the orbit shown to the left of FIG. 2.5.

If we showed the velocities at many successive positions instead
of at only twelve, the vectors representing the changes of velocities

between successive positions would be very short and would very nearly form the circumference of a circle. The radius of this circle, the magnitude of v_1, and of v_2, and of v_3, and of v_4, and of all other intermediate velocities at various orbital positions, would be the speed of the moon in its orbit. This speed is 3,360 feet per second. The circumference of the velocity circle would represent the sum of all the changes in velocity the moon experiences in moving clear around the orbit, successively changing from one orbital position at one time to another orbital position a short time later. This total change in velocity is clearly 2π times 3,360 feet per second, that is, 21,100 feet per second. This change in velocity takes place in one orbital period of 235,000,000 seconds. Thus, the change in velocity in feet per second per second is 21,100 divided by 235,000,000; this is .00899 feet per second per second. This is the constant acceleration which the moon experiences as its velocity continually changes in direction while it moves around its orbit.

The figure .00899 feet per second per second is very close to the acceleration of gravity at the moon's position, which, by using Newton's inverse square law, we earlier computed to be .00892 feet per second per second. According to Newton's second law, the acceleration of the moon in its orbit should be equal to the acceleration of gravity at the moon's position. The small discrepancy is accounted for by inaccuracies in our assumptions. The moon does not actually revolve about the earth's center, but about the mutual center of mass of the moon and the earth, which lies within the earth but a little toward the moon. Further, the moon's orbit is not exactly circular.

When we look back to see what we have done, we see that the acceleration of a body in a circular orbit can be written in several forms; for instance:

$$a = \frac{2\pi v}{T} = \frac{v^2}{r} = \frac{(2\pi)^2 r}{T^2}$$

These various forms, which involve the orbital velocity v, the orbital period T, and the orbital radius r, are related by the fact that the velocity is the circumference of the orbit divided by the orbital period; that is,

$$v = \frac{2\pi r}{T}$$

Through astronomical observations and by the application of Newton's laws we can measure the masses of the planets which have satellites. To see how this may be done, let us consider a particular case. Astronomical observations tell us that Jupiter's satellite Io is 262,000 miles, or 1,380 million feet, from the center of Jupiter and has an orbital period of 1.77 days, or 153 thousand seconds. The acceleration, $(2\pi)^2 \ r/T^2$, is thus 2.34 feet per second per second. This must be the acceleration of Jupiter's gravity at Io's orbit.

At the surface of the earth, 3,960 miles from the center, the acceleration of the earth's gravity is 32.2 feet per second per second. At the same distance from earth as Io is from Jupiter, by Newton's inverse square law of gravitation the acceleration of the earth's gravity would be .00736 feet per second per second. Our observations have enabled us to calculate that the acceleration of Jupiter's gravity at this same distance from Jupiter is 2.34 feet per second per second, or 318 times as great. Newton's law of gravitation tells us that the acceleration of gravity at a given distance from an object is proportional to the mass of the object, so we conclude that Jupiter's mass must be 318 times as great as that of the earth.

Newton's laws of motion and of gravitation changed astronomy from an empirical to a theoretical science. Newton showed that Kepler's laws governing the motions of the planets in their elliptical orbits are consequences of the laws of motion. The open parabolic orbits and hyperbolic orbits in which some comets approach the sun and leave it again, never to return, were deduced from Newton's laws. By the beginning of the nineteenth century, Laplace had shown that the planets are stable in their orbits about the sun despite the perturbing forces they exert on one another, and the solar system seemed to be reduced to an eternal, frictionless machine.

Today, save in exceptional cases involving relativity, astronomers no longer test Newton's laws; they use them. They use them to calculate the motions of stars, planets, satellites and comets, and to explain such phenomena as tides. Some astronomers are now busy calculating the unusual orbits which space ships and artificial satellites will follow if we ever build such devices.

We have come a great way in understanding the laws of motion; in fact, we have covered most of what we need to know in understanding how electrons travel through vacuum tubes. There are, however, vital things which we have not discussed, and which it would be a shame to miss.

Newton's first law of motion states that a body remains at rest or in motion in a straight line with constant velocity unless it is acted on by a force. Newton's second law states that when a body is acted on by a force, the change in velocity lies in the direction of the force, and the magnitude of the change in velocity is proportional to the period of time during which the force acts times the force (the change will be twice as great for the same mass if we double the force) and is inversely proportional to the mass (the change will be half as great for a given force and time if we double the mass).

Newton had something else to say about motion. He said in his third law that every action has an equal and opposite reaction. By this he meant that if a body A exerts a force on a body B, then body B exerts an equal and opposite force on body A. If I push a skater, who feels a force pushing him ahead, I feel the skater's back pushing back against my hands. The same principle is illustrated by the kick of a gun when it shoots out a bullet. If I am gliding on skates and bump into the back of another skater who is going in the same direction, a force acts which speeds him up, and an equal and opposite force acts which slows me down.

The product of the mass of a body times its velocity is called the *momentum* of the body. The momentum is a vector, just like the velocity, and it has the same direction as the velocity. From Newton's laws of motion, including the equality of action and reaction, a *theorem* called the *conservation of momentum* can be proved by mathematical manipulation. This theorem states that if we consider together all of a set of bodies which exert forces on one another, and if we add the *momenta* (plural of *momentum*) of all of these bodies, the vector sum of these momenta, which is the momentum of the system as a whole, is a constant, and does not change during all the complicated motions which the mutually interacting bodies undergo. Should we momentarily intervene from outside and push any one of the interacting bodies so as to change its momentum, the momentum of the system is changed by the same amount, and the new momentum is henceforward conserved.

The conservation of momentum is a fundamental and vital part of physics. With the years, it has been generalized to include the non-mechanical momentum of electromagnetic waves. The conservation of momentum will not concern us much in connection with simple motions of electrons, because we are usually interested only in the tiny forces necessary to change the motions of electrons themselves in the manner we desire. We are little interested in the forces which the electrons exert in return. The case is a good deal like that of jumping straight up from the surface of the earth. The conservation of momentum tells us that when we attain a certain upward velocity and upward momentum, the earth must move downward with such a velocity as to give it an equal and opposite momentum. The earth is very massive compared with you or me, and as momentum is mass times velocity, the velocity with which the earth moves down when you or I jump up is very small; ordinarily, we simply disregard it. In the same way, a vacuum tube is much heavier than billions of electrons, and we don't worry about the forces that the electrons exert on the structure of the tube.

Equally important with the conservation of momentum is the *conservation of angular momentum*. When the moon moves around the earth, the magnitude of its angular momentum is its distance from the earth times its mass times its velocity in its orbit (assuming the orbit to be circular). More generally, for non-circular motion, to obtain the angular momentum of a particle about a given point we first connect the point and the particle with a straight line. We then find the component of the particle's momentum normal to this line, and we multiply this component of momentum by the length of the line; this gives the magnitude of the angular momentum. The meaning of *component* will be made clear shortly. Angular momentum is a vector, and its direction lies normal to both the line connecting the point and the particle and to the component of momentum normal to the line. Thus, the vector representing the moon's angular momentum about the earth lies normal to the moon's orbit.

Like linear momentum, the angular momentum of a system of bodies acting on one another is conserved. If we broadjump west to east, we gain a certain angular momentum, and the earth slows in its rotation from west to east just enough to lose an equal amount of angular momentum.

When a skater whirls about, arms outstretched, and then draws his arms in, he spins faster. This is because angular momentum is conserved. Since the angular momentum of his arms is proportional to their velocity times their distance from the center of rotation, when the skater draws his arms closer to his center of rotation they must move faster in order for the product of velocity and radius to remain constant. Acrobats hanging by their teeth also speed up their whirling by drawing in their arms.

It is perhaps more striking to note that the angular momentum of the moon revolving about the earth plus the angular momentum of the earth turning on its axis is conserved. The friction of the tides which are caused in the earth's seas by the pull of the moon continually slows down the rotation of the earth. This continually speeds up the revolution of the moon in its orbit. This speeding up causes the moon to recede from the earth at a rate of 5 feet per century. Eventually, the rotation of the earth and the revolution of the moon will have the same period. Thereafter, the smaller solar tidal effect, which we have hitherto disregarded, will slow the common speed of revolution and rotation, and the moon will slowly fall toward the earth. This event lies so far in the future that it need not seriously concern us.

Angular momentum is also extremely important in connection with nuclear physics. Each elementary particle of physics, such as the proton and the neutron, has an angular momentum called *spin*. Total angular momentum, that is, the total spin, plus the angular momenta of particles with respect to one another, as well as the total linear momentum of the particles in their motions, must be conserved in nuclear reactions in which particles and photons change bewilderingly into other particles and photons.

We have dealt with the dynamics only of particles, that is, of tiny bodies of negligible dimensions. When many particles are held rigidly together, the motion of the whole consists of *rotation* as well as of *translation*. The astonishing behavior of the gyroscope is an example of a rigid body following Newton's laws of motion. The reader will have to look elsewhere and to think very hard in order to understand this and many other intriguing aspects of the motion of rigid bodies.

While we will be little concerned with the conservation of momentum and the conservation of angular momentum in connection with electronic devices, there is another law that can be deduced from Newton's laws of motion which we cannot disregard. This is the law of conservation of energy.

In order to understand the law of conservation of energy we must know what a *component of velocity* is. Suppose that vector v in FIG. 2.6 is the velocity of a body at some instant. Suppose that vector f of FIG. 2.6 is the force acting on the body. We can represent f as the sum of two vectors f_p and f_n which, added vectorially, equal f. These two vectors f_p and f_n together *are* the force—for, added, they are equal to the force f; this is as true as that 2 plus 3 is 5; $2 + 3$ is just another way of writing 5, and f_p plus f_n is just another way of writing f.

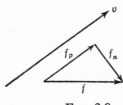

FIG. 2.6

In FIG. 2.6, f_p and f_n have been chosen so that the component of force f_p is parallel to the velocity v, and the component of force f_n is normal to the velocity v. f_p is the component of the force f which acts in the direction of motion of the body, and f_n is the component of the force f which acts normal to the motion of the body. f_p acts to speed the body up; f_n acts to turn the body in its path without changing its speed. The force may be so directed that the component parallel to the velocity points in the opposite direction from the velocity, as shown in Fig. 2.7. The component f_p may then be said to be negative, and it acts to slow the body down.

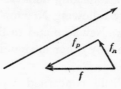

Fig. 2.7

In mechanics, *work* is defined as force exerted in direction of motion times distance of motion. Work is the component of force in the direction of motion, f_p, times the distance the body moves while the force acts. The force f_n does no work on the body, because the body does not move in the direction in which f_n acts.

Think of an example. When a body whirls about at the end of a string, the string exerts a force normal to the direction of motion. We don't have to do work in applying this force; we could merely tie the string to a fixed pivot.

When we push a skater ahead, however, we exert a force in the direction of motion. We speed the skater up, and we do work (and get tired) in doing this.

The earth does no work on the moon in holding it in its orbit, but it does do work on a falling apple as the apple falls.

Work is force in the direction of motion times distance moved. We can write it:

$$W = f_p l$$

Here W stands for work, f_p for force in the direction of motion, and l for distance moved. Work done on a freely moving body changes its speed.

We can define a quantity called the *kinetic energy*, E_k, of a body:

$$E_k = \tfrac{1}{2}mv^2$$

Here m is the mass of the body and v is the magnitude of its velocity. It can be shown from Newton's laws that the change in the kinetic energy of a body is equal to the work done on it.

What does the work? When a sliding or rolling body slows down, it loses kinetic energy; it does work against the force of friction. When a body falls toward the ground it gains kinetic energy. The work is done on the body by the force of gravity. If we lift a fallen body to its original height we have to do work, an amount of work equal to the kinetic energy it gained in falling. In lifting the body, we give it *potential energy*. If it falls again, this energy is changed to kinetic energy.

When we draw a bow, we do work, which is stored in the bow as potential energy. When we release the string, the string does work on the arrow; the potential energy of the bow is gone and the arrow has an equal (for a 100%-efficient bow) amount of kinetic energy.

All of this can be derived from Newton's laws of motion. It can be applied directly to the motions of electrons. We now know of many sorts of energy with which Newton was unfamiliar: thermal energy, electromagnetic energy, nuclear energy. The law of conservation of energy has been generalized to include them all. In reckoning up all the energy, kinetic energy and mechanical work still appear in their familiar forms. When an electron is accelerated, its kinetic energy, which is one half the product of its mass times the square of its velocity, increases. This increase is equal to the work done on the electron—the component of force acting in the direction of motion times the distance over which the electron moves while the force acts. To increase the kinetic energy, energy must be supplied from some source, though it be from a source never dreamed of by Newton.

CHAPTER III

Electric Fields and Electrons

Ions and electrons are called *charged particles:*
particles because they are small, and *charged* because an electron
or an ion has an *electric charge,* a quantity of electricity, associated
with it.

Two charged particles at rest act on each other with an inverse-
square law of force just as do two gravitating masses. The differ-
ences are that the magnitude of the force is proportional to the
product of the charges, not of the masses; that like charges (two
positive charges or two negative charges) repel one another and
unlike charges attract one another; and that electric forces are much
stronger than gravitational forces.

The interaction of charges in motion and the way in which this
interaction depends on the velocities of the charges are very complicated. Moreover, electrons, unlike planets, are far too numerous
in practical devices for us to reckon their mutual interactions individually. How, then, are we to deal with the forces on electrons?

Michael Faraday, a great physicist of the nineteenth century,
knew almost no mathematics. He was puzzled about the interaction of charges and of currents of electricity (particles of electricity such as electrons had not been discovered in his day). He
sought some graphic way of representing the nature of the forces
he found, and he hit on the idea of electric and magnetic fields,
represented graphically by lines of force. To understand anything
about electronics, we must understand something about electric
and magnetic fields.

Fields have become a prized and universal tool of physics. They
can represent gravitational forces as well as electric forces. Because

we have already discussed gravity, it will be easiest first to illustrate fields in the case of the gravitational field, and to see how this is connected with Newton's inverse-square law of force.

We really define what we mean by a "gravitational field" by saying that in a gravitational field an object experiences a force. The magnitude of the force is given by the product of the strength of the field and the mass of the object. The direction of the force is given by the direction of the field.

The gravitational field of a single spherical body like the earth or the sun is everywhere directed toward the center of the sphere. The strength of the field is proportional to the mass of the body, m, and inversely proportional to the square of the distance from the center, r. Thus, the strength, F, of the gravitational field of a mass m is written:

$$F = \frac{gm}{r^2}$$

We can, if we like, represent the field pictorially by drawing gravitational lines of force. These come in from infinity toward the center of the object, as shown in Fig. *3.1*. Of course, the figure

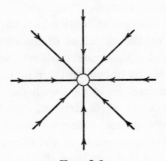

FIG. *3.1*

is a flat picture and shows the lines in one plane only, but we can imagine lines of force coming in from all directions, like the toothpicks stuck in a grapefruit to support canapes.

The gravitational field at any point is a vector; that is, it has direction and magnitude. We should not, however, confuse the lines of force with vectors just because I have put arrowheads on them in

FIG. *3.1* to show their directions. The lines of force are merely a picture of the field. They may be, and usually are, curved, although they are straight in the simple case we have been discussing. The direction of the lines of force is at each point the direction of the field, which is a vector.

In FIG. *3.1*, we can draw in as many lines of force as we wish. However, we will note that the lines of force get farther apart the farther away we go. Let us imagine a spherical surface a distance *r* from the center of the mass which produces the gravitational field and its lines of force. The area of the surface of the sphere is $4\pi r^2$, so we see that the number of lines of force which cross a given area—one square meter, or one square foot, or one square mile—is inversely proportional to the square of the radius. Thus, if four lines of force cross an area of a square mile at a distance of 10,000 miles from the center of the earth, one line of force will cross each square mile at a distance of 20,000 miles from center of the earth, since the square of 1,000 divided by 2,000, that is $(1,000/2,000)^2$, is $\frac{1}{4}$.

Newton said that the gravitational force is directed toward the attracting mass and is inversely proportional to the square of the distance. That means that it is directly proportional to the density of lines of force which is, in our picture, the number of lines of force which cross a unit area. Thus, our lines of force give a very complete picture of the gravitational field. Not only do they show the direction of the force it produces on masses, but their density gives the strength of the field, that is, the magnitude of the force.

What of the gravitational field of many objects? Like velocity, the gravitational field of a body at a given point has magnitude and direction, and we can represent it by an arrow or vector, just as we did in the case of velocity. For instance, suppose that in the left part of FIG. *3.2* the vector *A* represents the gravitational field of planet *a* at a given point, while *B* represents the gravitational field of planet *b* and *C* represents the gravitational field of planet *c*. The total gravitational field at the point is the vector-sum *D* of the individual field vectors *A*, *B*, and *C*. Thus, if we know the field at every point produced by the masses individually, we can get the total field at every point by vector addition.

While we can find the field produced by a number of bodies by adding vectorially the fields produced by each, this is impractical in many cases. Faraday showed that electric and magnetic fields obey certain general rules, however they are produced, and Maxwell later expressed these mathematically in the wonderful equations which describe completely the behavior of electric and magnetic fields. We will encounter these in Chapter VI.

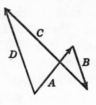

FIG. 3.2

Nowadays we think of fields as things in themselves, of which the form is specified, and which fully represent the forces which bodies will encounter at various points in space. The lines of force of a complicated field may be very complicated curves, yet the strength of the field at any point is proportional to the density of lines of force at that point. Thus, the representation of a field by lines of force gives a striking picture of its properties.

Fields are very important to us, because it is in terms of fields that the forces on electrons are expressed. Like skaters and planets, electrons obey Newton's laws of motion. When a force acts in the direction of motion of an electron, the electron speeds up; when a force acts against its direction of motion, it slows down; and when a force acts exactly normal to (perpendicular to, at right angles to) its direction of motion, the electron turns without changing speed.

The force acting on a skater may be a friendly push, a gust of wind, or the friction of his skates on the ice. The force acting on a star or on a planet is the gravitational attraction of other celestial bodies. From a slightly different point of view, we say that it is the force due to the gravitational field of these bodies.

Electrons are acted on by electric and magnetic fields. Electrons and currents of electrons produce electric and magnetic fields, and we express the forces that they exert on other electrons in terms of the fields themselves.

Let us consider electric fields first, and leave magnetic fields until later. Electric fields are very closely akin to gravitational fields. The action of the electric field on an electron is analogous to that of a gravitational field on a mass. Because the charge of an electron is negative, the force on an electron is in the opposite direction from the direction of the electric field. However, when I put arrows on electric lines of force in this chapter these arrows will indicate the direction in which the electric field pushes an electron. The same field would push a positive particle, such as a proton or positron, in the opposite direction, which is truly the direction of the electric field. The magnitude of the force is given by the product of the strength of the electric field and the charge of the electron.

The astronomer who deals with gravitational fields is confronted with particular fields that already exist in a world he never made. His problem is to calculate the motions of heavenly bodies in these fields. The problem of the electronics engineer is quite different; it is to produce inside of a vacuum tube fields which will cause electrons to go where he wants them to go and to do what he wants them to do. He is fundamentally a maker of universes, on a small scale of course, rather than a student of a universe already given.

The electronics engineer produces the electric fields which he desires by applying a voltage between electrodes, that is, pieces of metal which conduct electricity.

A conductor is full of electrons which are free to move within the conductor but in general cannot escape through its surface. It also contains fixed positive charges equal in total charge to the charge of the free electrons. Suppose we tried to produce an electric field in a conductor. If we succeeded in producing such a field, the field would cause the electrons in the conductor to move. They would move into such a pattern as to reduce the electric field. They would move into some regions, causing an excess of electrons and a net negative charge in those regions, and they would move away from other regions, leaving a net positive charge in those regions. These charges would tend to reduce the field, and when the field finally became zero the electrons would cease to move. Hence, there is never any electric field inside of a conductor.[1]

If we connect one electrode to the positive terminal of a battery and another electrode to the negative terminal of a battery, there will be an electric field between the two electrodes, and this field will exert a force on any electron in it. The general direction of the force will be away from the negative electrode and toward the positive electrode.

The field extends right up to the surface of the electrodes. A fundamental law of electric fields is that very near the surface of an electrode—that is, a conductor, any piece of metal—the direction of the electric field must be normal to the surface of the conductor. The electric field exerts a force on the electrons near the surface of the conductor. If the electric field is normal to the surface, this force is straight inward or outward. An outward force draws an excess of electrons to the surface. An inward force pushes the electrons in from the surface and leaves an excess of positive charges. If, however, there were a component of the electric field parallel to the surface, it would cause the electrons to slide along parallel to the surface just inside the conductor, and this would so rearrange the electrons as to change the electric field so as to make it normal to the surface of the conductor at all points.

Thus, we have two important rules or laws concerning electric fields: (1) there is no electric field within a conductor; (2) the electric field just outside of a conductor is always normal to the surface of the conductor.

Let us consider the sort of conducting electrodes that may be used in a particular type of vacuum tube. The simplest form of vacuum tube is the *diode*. FIGURE 3.3 shows the parts of a diode. The drawing does not resemble closely an actual practical diode such as one will find in a TV set. Such a diode is very compactly made and a drawing of it would be confusing.

[1] This is strictly true only for perfect conductors. A feeble electric field can be maintained even in a good conductor like copper. Such a field causes a continual strong flow of electrons, that is, an electric current, through the material. The electrons heat the copper by continually bumping into imperfections, and electric energy must be supplied continually to maintain the field.

The two electrodes of the diode are the *cathode* and the *anode*. In FIG. 3.3, the cathode is a sort of rectangular pipe or sleeve made out of thin nickel and coated on the outside with a mixture of barium and strontium oxides. The purpose of the coating is to make it easy for electrons to leave the cathode when it is heated. The cathode is heated by an internal electric heater of tungsten

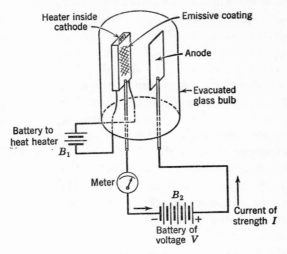

FIG. 3.3

wire. In the drawing, power from battery B_1 heats the heater and the heater heats the cathode. When the cathode is hot, the electrons inside it rush about with increased velocities, and some are able to pass through the surface of the cathode and into the vacuum inside the glass envelope.

The anode is simply a flat piece of metal. When the anode is held positive with respect to the cathode, as it is by battery B_2, of voltage V, in FIG. 3.3, there is an electric field between cathode and anode, and the electric field is such as to force electrons toward the anode. Thus, when the anode is positive with respect to the cathode, an electric current flows between anode and cathode and through the external circuit, that is, the wires connecting the battery to the anode and the cathode, and through the battery itself.

In FIG. 3.3, the direction of the current is indicated by arrows next to the wires. The arrows point away from the positive (+) pole of the battery and toward the negative (−) pole. Long ago, the direction of electric current flow was defined as being from positive to negative. Actually, in wires and in diodes the electric current consists of electrons moving in just the opposite direction, from negative to positive. However, the old definition persists, and the convention is that current flows from positive to negative.

Nonetheless, the electrons flowing from cathode to anode constitute the electric current between anode and cathode. The strength of this current might be reckoned by the number of electrons which leave the cathode each second. Actually, the current of electrons is measured in *amperes*. A current of one ampere means 6.3 billion billion (6.3 × 10^{18}) electrons per second. While we cannot count the electrons leaving the cathode and striking the anode, we can connect an *ammeter* (which measures amperes), a *milliammeter* (which measures thousandths of amperes) or a *microammeter* (which measures millionths of amperes) between the cathode and the negative terminal of the battery. Then, all the electrons emitted by the cathode, which are supplied to the cathode from the negative terminal of the battery, must pass through the meter. The meter in effect measures the number of electrons which pass through it each second, reckoned in amperes, milliamperes (thousandths of an ampere) or microamperes (millionths of an ampere).

How much current flows when a given voltage, V, is applied across the diode? If electrons are emitted copiously from the cathode, not all those emitted reach the anode, for as the negative electrons move out toward the anode they produce an electric field opposite to that produced by the positive anode, a field that tends to prevent electrons from leaving the cathode. Thus, when a given voltage, V, is applied to the anode, a particular current, I, flows, a current such that near the cathode the *space charge* of electrons flowing from cathode to anode just counteracts the field due to positive anode. For a given voltage, more current will flow per unit area of cathode if the spacing between cathode and anode is small, so that there is little room for space charge.

Suppose we start out with the anode negative with respect to the cathode. No current will flow, because the field is such as to force electrons back toward the cathode. As we make the anode positive, current starts to flow. As we make the anode more positive, more current flows. If we plot current I vs. voltage V, the plot will look somewhat as shown in Fig. 3.4. This shows zero current at a voltage of -10 volts and a current of 100 milliamperes at a voltage of $+10$ volts.

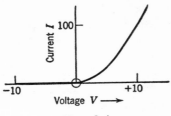

FIG. 3.4

Such a curved or *non-linear* relation between voltage and current is in contrast to the relation between voltage and current which is characteristic of imperfect conductors, or *resistors*, such as coils of fine wire or mixtures of carbon and non-conducting material. For

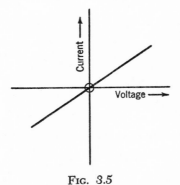

FIG. 3.5

such *linear* devices the plot of current I vs. voltage V is a straight line, as shown in Fig. 3.5. Mathematically, we can write:

$$V = IR, \qquad I = \frac{V}{R}$$

Here, R is a constant called the *resistance* of the device. This relation is called *Ohm's law,* and the unit of resistance is the *ohm.* If a coil of wire has a resistance of 10 ohms, and if we connect it to a battery with a voltage of 1 volt, a current of 1/10 amperes will flow.

Diodes simply do not obey Ohm's law. Therein lies their value. They can be used in obtaining a *direct current* (a current which flows in one direction only) from an alternating voltage (one which is sometimes positive and sometimes negative). Also, the curved nature of the characteristic of the diode is valuable in changing a signal of one frequency to a signal of another frequency, as we shall see in Chapter VIII.

Essentially the same parts as are used in a diode appear in another important electron device, the *electron gun.* Electron guns are used to produce beams of electrons in TV picture tubes, in amplifiers for radio signals of extremely high frequencies, and in many other devices.

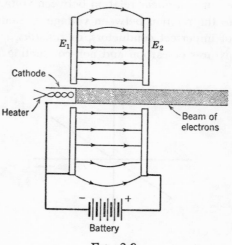

FIG. 3.6

FIGURE 3.6 shows the electrodes of a simple electron gun. Here no attempt is made to show the parts in perspective or to include the evacuated envelope. The chief electrodes, E_1 and E_2, are two parallel sheets of metal, each with a central aperture. One of these is connected by a wire to the negative terminal of a battery (marked —) and the other is connected to the positive terminal of the battery (marked $+$). The electric lines of force between the two electrodes are shown as lines with arrowheads indicating the direction of the force the field produces on electrons. The lines of force must, as we have seen, be normal to the electrodes at the surface. In this case, the electric lines of force between the two plane parallel electrodes are very simple. They are straight, parallel, and uniformly spaced except near the edges of the plates. The electric field between the two parallel-plane electrodes is everywhere the same in magnitude and direction.

In the electron gun of FIG. 3.6, a little metal cup with an electric heating coil inside acts as the cathode. This cathode is centered in the aperture in the negative electrode, and it is connected with a wire to the negative electrode E_1, and hence to the negative terminal of the battery.

The electric field between the electrodes E_1 and E_2 accelerates the electrons to the right, so that a *beam* of electrons (by analogy with a beam of light) travels from the cathode toward the positive electrode E_2, which is the anode of the electron gun. The electrons do not strike the anode, however; they pass through the aperture in the anode and travel on through the vacuum beyond to perform any of a variety of functions.

As in the case of the simple diode, the current leaving the cathode is limited by the space charge of the electrons in the beam, so that the greater the voltage between cathode and anode, the greater the current flow. In some electron guns the electrode E_1 is not attached directly to the cathode, but a voltage V_1 is applied between it and the cathode. If E_1 is made negative with respect to the cathode, fewer electrons will leave the cathode. Thus, the voltage V_1 can be used to control the current of the electron beam produced by the gun.

An electron gun much like that of FIG. 3.6 may supply electrons to "illuminate" the specimen in an electron microscope and so enable a chemist or a biologist to see details far smaller than a wave of light, and scarcely larger than molecules. The electrodes of such a gun look somewhat as shown to the left in FIG. 3.7. The cathode is a mere hairpin of tungsten, heated by passing current through it as in the filament of an electric lamp, and the electrodes E_1 and

E_2 have shapes somewhat different from those shown in Fig. 3.6. The electrons from an electron gun may travel from the gun in a beam in the picture tube of your television receiver and paint on the screen scenes of astounding variety. A somewhat larger electron gun may supply the electron beam in a microwave amplifier tube, which amplifies television signals at relay points while sending them from coast to coast. Or it may be a part of a powerful amplifier for radar, which sends out radio pulses of millions of watts'

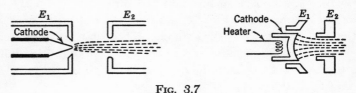

Fig. 3.7

power in search of enemy planes or missiles. Electron guns for such tubes look much as shown to the right in Fig. 3.7. The cathode is concave, and electrodes E_1 and E_2 are curved so that the electric lines of force converge or draw closer together in going from E_1 to E_2. This arrangement of electrodes, and the concave cathode, result in a converging beam of electrons. Electron guns form a part of many other electronic devices besides electron microscopes, picture tubes, and microwave amplifiers.

The French call an electron gun a *canon électronique*. This does not mean that French electron guns are of a larger caliber than the American variety. Physically, they both come in various sizes. Some which are used in low-power microwave amplifiers have a cathode only a fiftieth of an inch in diameter. Those used in microwave amplifiers which produce millions of watts of power have cathodes broader than one's hand. The electron gun in an electron microscope may furnish only microamperes. The electron gun in a powerful microwave amplifier for producing radar pulses may furnish beams of tens of amperes—millions of times as many electrons per second. For comparison, the electric current in the filament of a 100-watt light bulb is a little less than an ampere.

In the electron gun, an electric field is used chiefly to increase the velocity of electrons, to speed them up. An electric field applied transverse to the direction of motion of electrons will change their direction of motion. For instance, in Fig. 3.8 a beam of electrons passes between two parallel-plane electrodes, E_1 and E_2, and E_2 is held positive with respect to E_1 by means of a battery. The electric lines of force are about as indicated. As the

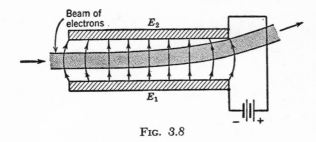

FIG. 3.8

electrons move from left to right, they are accelerated upwards, so that the electron beam emerging at the right travels up at an angle, not horizontally. The electron beam has been *deflected* from its original direction.

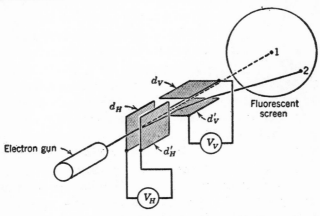

FIG. 3.9

Deflection is made use of in the cathode-ray oscilloscope tube, which is used to display the variation of voltage with time in various electronic circuits. FIGURE 3.9 shows the parts of a cathode-ray oscilloscope. A narrow electron beam from an electron gun is directed at the center of a *fluorescent screen*. This screen is a coating of some substance on the inside of the flat end of a cone-shaped glass envelope which encloses the gun and the other parts of the device. The coating, which is the same sort of material which is used in fluorescent lights, glows when the electrons of the beam strike it, producing a bright spot of light.

Between the electron gun and the fluorescent screen are two sets of deflection plates, the horizontal deflection plates d_H and d'_H and the vertical deflection plates d_V and d'_V. A voltage V_H applied between d_H and d'_H deflects the beam sideways and moves the spot left or right on the fluorescent screen. A voltage V_V applied between d_V and d'_V deflects the beam vertically and moves the spot up or down on the fluorescent screen. If V_H and V_V were zero, the beam would go straight through the tube, as indicated by the dotted line, and would strike the screen at the center, at 1 of FIG. 3.9. With some particular voltages applied, the spot will go to some particular point on the fluorescent screen, as to 2 in FIG. 3.9.

FIGURE 3.10 shows at the top the general appearance of a cathode-ray tube. We look at the fluorescent screen through the glass of the envelope. If the bright spot produced by the electron beam on the fluorescent screen is moved rapidly about in a repeating pattern, it will appear as a bright line, just as Fourth-of-July sparklers appear to trace out bright lines when we swing them about. The form of the bright trace or pattern on the screen of the oscilloscope depends on the voltages applied to the deflecting plates. If V_H and V_V are as shown at the bottom of FIG. 3.10, the trace will be of the form indicated on the face of the tube.

Oscilloscopes are invaluable tools in studying the behavior of electric circuits. They can be used to display phenomena which occur in a few billionths of a second. Electronic-research workers, design engineers and TV repairmen, all would be helpless without oscilloscopes to map out for them the complicated behavior of the voltages in various electronic devices.

Various electron tubes and other electronic devices make use of magnetic fields as well as electric fields. Before going on to magnetic fields, however, it is wise to consider some fundamental matters concerned with electric fields; these are the relation between the flow of electrons between electrodes and the current in the wires connected to the electrodes, and the conservation of energy. These matters can be very complicated when the voltages applied to the electrodes change rapidly with time. We will not

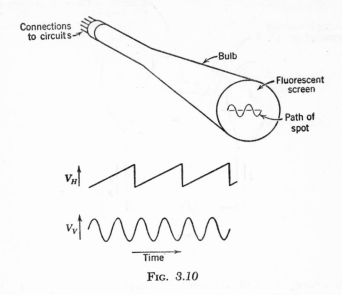

FIG. 3.10

consider this difficult case. Matters are much simpler when the voltages are constant with time, or when they change negligibly in the time it takes an electron to get from one electrode to the other.

Electrostatic fields—that is, electric fields which do not change with time—have a particularly important property. When an electron travels between two points in such an electric field, the work done on it by the electric field is the same regardless of the path, direct or indirect, by which the electron travels between the two points. Consider two conductors or electrodes, A and B, which are connected to the negative and positive terminals of a battery, as shown in FIG. 3.11. There is no field inside the conductors. Hence, the same work is done on any electron traveling from any point on electrode A to any point on electrode B, regardless of just where the electron leaves or where it arrives or what path it follows. Thus, all electrons which leave electrode A at rest will have the same velocity and the same kinetic energy when they strike electrode B. Where does this energy come from?

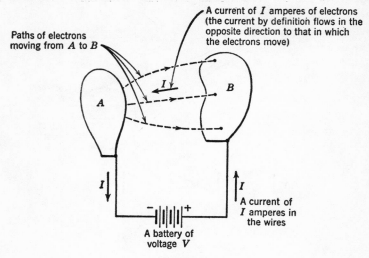

Fig. *3.11*

The energy is supplied from the battery as electric power. If the flow of electrons between electrodes A and B constitutes a current of I amperes, a current of I amperes will flow from one terminal of the battery connecting the electrodes and back into the other, as shown in Fig. *3.11*. We should remember that, by a definition made long before electrons were discovered, the current flows in a direction opposite to that of electron flow. In Fig. *3.11*, the small arrowheads on the electron paths from A to B indicate direction of electron motion and the large-headed arrows indicate current flow.

Power is work done per second. Electric power is measured in watts. The electric power P supplied by the battery of Fig. *3.11* is the voltage V of the battery times the current I which flows from it and back to it:

$$P = IV$$

Suppose we divide a line of force between A and B into little lengths, and multiply each little length, each fraction of a meter, by the electric field strength, which is measured in volts per meter. If we sum up all these products, all the way from A to B, we get the voltage of the battery, measured in volts. The battery supplies electric power. It also causes the electric field, the field which produces a force on the electrons between electrodes A and B and gives the electrons kinetic energy. The conversion of electric power from batteries or other electric generators into kinetic energy of electrons is something we encounter over and over again in electron devices. In these, as in all of the universe, the books always balance. The electric energy which disappears from the electric generator (the battery, in this case) all reappears as kinetic energy of accelerated electrons.

CHAPTER IV

Magnetic Fields, Too

WHILE in some ways electric fields are more important in vacuum tubes than are magnetic fields, many tubes require both for their operation. Indeed, we will find out in Chapter VI that both are so closely related that when we have one we usually have a certain amount of the other. However, the ways in which electric and magnetic fields are produced and the ways in which they act on electrons are quite distinct.

We have seen that electric fields are associated with electric charges, and they are usually produced by applying a voltage to a pair of electrodes, as by means of a battery. There are no magnetic charges or isolated *poles*. There is no analogue of a magnetic battery. An electric battery can cause a flow of electric charges; an electric battery changes chemical energy into electric energy. There are no magnetic charges to flow.

Magnetic fields can be produced by permanent magnets, but often they are produced by an electric current, that is, a flow of electrons, through a coil of copper wire. A coil of wire connected to the terminals of a battery as shown in FIG. *4.1* produces a magnetic field inside the coil in the direction shown. The arrows beside the wire show the direction of current flow, which is from the positive terminal of the battery, through the coil, and back to the negative terminal.

We know that what is actually flowing in the wires is electrons and that these move through the wire from the negative terminal of the battery to the positive terminal. We should remember that a direction of current flow was defined long before anyone knew about electrons, and that the direction of current flow is contrary to the direction of electron flow.

We can draw the coil of Fig. *4.1* in cross section and show the lines of force, as in Fig. *4.2*. Inside the coil or *solenoid* the mag-

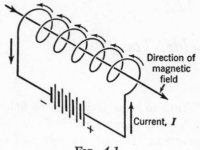

Direction of magnetic field

Current, *I*

FIG. *4.1*

netic lines of force are nearly parallel, and the strength of the field is thus very nearly constant. Hence, we can use such a solenoid to produce a uniform magnetic field.

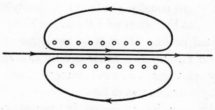

FIG. *4.2*

More often, we use an electromagnet with a *core* of iron or, often, of an iron alloy with desirable magnetic properties. Such an electromagnet for producing a uniform magnetic field is shown in Fig. *4.3*. The magnetic lines of force which stray far out in the solenoid of Fig. *4.2* are confined to the iron in electromagnet of Fig. *4.3*, and a very strong magnetic field appears between two projecting portions of the core called *pole pieces*.

If there were isolated magnetic poles, as Ehrenhaft tried to persuade us a few years ago, a magnetic field would exert a force on them in the direction of the magnetic lines of force. Actually,

there are no isolated magnetic poles. In describing a magnetic
field we use lines of force, just as in the case of an electric field, and
the field is strongest where the lines of force are crowded closest
together. However, a magnetic field produces a force on a charge
only when the charge is moving. The magnitude of the force is
proportional to the product of the magnetic field strength, the

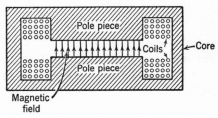

FIG. 4.3

charge, and the component of the charge's velocity normal to the
magnetic field. Thus, if a charge moves parallel to the magnetic
lines of force, the magnetic field produces no force on it, while
for a given speed the maximum force is produced if the charge
moves normal (perpendicular) to the magnetic lines of force. In
fact, we can accurately say that the force due to the magnetic field
is proportional to the charge times the rate at which it passes lines
of force. The direction of the force may astound the uninitiated.
The force is perpendicular to both the velocity of the charge and to
the direction of the magnetic field. Thus, the force always acts
to turn the charged particle and never to speed it up or to slow it
down. The force due to a magnetic field never does any work on
a moving charge.

We may express the magnitude of the force F acting on a charged
particle moving in a magnetic field by

$$F = q\mu H v_n$$

Here q is the electric charge of the particle, μ (mu) is a constant
called the permeability of space, H is the magnetic field strength,
and v_n is the component of velocity normal to the magnetic field.

Let us imagine that we have a uniform magnetic field of strength
H such as might be produced by the electromagnet of FIG. 4.3.

Suppose we set a charged particle in motion with a velocity v in a horizontal plane, normal to the lines of force. What will the motion of the particle be?

The force of the magnetic field is normal to the velocity, so the particle will be neither speeded up nor slowed down. It will be acted on by a constant force,

$$q\mu Hv,$$

normal to the direction of motion. It will turn at a constant rate; it will travel in a circle.

How long will it take the particle to go once around the circle? We have seen in Chapter II that the acceleration a of an object traveling in a circle is:

$$a = \frac{2\pi v}{T}$$

From Newton's second law, the mass m times the acceleration must be equal to the force acting on the particle. That is,

$$\frac{m2\pi v}{T} = q\mu Hv$$

As v appears as a factor on each side, we see that the period does not depend on the velocity. In fact, we see that

$$T = \frac{2\pi}{\mu H(q/m)}$$

Thus, in a uniform magnetic field, charged particles go around in circles with a constant period T. The radius of the circle depends on the velocity. The circumference of a circle of radius r is $2\pi r$, so we must have

$$v = \frac{2\pi r}{T}$$

and

$$r = \frac{T}{2\pi} v$$

If we were able to increase the speed of a charged particle circling in a uniform magnetic field, the period would remain constant but the particle would swing around in larger and larger circles.

This is just what happens in the *cyclotron,* a device used for accelerating positive ions to atom-smashing speeds.

In a cyclotron, a flat, pillbox-shaped vacuum chamber is located between the poles of a powerful magnet such as that of FIG. 4.3. Inside the chamber is a pair of dees (named from the shape), as shown at the top of FIG. 4.4. The ions travel around between the

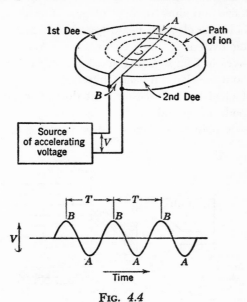

FIG. 4.4

dees. An accelerating voltage, V, which varies periodically with time as shown at the bottom of FIG. 4.4, is applied between the dees. This voltage changes from positive to negative to positive again in just the time it takes the ion to circle once between the dees. Thus, if the second dee is negative with respect to the first as a positive ion passes between the two at A, so that the ion will be accelerated, then when the same ion reaches B the first dee will be negative with respect to the second and the ion will be accelerated again. Thus, the ion will spiral outward as shown. Out at the edge of the dees, an aperture is provided, and a strong electric field is used to get the ions out of the cyclotron at that particular point.

Cyclotrons with diameters as great as 17 feet have been made. Such a huge beast will accelerate particles to energies of almost a half a billion volts (that is, to the velocity that would be given by a battery of that voltage). In such devices, Newton's laws of motion are in error; something will be said about this in Chapter XVI.

Of course, magnetic fields are put to work in devices of much more modest size and aims than cyclotrons. In fact, magnetic fields are used to hold the electron beam together in most vacuum tubes for amplifying extremely high frequencies. We will discuss the tubes themselves in Chapters VII and VIII, but it is worth while to say a word about the electron beams here.

A beam of electrons, consisting as it does of changes all of the same sign, tends to spread apart. The electrons themselves produce an electric field with lines of force pointing out radially, and

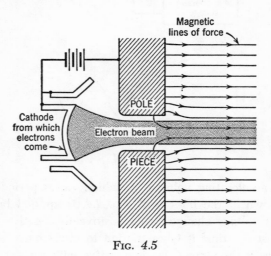

Fig. 4.5

this field tends to deflect the outer electrons outwards. Fig. 4.5 shows how a uniform magnetic field is used to hold a beam of electrons together.

The uniform field extends from a flat iron-pole piece to another pole piece located somewhere to the right. The electron beam enters the field through a hole through the pole piece. Near the hole the lines of force spread out as shown, and some of them terminate on the inside of the hole through the pole piece. Thus, as the electrons of the beam go through the hole they must cross a radial component of magnetic field. This produces a force directed around the axis of the hole and sets the electrons whirling around the axis. Now, because of this motion about the axis, the electrons have a component of velocity normal to the parallel lines of magnetic force in the main, uniform portion of the magnetic field. As the electrons move across the parallel lines of force, the magnetic field produces a constant inward force on them. If the magnetic field has just the right strength, and if the electrons enter it parallel, the force will be just right to overcome the outward force due to the electric field produced by the electrons in the beam, and the beam diameter will remain constant as the electrons travel in helical paths through the magnetic field.

Magnetic fields are used to confine electron beams as in Fig. 4.5 only in cases of the fairly large beam currents used in amplifier tubes. However, both magnetic and electric fields are used to *focus* electrons in beams of small current, much as glass lenses are used to focus light. Electrodes or pole pieces which produce such focusing fields, together with the fields themselves, are called *electron lenses*. Here we will consider both electric lenses and magnetic lenses and compare the two.

Lenses used in focusing light are round glass disks with concave or convex surfaces. The properties of convex or *positive* or *converging* lenses are illustrated in Fig. 4.6. Light rays emanating

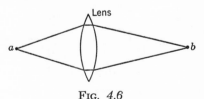

FIG. 4.6

from a source *a*, perhaps the hot filament of a flashlight bulb, and passing through the lens are focused, that is, brought together, by the lens at some point, *b*. Suppose light leaves several points the same distance to the left of the lens; such points as a_1, a_2, a_3 in Fig. 4.7. The lens will bring the light from these points to a focus at 3 points, b_1, b_2, b_3 which are all at the same distance to the right of the lens. Thus, the lens forms an *image* of points a_1, a_2, and a_3.

We might replace the source of light a_1, a_2, a_3 by an illuminated object, such as a slide in a projector. Where the image falls at

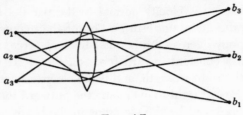

FIG. 4.7

b_1, b_2, b_3 we could put a white screen and see the slide projected. Or a_1, a_2, a_3 might be stars, and b_1, b_2, b_3 the images of stars, to fall on a photographic plate or to be examined with the eyepiece of a telescope. Or a_1, a_2, a_3 might represent light coming from the illuminated specimen of a microscope, and b_1, b_2, b_3 parts of the image, again either to fall on a photographic plate or to be examined with an eyepiece.

An *electron lens* focuses the paths of electrons just as a glass lens focuses rays of light. A typical electron lens consists of two coaxial metal tubes with a short gap between the ends, as shown in FIG. 4.8.

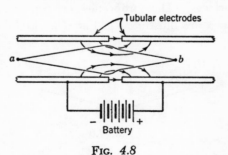

FIG. 4.8

The lines of force of the electric field are shown, with arrowheads to show the direction of force on the electrons. The field is strongest near the short gap between the ends of the two tubes. It is weaker at the center of the tube, where its direction is entirely horizontal—that is, parallel to the axis of the tubes. The field dies away rapidly to the left and to the right of the gap.

Two typical electron paths show what happens to electrons which leave a point *a* at different angles and go through the electron lens. They are *focused* and brought together at a common point *b*. So (disregarding certain aberrations or imperfections in focusing) are any other electrons going through the electron lens from point *a*; all are brought to a focus at point *b*.

How does this come to be? Let us go along the electron path from *a* to *b*. As we approach the gap, the electrons cross the electric lines of force; as we can see, these are so directed as both to speed the electrons up and to push them in toward the axis. In passing the gap, the field is parallel to the axis and the electrons are merely accelerated without being pushed either toward or away from the axis. To the right of the gap, the lines of force are so directed as to push the electrons away from the axis.

At the same distance from the axis the outward force to the right of the gap is just as great as the inward force to the left of the gap. Why, then, is there a net overall effect of pushing the electrons toward the axis, as shown by the electron paths or trajectories in Fig. 4.8? There are two reasons: First, change of velocity is proportional to force times time. The electrons are accelerated, speeded up, in passing the gap, so that they are going faster in passing through the outward-directed field to the right than they are in passing through the inward-directed field to the left. Thus, the outward-directed field has less time to act on the electrons than does the inward-directed field, and so it produces less change in velocity. The second reason depends on the fact that the inward-directed and outward-directed fields are stronger the farther we go from the axis. The paths are such that the electrons are farther from the axis to the left of the gap than to the right; hence *along the actual path* the inward-directed force to the left of the gap is greater than the outward-directed force to the right.

If we consider what happens to an electron moving from *b* toward *a*, we see that the electron paths are the same for the electron traveling in either direction. In either case, the system of two tubes with an applied voltage acts as does a converging or convex lens for light, like a magnifying glass, a burning glass, or a camera lens. Electron lenses are always converging lenses, and there is no analogue of the concave lens, such as the eyepiece of an opera glass! Too, electron lenses turn out to be of very poor quality compared with the glass lenses used in conventional optics.

Magnetic fields can also be used to produce electron lenses, just as electric fields can. The configuration of the magnetic lines of force used is like that of the electric lines of force of the electric electron lens of Fig. 4.8. To produce such a magnetic field, two tubular iron-pole pieces are used, separated by a short gap. In the electric lens, the electric field between the electrodes was obtained by connecting the electrodes to the terminals of a battery. In the magnetic lens, the magnetic field is produced by current flowing

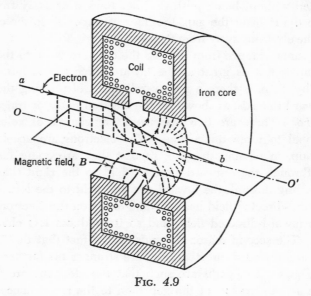

FIG. 4.9

through a coil wound around the hollow pole pieces, as shown in the cutaway view of Fig. 4.9. The coil is surrounded by an iron shell which connects the pole pieces outside of the coil.

While the magnetic lines of force of the magnetic lens are much like the electric lines of force in the electric lens, the way in which they affect the electrons is quite different. This is illustrated by the electron path between *a* and *b* in Fig. *4.9*. As the electron approaches the gap between the pole pieces, it cuts lines of force which go from the inside of the tubular pole piece toward the axis; this causes a force normal to the magnetic lines of force, and this force starts the electron rotating clockwise about the axis. As the electron rotates about the axis it cuts the longitudinal lines of force near the center of the lens, and this produces an inward force which pushes the electron in toward the axis. The electron then passes through the magnetic field beyond the gap where the lines of force are headed outward toward the inside of the pole piece. In cutting these lines of force the rotation of the electron about the axis is stopped. It is the inward push on the rotating electron near the center of the lens which is responsible for the focusing action of the magnetic lens.

Like electric electron lenses, magnetic electron lenses are very poor compared with the glass lenses used to focus light. Nonetheless, both electric and magnetic lenses are used in various important electronic devices.

Electric lenses are used in conjunction with electron guns in cathode-ray oscilloscope tubes such as that described in Chapter III. An electron lens focuses the beam on the fluorescent screen so as to form the fine spot which writes out the pattern.

The picture tube of the TV receiver is a close relative of the oscilloscope tube, but the picture tube usually makes use of a magnetic lens, and the electron beam is deflected by transverse magnetic fields produced by an electromagnet structure called a *deflection yoke*. Fig. *4.10* shows the principal parts of a picture tube. An electron gun produces a beam of electrons which is sharply focused into a spot on a fluorescent screen. In order to form the picture, the spot is swept back and forth across the fluorescent screen, painting out the picture a line at a time. As the electron beam is swept across the screen the beam current, and hence the brightness of the spot, is controlled by a voltage applied to an apertured electrode near the cathode of the electron gun.

The electron microscope is a powerful tool, useful in research and in much routine medical and engineering work. It is superior to a light microscope because it will disclose finer details. Electron microscopes usually make use of magnetic lenses. If powerful electric lenses were used, it would be necessary to apply a high voltage between the electrodes of the lenses, and this could lead to sparks or arcs between the electrodes, which would damage them. There is no such danger with magnetic lenses.

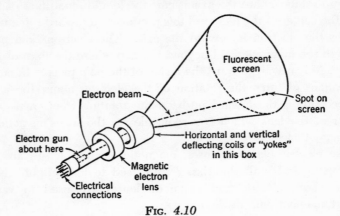

FIG. *4.10*

FIG. *4.11* shows the essential parts of an electron microscope without showing the vacuum-tight casing which goes around the parts. To the left are shown the equivalent optical lenses as they might be used in an optical microscope of similar function. In the optical microscope, there is a light source at the top. Next down is a convex *condenser lens,* which concentrates the light on the specimen below it. Just below the specimen is a powerful convex *objective lens,* which forms an image of the specimen, a first image, some distance below it. Just below the plane of the first image is a *projector lens,* which casts a magnified image of the first image on a photographic plate below. In the electron microscope to the right, an electron gun is used to illuminate the specimen with electrons instead of a light source to illuminate it with light. Otherwise, the parts of the electron microscope are exactly analogous to those of the optical structure just described.

In an actual electron microscope all these parts may be mounted in an evacuated vertical metal tube about 3 feet tall and 8 inches in diameter, which rests on a platform providing a working space.

The electron gun will be at the top. Near the top, below the gun, there will be an opening, with an airtight cover, for inserting the specimen to be observed. At the bottom of the tube there will be large airtight glass windows for observing a horizontal fluorescent screen on which the electron image falls during focusing and adjust-

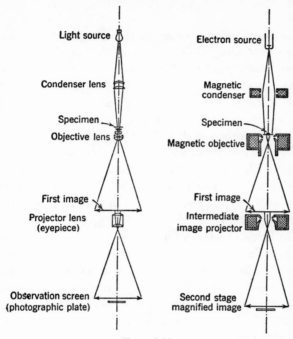

Light source

Condenser lens

Specimen
Objective lens

First image
Projector lens
(eyepiece)

Observation screen
(photographic plate)

Electron source

Magnetic
condenser

Specimen
Magnetic objective

First image
Intermediate
image projector

Second stage
magnified image

FIG. 4.11

ment. By means of a mechanism which operates through airtight joints, the fluorescent screen can be replaced by a photographic plate, and the electrons falling on the plate record the image photographically.

The tube of the microscope and the platform below it are mounted on the front of a cabinet perhaps 2 feet square and 6 feet high. This cabinet contains a 50,000-volt power supply for accelerating the electrons and carefully regulated current supplies for the coils of the magnetic lenses. It also contains vacuum pumps which can remove the air from the metal tube housing the microscope in less than a minute after a specimen has been inserted or a photographic plate changed.

Electron microscopes may magnify objects hundreds of thousands of times and show details as fine as a ten-millionth of an inch. An ordinary light microscope can reveal details down to only about a hundred-thousandth of an inch. We will see in Chapter V why this is so.

We have now explored many of the things we need to keep in mind in understanding electronics and electron devices. We have encountered electric fields. There is an electric field at a point if a fixed charge experiences a force. The magnitude and the direction of the force give the magnitude and direction of the electric field. We can draw a picture which represents an electric field in terms of lines of force which are everywhere in the direction of the field, and whose density or closeness is proportional to the strength of the field. Electric fields are produced by applying a voltage between electrodes. The lines of force are everywhere normal to the surface of the electrodes. Electric fields can speed up charges, doing work on them.

Magnetic fields can be produced by the flow of electric current, as in coils. We can represent magnetic fields by lines of force. Magnetic fields, however, produce a force on moving charges only. The force is always normal, not only to the direction of the field, but also to the direction of motion of the electron. There is no component of force in the direction of motion. Magnetic fields cannot change the speed of an electron; they merely turn it in its path. Magnetic fields cannot do work on electrons.

These are matters which we should keep in mind for future use.

CHAPTER V

Waves

THERE are some concepts so general and so far-reaching that they give us important information even about things whose precise physical nature is not well understood. Greatest of these concepts certainly is that of number. We know that two pigs and two pigs are four pigs, just as two men and two men are four men, or two canoes and two canoes are four canoes. The ideas of counting, of numbers, and of the correspondence between numbers and groups of objects apply to all distinct, relatively permanent things and collections of things, regardless of the nature of the objects.

Should we take this for granted? I have been told that there are primitive tribes which have words for one man, two men, three men, or many men, and quite separate words for one dog, two dogs, three dogs, and many dogs. Indeed, something of this attitude may survive in the engaging terms of venery; a gaggle of geese, a pride of lions, an ostentation of peafowl, and the rest.

Among the greatest of the great unifying concepts of physics is the idea of waves. Men must have observed waves from the earliest times. In the fifteenth century, Leonardo da Vinci wrote of waves, "The impetus is much quicker than the water, for it often happens that the wave flees the place of its creation, while the water does not; like the waves made in a field of grain by the wind, where we see the waves running across the field while the grain remains in place." Clearly, Leonardo recognized that when a wave of water moves from one place to another the water does not go bodily with it.

Modern physics is full of waves: the earthquake waves which

seismologists study; the waves and ripples on oceans, lakes and ponds; the waves of sound which travel through the air; the mechanical waves in stretched strings and in the quartz crystals which are used to control the frequency of radio transmitters; the electromagnetic waves which constitute light, and which are radiated by radio transmitters and received by radio receivers; and finally, the waves of what?—probability, perhaps—which are used in quantum mechanics to predict the behavior of electrons, atoms, and complex substances.

What are waves? They are not earth, or water, or air; steel, or catgut, or quartz; yet they travel in these substances. Nineteenth-century physicists felt constrained to fill the vacuum of space with an *ether* to transmit electromagnetic waves, yet so arbitrary a substance seems more a placebo to quiet the disturbed mind than a valid explanation of a physical phenomenon. When we come to the waves of quantum mechanics, the physicists do not even offer us a single agreed-upon physical interpretation of the waves with which they deal, although they all agree in the way they use them to predict correctly the outcome of experiments.

Rather than asking what waves are, we should perhaps ask, what can one say about waves? Here there is no confusion. One recognizes in waves a certain sort of behavior which can be described mathematically in common terms, however various may be the physical systems to which the terms are applied. Once we recognize that in a certain phenomenon we are dealing with waves, we can assert and predict a great deal about the phenomenon even though we do not clearly understand the mechanism by which the waves are generated and transmitted. The wave nature of light was understood, and many of its important consequences were worked out, long before the idea of an electromagnetic wave through space was dreamed of. Indeed, when the true explanation of the physical nature of light was proposed, many physicists who recognized clearly that light was some sort of wave refused to accept it.

We can study the important principles of waves in simple and familiar examples. As we come to understand the behavior of these waves, we can abstract certain ideas which are valid in connection with all waves, wherever we may find them. Such a study is the purpose of this chapter.

Suppose that we watch the waves of the sea from a pier. Let us imagine that today the waves are particularly smooth and are very regular in height. We see a certain number of crests pass us each second—let us say a number f. This number f is the *frequency* of the waves. Frequency is reckoned in *cycles per second,* or *cycles* for short. The cycle referred to is simply a complete cycle of change; the departing of a wave crest, the passing of the trough, and finally, the arrival of the next crest. As a complete wave, from crest through trough to crest again, passes us, the height of the water goes through a complete cycle of change, from high to low to high again.

A cycle is a complete cycle of change, at the end of which we are back to the original state. It is the same in the case of 60-cycle electric power. The 60-cycle electric current alternates in direction of flow and goes through a complete cycle of change 60 times a second. Broadcast waves reach your receiver about a million crests a second; some television waves a hundred million crests a second, and radar waves leave the radar antenna and are reflected back again at a rate of billions of waves or cycles per second.

The waves in the ocean each take several seconds to pass us, so that the frequency of the ocean waves is a fraction of a cycle per second. We can if we wish measure, instead of the frequency, the time between the passing of two crests; this is the *period* of the wave, which we will call T. We see that T is the *reciprocal* of f, that is,

$$T = \frac{1}{f}$$

Looking out at the waves, we may estimate or measure the distance between the crests of the waves; this is the wave length, which is always denoted by the Greek letter λ (lambda). Among radio waves, from radar to broadcast, the wave length ranges from a little over an inch to around 1,000 feet.

The time between the passage of wave crests is T. In this time the next crest must travel just one wave length, λ, to reach the position of the preceding crest. Thus, the wave travels with a velocity v which is the distance of travel, λ, divided by the elapsed time, T, so that

$$v = \frac{\lambda}{T} = \lambda f$$

Thus, we can express λ in terms of f and f in terms of λ by using the velocity, v:

$$\lambda = \frac{v}{f}$$

$$f = \frac{v}{\lambda}$$

Light waves and radio waves are both electromagnetic waves, and for such electromagnetic waves traveling through space, the velocity, v, is the velocity of light:

$$v = 186{,}000 \text{ miles per second}$$
$$v = 3 \times 10^8 \text{ meters per second}$$

Waves may have various shapes. We have been considering smooth rollers which come in one after another, regularly spaced. We can also have a single wave or a short *train* or waves such as those caused by throwing a single stone into a pond. There is a reason, however, for considering a particular regular, smooth, persistent kind of wave called a *sinusoidal* wave.

The waves we consider are waves of what is called *linear* systems. We will see what this means later on. Now, we will merely say that while for some linear systems a wave of any form travels along preserving that same form, in many other linear systems a wave of arbitrary form will change form as it travels. Consider, however, a wave such that as it passes a given point, the height of the water or the magnitude or *amplitude* of some other significant quantity, varies *sinusoidally* with time with some frequency f. If this is so at any point in any linear system, the wave will also vary sinusoidally with time, with the same frequency f, at any other point. Strictly, the term frequency should be applied to sine waves only.

A sinusoidal variation can be understood in terms of a crank on a shaft which rotates at a constant rate, f turns per second, as shown in FIG. *5.1*. The height, h, of the end of the crank above the level of center of the shaft varies sinusoidally with time. If we plot height or amplitude vs. time in seconds, as in FIG. *5.2*, we get a

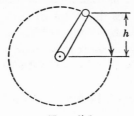

FIG. *5.1*

sine curve or *sine wave*. This is the way the waves we will talk about vary with time. As long as the wave travels with a constant velocity, this is also the way the height above the mean or zero level, which is called the *amplitude,* varies with distance.

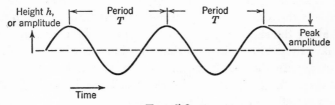

FIG. *5.2*

In instances in which a wave other than a sine wave will change in form as it travels, sine waves of different frequencies (and hence of different wave lengths) travel with different velocities. Henceforward, unless we say otherwise, we will mean a sine wave of some particular frequency when we speak of a wave, and the wave velocity will refer to the velocity of a sine wave of a particular frequency.

Let us think back to the waves that we watch from a pier in the ocean, and think of them as being sine waves. Imagine that they roll past a single pile sticking up from the water. The waves are very long compared with the diameter of the pile. We can imagine the water rising smoothly up the height of the pile and sinking smoothly down again, the height varying sinusoidally with time as the wave passes. Does the pile disturb or scatter the wave? Scarcely at all; a very little, perhaps. This is a fundamental rule concerning waves. They go right past objects small compared with the wave length. The individual molecules of air are so small compared with light waves that they do not appreciably scatter the light waves. The droplets of fog, which are larger, scatter light waves but do not affect the short radio waves of radar. Rain drops will scatter short radar waves but do not affect waves of broadcast wave length.

Obstacles can stop waves, however. Visualize a long breakwater extending parallel to the shore. Behind it, well away from the ends, the sea will be calm. Near one end, the waves will in effect bend around and get behind the breakwater a little. If we liken the waves of the ocean to light waves, and say by analogy that the shore is illuminated by the waves where the waves fall on it, then the breakwater casts a shadow on the shore. The shadow is not sharp, however; it is diffuse near the ends of the breakwater. The water near the shore passes gradually from calm to rough as we travel along the shore and pass one end of the breakwater.

It takes little to convince us that the sharpness of the shadow is connected with the length of the waves, and it indeed turns out that the length of the region between calm and rough, light and shade, is directly proportional to wave length.

The great Newton rejected the wave theory of light because light casts sharp shadows, and waves which he observed, such as waves of sound, do not. He was deceived, for optical shadows are so sharp merely because light waves are so short (they are around 20 millionths of an inch long). If one looks closely, however, he can see the diffuseness of shadows which is associated with the wave nature of light.

Can we understand the "shadows" cast by light more quantitatively? We can, and quite simply, too. In doing this, we must make use of the property of linearity of the waves of which we speak.

In order to explain linearity in a simple case, let us imagine that apples sold always for 5 cents each. Then, if we had 100 apples, we would know the total cost: 500 cents. We could if we wished point out any 10 apples and say those 10 apples cost 50 cents and all the rest together cost 450 cents. There is in this case a *linear* relation between the cost and the number of apples. The word linear is used because if we plotted cost of apples vs. number of apples, we would get a straight line.

If, however, apples were 5 cents for one and 6 for a quarter, we could make no such sweeping statements about a collection of 100 apples. We could not even say what the 100 apples cost, unless we knew the details of the transactions in which they were bought.

Linearity is an overwhelmingly important concept in physics. We can say a great deal about linear systems. We know how to handle them mathematically. Non-linear systems comprise that overwhelming total of all systems which are not linear, in any of many fashions. We can deal much less effectively with this huge variety of systems. Alas, most actual devices are more or less non-linear. It seems great good fortune that sound waves of ordinary amplitudes are linear, and that electromagnetic waves, embracing light and radio waves, are exactly linear.

It was because velocities add linearly that we could break up the velocity vector into two components. It was because the force on a body attracted by two other bodies is the linear vector-sum of the attractions taken separately that we could represent the overall action by a field which is the sum of the fields of the individual bodies. It is because of this linearity that we could represent electric and magnetic fields by components, and the total field by the sum of the components. We can also represent waves in linear systems as a sum of components.

For instance, consider the small ripples on the surface of a pond which are caused by dropping a pebble into it. These ripples go out in concentric circles. If we simultaneously drop another pebble near by in the pond, the circular ripples or waves from it will pass right through the waves caused by the first pebble. If we concentrate our attention on the waves from either, we will see them as a simple circular pattern, undisturbed by the presence of the other pattern. If we look at the waves due to both pebbles, we will see them as a more complicated pattern, but everywhere the amplitude of this pattern, the height of the water, that is, is just the sum of the heights of the two circular patterns.

This sort of behavior is unusual in our world. If we shot two charges of shot through the same space, each would pass through the other undisturbed only if the shot were spaced very far apart, and even then not with certainty. We can imagine an even more striking example of a non-linear system. Imagine walking between a target and a gun. Imagine, separately, firing the gun at the target. Now imagine doing both simultaneously. The result is in no sense simply the sum of the separate acts. This example is extreme, perhaps, but it is not ridiculous; it merely shows how truly extraordinary linearity is in our world.

If we consider again the linear behavior of the pattern of ripples caused by the two pebbles dropped into the pond, we may well ask, what is the *true* pattern? Is it the sum of the two circular patterns? Is it the one complicated pattern? In the case of a linear system the question is meaningless. It is like asking, concerning 100 apples each of which was bought for 5 cents, whether the cost is 500 cents per hundred apples or 50 cents for each 10 apples. It is either and both. It is like asking, in the case of a velocity, whether the velocity is the vector, v, or the sum of the horizontal component of velocity, v_x, and the vertical component of velocity, v_y. The two components are merely an alternative way of representing the velocity, v.

Linearity makes it possible for us to talk of a complicated wave as the sum of a number of simpler component waves. This is not a matter of mere philosophical interest. It is a matter of the greatest practical significance.

Let us approach this problem by considering the pattern of two wave sources, from each of which concentric circles of sinusoidal waves travel out, with the same frequency, f, and the same velocity, v. I have tried to show a snapshot of this, a picture at one instant of time, in FIG. 5.3. Because it is hard to show sine waves, I have surrounded each of the sources, S_1 and S_2, by concentric rings of equal width, alternately blank and filled in with parallel lines. A blank circle plus a lined circle is one wave length. I have drawn the lines of the lined circles at different angles for the circles from the two sources.

Let us imagine that the lined areas represent the crests of the waves and the white areas represent troughs. Then, for both patterns together, a black area is the sum of two crests, or a double

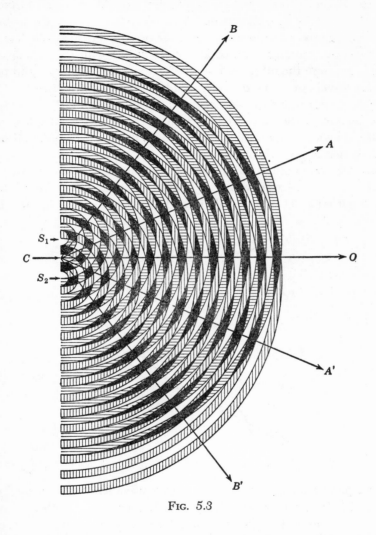

Fig. 5.3

crest. A blank area is the sum of two troughs, or a double trough. A lined area is the sum of the crest of one wave and the trough of the other; that is, the lined areas represent zero amplitude.

Let us examine the total pattern due to the two sources S_1 and S_2. Look at the radial lines drawn out from the center point, C, which is midway between the two sources to O, A, A', B, B'. Along these lines a double crest alternates with a double trough. Strong waves travel in these directions. Midway between these lines—for instance, midway between the line to O and the line to A—the crest of the wave from one source always coincides with the trough of the wave from the other source; the total amplitude is zero, and no waves travel out in the directions midway between the lines.

FIG. 5.3 illustrates *wave interference* or *diffraction*. Waves from two sources of the same frequency *interfere* to give a complicated pattern, and, in the overall pattern, waves travel in some directions and there is no wave in other directions.

Is there some other way of finding out in what direction waves will travel, some way which is simpler than drawing the whole wave pattern? There certainly is, and FIG. 5.4 illustrates it. In the

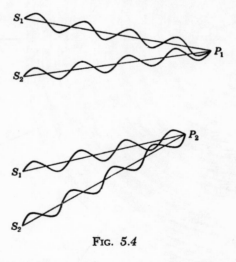

FIG. 5.4

upper part of the figure, point P_1 is four wave lengths from source S_1 and it is also four wave lengths from source S_2. Both sources produce crests or troughs at P_1 simultaneously as the waves travel out from them, so the crests and troughs add up and there is a strong wave at P_1. In the lower part of FIG. 5.4, point P_2 is three and one half wave lengths from source S_1 and four wave lengths from source S_2. Always, when a crest reaches P_2 from S_1, a trough reaches P_2 from S_2; there is never any wave at P_2, for the waves from the two sources always cancel at this point and, indeed, everywhere in this direction from the two sources.

By means of the principles we have just discussed, we can explain how it is that *microwaves*—that is, radio waves a few centimeters or less in length—as well as the rays of light, can be focused by a lens. A material such as glass will transmit electromagnetic waves, but in it the waves go slower than they do in air. Thus, the wave length, which is the velocity divided by the frequency, is shorter in the glass of a lens than it is in the air about the lens. FIG. 5.5 illustrates a lens focusing electromagnetic waves from point a onto point b.

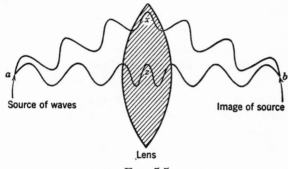

Source of waves   Image of source

Lens

FIG. 5.5

We know that to the left of the lens the waves travel out in straight lines from the source a, as shown. We can see how they must travel to a focus to the right of the lens if at the focus crest is to be added to crest and trough to trough. They must travel as shown, in such a way that the indirect path a–x–b, which is longer than the direct path a–z–b, contains just the same number of wave lengths as the direct path. The shorter path a–z–b passes through a greater thickness of glass, and the wave length is shorter in the glass than in the air, just as shown. Thus it is that the shorter and longer paths contain the same number of wave lengths. The lens will focus all the waves from a at b because it is so shaped that all the paths similar to path *a–x–b* which pass through it contain the same number of wave lengths, so that at *b* crest will be added to crest and trough to trough for all paths.

This explanation of how lenses focus light may come as somewhat of a shock even to people who think they know a little about optics. One aspect of optics is called *geometrical optics.* In geometrical optics we grandly draw in lines representing *rays* of light, and we show how rays are bent when they pass from air into glass. All this was worked out before the physical nature of light, that is, its wave nature, was understood. Even now that we know the nature of light we still use geometrical optics for many purposes. It is a good approximation to the behavior of the waves when, and only when, the waves are very short compared with the size of the lenses and of the images we are considering.

To find the full truth about the behavior of lenses and other optical devices, however, we must turn to *physical optics,* that is, to explanations based on waves. This is what we have just done in explaining how a lens focuses waves. Such an explanation is important not only because it explains how a lens focuses light but also because it explains certain limitations on focusing which are vitally important in microwave radio and in optics.

To understand the limitations of focusing, let us ask, what do we mean by saying in connection with Fig. 5.5, that the waves are *focused* at *b*? If we move a little up or down from *b*, the waves from *a* will still add up, crest with crest and trough with trough. It is clear that the waves cannot be focused precisely on one point, but rather that they will spread out over an area. Just as waves don't make perfectly sharp shadows, they don't make perfectly sharp images.

In fact, we can easily estimate how sharp the image can be. Fig. 5.6 shows a lens of width *D* which focuses waves on a point *b* a distance *L* from the lens. The lens has been divided into two halves; the centers of each half, at *x* and *y*, are a distance *D*/2 apart. Suppose that we move up a distance *W* from *b* to a point *b'*. The distance *W* is such that the distance from *b'* to the center of the lower half of the lens is just half a wave length, $\lambda/2$, greater than the distance from *b'* to the center of the upper half of the lens.

Roughly speaking, at this point, b', crests of the waves from the lower half of the lens will arrive when peaks of the waves from the upper part of the lens arrive. That is, there will be no waves at b'.

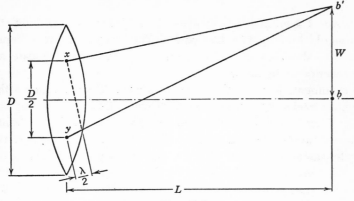

FIG. 5.6

Those with geometrical or mechanical instincts will easily see that, as L is much greater than W or than λ, very nearly

$$\frac{W}{L} = \frac{\left(\frac{\lambda}{2}\right)}{\left(\frac{D}{2}\right)} = \frac{\lambda}{D}$$

Thus, waves will fall above and below b, but at approximately W above and below b there will be no waves at all. As a matter of fact, a great fraction of the waves will fall in a range from $W/2$ above b to $W/2$ below b.

This is an extremely important fact, both in radio and in optics. It can be shown to apply when waves are focused by concave mirrors as well as when waves are focused by lenses. It says, for instance, that if we have a radar antenna of width D and send out a beam of microwaves of wave length λ to a distance L, the beam will have a width W given by this relation. For instance, for radar waves 10 centimeters, or ⅓ feet, long and an antenna 10 feet wide, at a distance of one mile, or 5,280 feet, the width, W, of the radar beam will be about

$$W = \frac{\frac{1}{3}(5,280)}{10}$$

$$W = 176 \text{ feet}$$

For waves 1 centimeter long instead of 10 centimeters long, the beam would be only 17.6 feet wide. This shows why it is important to use short waves and large antennas in order to locate airplanes accurately by radar.

By arguments just like those we have used, it can be shown that if we have a telescope lens or mirror of width D, and if we use light of wave length λ, and if we look at two points or patches of light a distance L away, we can *resolve* them, that is, see them as two separate patches or points of light, only if they are at least a distance W apart, where W is given by this same relation.

For instance, light waves are about 2×10^{-6} feet long. The distance to Mars at its nearest is about 3.5×10^7 miles, or about 1.8×10^{11} feet. If we have a telescope with a lens or mirror 1 foot in diameter, we can resolve objects if they are a distance W apart, given by

$$W = \frac{(2 \times 10^{-6})(1.8 \times 10^{11})}{1}$$

$$W = 360,000 \text{ feet}$$

$$W = 70 \text{ miles}$$

Giovanni Schiaparelli, who in 1877 first reported seeing canals on Mars and who asserted later that they were sometimes double, used a telescope with a lens a little less than ¾ feet in diameter. Thus, he could not have seen double canals unless they were at least 100 miles apart, and he could have scarcely detected single canals unless they were around 100 miles wide. Even the 200-inch telescope could not possibly resolve details on Mars of a size smaller than about 4 miles. On the moon, however, it could resolve details down to about 160 feet.

The same limits to resolution which apply in telescopes apply in microscopes also. This explains why we can see so much finer detail with an electron microscope than with a light microscope. Biologists had to wait for the advent of the electron microscope to be able to see viruses, and the electron microscope has revealed hitherto hidden details of the structure of metals to metallurgists.

Quantum mechanics tells us that when we examine the behavior of electrons in very fine detail, we see phenomena of a wave nature. In fact, the simple behavior of electrons as particles, which we discussed in the preceding chapter, bears much the same relation to the fine-grained quantum-mechanical behavior of electrons that geometric optics does to wave optics. We must consider the wave nature of electrons when we ask how good the resolving power of an electron microscope can be.

The wave length of an electron varies inversely as the square root of the voltage used to accelerate the electrons. For a 50,000-volt accelerating voltage, which is common in electron microscopy, the electron wave length is about 2×10^{-9} inches. This is roughly a ten-thousandth the wave length of visible light.

Using optical microscopes with visible light, we cannot possibly achieve resolutions of better than about a hundred-thousandth of an inch (10^{-5} inches). If we could judge by wave length only, an electron microscope would be ten thousand times as good as a light microscope. Because electron lenses are much inferior in quality to lenses for light, an electron microscope has a resolving power only about two hundred times better than a light microscope. Thus, with an electron microscope we can resolve objects down to about a half a ten-millionth of an inch (5×10^{-8} inches).

Resolution is important in telescopes and microscopes. The width of a radio beam is important in microwave communication. Microwave transmitters send out beams of microwaves from horns, lenses, or reflectors which are called *antennas*, and pick them up with similar antennas. FIG. 5.7 illustrates some common types of antennas used in transmitting and receiving microwaves. Microwaves are often guided for short distances through metal tubes or *wave guides*. In the antenna shown to the left in FIG. 5.7, the wave guide flares out to form a horn like a megaphone, and a lens is placed at the end of the horn. In the antenna shown at the center, the waves from the end of the wave guide are focused into a beam by a concave metal dish in the form of a *parabola*. Most radar antennas are of this sort. In the *horn-reflector* antenna shown at the right of Fig. 5.7 the waves from the horn are focused by a concave surface set at an angle.

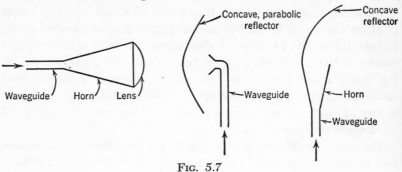

Fig. 5.7

Large antennas are necessarily highly directive. Large, highly directive antennas are used in microwave communication systems so that the transmitted power can be sent toward the receiver rather than scattered in all directions, and so that the receiver can pick up power over a large area. We can see just how this works out. Fig. 5.8 shows a microwave transmitter and a microwave receiver.

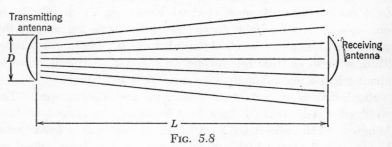

Fig. 5.8

The transmitter sends out a beam of microwaves. A receiving antenna a distance L away picks up a part of this beam. According to our relation, if D is the diameter of the transmitting antenna and λ is the wave length, the width, W, of the microwave beam at the receiving antenna is about

$$W = \frac{\lambda L}{D}$$

If we assume the beam to be circular, the area, A, over which it falls is approximately the area of a circle of diameter W, that is,

$$A = \frac{\pi}{4} W^2 = \frac{\pi \lambda^2 L^2}{4 D^2}$$

If A_R is the area of the receiving antenna, the ratio of the power, P_R, which falls on the receiving antenna and is received to the total power transmitted in the beam, which we will call P_T, is

$$\frac{P_R}{P_T} = \frac{A_R}{A} = \frac{4 A_R D^2}{\pi \lambda^2 L^2}$$

If the transmitting antenna is circular, its area, A_T, is

$$A_T = \frac{\pi}{4} D^2$$

or

$$D^2 = \frac{4}{\pi} A_T$$

Thus, we can write approximately for the ratio of received power to transmitted power,

$$\frac{P_R}{P_T} = \left(\frac{4}{\pi}\right)^2 \frac{A_R A_T}{\lambda^2 L^2}$$

This relation has been arrived at right before our eyes. We have derived everything in it, including the expression for the width of the beam. The result is only approximate because we have used an approximate expression for the diameter of the area over which the transmitted power falls. The correct expression is

$$\frac{P_R}{P_T} = \frac{A_R A_T}{\lambda^2 L^2}$$

This simple and basic equation governing microwave transmission was derived by H. T. Friis. It tells us that to increase the fraction of the transmitted power which is received at a distance L from the transmitter we should increase the area of the transmitting antenna, or the area of the receiving antenna, or we should use a shorter wave length. In this expression, A_R and A_T are the actual physical areas of the transmitting and receiving antennas only for ideal antennas. An ideal transmitting antenna sends out a wave of equal strength over its whole area. If an antenna is ideal as a transmitting antenna, it is ideal as a receiving antenna. Actual practical antennas are not ideal, and we must use instead of A_T and A_R the *effective areas,* which are less than the actual geometrical areas but usually somewhat greater than one half of the geometrical areas. The effective area of antenna is the same for transmitting as for receiving.

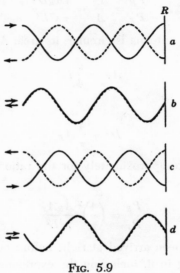

FIG. 5.9

For a typical microwave radio circuit, the distance L is around 30 miles, or 150,000 feet. The antennas may be square and 10 feet on a side. The effective area may be one half the geometrical area, so that A_T and A_R are each 50 square feet. λ may be around 7.5 centimeters—that is, 3 inches, or $\frac{1}{4}$ feet. Thus,

$$\frac{P_R}{P_T} = \frac{(50)(50)}{(\frac{1}{4})^2(150,000)^2} = 1.8 \times 10^{-6}$$

Only about two millionths of the transmitted power will be received.

So far we have considered the properties of waves traveling through open spaces: waves sent out and picked up by antennas and waves focused by lenses and mirrors. There is another very important kind of wave called a *standing wave*. It is a wave which has been trapped in one place. Let us consider how a wave can be trapped.

To understand this, we must understand how a wave is reflected. Fig. 5.9 represents the reflection of a wave coming from the left by a reflecting surface *R*. The wave coming from the left is shown as a solid curve; the reflected wave is shown as a dotted curve.

Reflections are of various kinds. Sometimes the reflection leaves the wave right side up, reflecting a crest as a crest and a trough as a trough. Sometimes (I will present evidence for this later) a reflection turns the wave upside down, reflecting a crest as a trough and a trough as a crest. The reflection in Fig. 5.9 is of this kind. In sketch *b* the wave traveling from the left has advanced a quarter wave length from where it was in sketch *a*, and so has the reflected wave. Sketch *c* shows another advance of a quarter wave length. Sketch *d* shows an advance of a quarter wave length more.

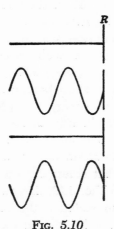

Fig. 5.10

In Fig. 5.10 the amplitudes of the incident and reflected waves have been added. We see that the wave pattern moves neither to the right nor to the left. We have a *standing*, not a *traveling* wave. At the reflector, and at half a wave length and three-halves of a wave length to the left of it, the total amplitude is always zero. At other points, the amplitude rises and falls periodically with time, with the frequency, f, of the wave.

Suppose we put two reflectors, R_1 and R_2, half a wave length apart, as shown in FIG. *5.11*. The solid curve shows the maximum upper excursion of the standing wave; the dashed curve shows the maximum lower excursion of the standing wave. The wave successively oscillates through all positions in between.

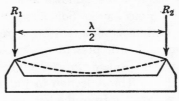

FIG. *5.11*

If FIG. *5.11* strangely resembles the vibration of a stretched rubber band, a door spring, or the string of a musical instrument, the resemblance is intentional. All of these are examples of standing waves, of waves which are reflected back and forth endlessly. If there were no dissipation of energy in friction or radiation of energy in the form of traveling waves, such waves would persist forever. Actually, in our ordinary experience such waves eventually die out, unless energy is supplied. The vibration of the struck string of a piano dies out because no energy is supplied subsequent to the blow of the hammer, while both friction and the radiation of sound carry energy away. The standing wave in the organ pipe persists because the blower continues to supply energy.

We see very clearly that unless the wave length is exactly $\lambda/2$ or $2\,\lambda/2$ or $3\,\lambda/2$, as in FIG. *5.12*, the wave will not be properly reflected at each end to maintain the pattern, and the pattern cannot exist. As the wave length and the frequency are related, this means that a standing wave between reflectors which are a fixed distance apart can exist only at certain particular frequencies and in certain particular patterns. If the velocity is independent of frequency, and if we say that the pattern of FIG. *5.11* corresponds to some fundamental frequency f_1, the pattern of the upper part of FIG. *5.12* will have a frequency $f_2 = 2f_1$, the *second harmonic* (also, the *first overtone*, which is an octave up). The pattern of the lower part of FIG. *5.12* will have a frequency $f_3 = 3 f_1$, the *third harmonic* (the second overtone, the fifth above the octave above). Because of linearity, many such patterns can exist simultaneously without interfering with one another. In striking a piano string we produce many overtones, and these and the way in which they decay with time are responsible for the characteristic tone quality of the piano.

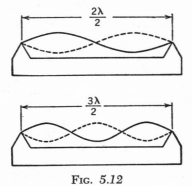

FIG. *5.12*

Sometimes, as in the case of stretched strings, the overtones have frequencies which are integral multiples of the fundamental frequency (an integer is 1, 2, 3, 4, etc.). This is true for stretched strings. Sometimes it is otherwise, as in the case of drums and bells.

Let us disregard the oversimplified illustrations we have used and talk about all waves which are trapped, waves which cannot escape because, no matter in which way they travel, they meet a reflecting barrier.

We can think of many such waves. The ripples on the surface of the water in a pan are reflected by the walls. If you tap the pan, you will (if you are lucky) see concentric rings on the surface; these are standing waves. Electromagnetic (radio) waves can be trapped in a metal box, for metal reflects radio waves.

Any closed (to the waves) system which can support waves traps them. The system may be a violin string, a tuning fork, a room, or a metal box. Such a system will support waves of certain frequencies only. Such frequencies, and the wave patterns associated with them, have been known for many years. They used to be called *normal modes. Modes* means merely patterns of oscillation. Since the advent of quantum mechanics, which came mainly from Germany, the patterns have been called *eigenfunctions* and the frequencies *eigenfrequencies.* On a small enough scale, electrons behave as waves, and in quantum physics the atom is an oscillator exhibiting certain patterns of standing waves.

We are not primarily interested in atoms; our interest is in radio and electronics. We should consider electromagnetic waves trapped in metallic enclosures, for they are very important.

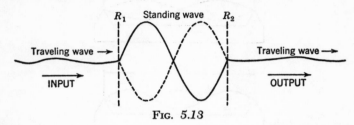

FIG. 5.13

Let us make a rather symbolic drawing, shown in FIG. 5.13. R_1 and R_2 represent somewhat imperfect reflectors. Between R_1 and R_2 there can exist a standing wave. Reflectors R_1 and R_2 have little holes in them, however, so that some of the waves leak out at each reflection. Thus, if nothing were done, the standing wave between R_1 and R_2 would die out as time passed. For instance, a weak wave would leak off to the right of R_2. An arrow shows its direction of travel, and the arrow is labeled *output.*

If we had the wave leaking off only, the standing wave pattern between R_1 and R_2 would gradually decrease in amplitude. Suppose, however, that we supply a wave from the left, which is shown together with an arrow indicating its direction of travel. The arrow is labeled *input.*

If the holes in the reflectors R_1 and R_2 are very small, we can hope to get a wave through this system only if the frequency is very exactly the value which makes the distance between R_1 and R_2 a wave length, so that the large standing wave which is indicated can exist. Imagine the opposite extreme; suppose we make the holes so large that the reflectors cease to exist. We have an uninterrupted medium for transmission of waves between input and output, and waves of any frequency can get through.

What we have just described is a *filter* for electromagnetic waves. Such a filter passes waves of a certain range of frequencies only, a narrow range or *band* of frequencies, or a wide range or band of frequencies, depending on its adjustment. In our example, small holes result in a narrow-band filter and large holes in a wide-band filter.

When you turn the tuning dial of your radio set you are in effect adjusting a filter which acts in essentially this manner. It allows to pass only the frequencies emitted by a certain radio transmitter and excludes (we hope) the frequencies emitted by other transmitters. If the filter passes too narrow a band of frequencies, the result will not satisfy a hi-fi man. If it passes too wide a band of frequencies, you will get two or more stations at once.

What have we learned about waves? Not much in minute detail. Saying that we have five horses tells us little about horses. Saying that we have five wives raises questions which cannot be resolved by mathematics.

Number is a very general concept, but one of overwhelming scope and importance. The idea of waves is a somewhat more complicated concept, and one of a smaller range of applicability. Yet, after the ideas of number and measurement, it is among the few concepts of very great generality. Without the concept of waves, we cannot understand the behavior of the ocean, of earthquakes, of sound, of musical instruments, of the vibration of structures, of radio, of light, nor, we must emphasize, of that bane of those who are imperfectly-adjusted-to-contemporary-physics; that is, quantum mechanics.

In studying waves further, we must pay some heed to the physical nature of the waves which we study. Ordinarily, a student of physics starts out with mechanical waves of some sort.

In mechanical waves, the propagation of waves always involves kinetic energy and potential energy. The material through which the wave propagates moves with an oscillatory motion. Because of the velocity associated with this motion, the material gains and loses kinetic energy. In sound waves the air is compressed as the wave travels; the air under pressure has potential energy. In large waves of water, the water has potential energy because at the crests it is raised above the mean level. In small ripples, the water has potential energy because of the stretching of the surface of the water against *surface tension*.

As the wave travels along, the material through which it travels alternately gains and loses kinetic and potential energy.

Newton's laws of motion tell us that in altering the velocity which accounts for kinetic energy, a force must be exerted; this force is the force associated with the increase or decrease of potential energy as the material is distorted during the passage of the wave.

If this were a conventional treatment of waves, we would analyze in detail the propagation of one or more types of mechanical waves, to show how the laws of motion explain their behavior and how the waves transmit energy away from the device that produces them and carry it to whatever absorbs them. This book is, however, primarily an account of electronics, and in explaining in detail the behavior of waves we will consider only the case of electromagnetic waves.

To understand electromagnetic waves, we must understand Maxwell's equations, which govern the behavior of electric and magnetic fields. Maxwell's equations form the subject of the following chapter in this book.

CHAPTER VI

Maxwell's Wonderful Equations

THERE are certain summits of achievement in the history of science, the formulation of certain general laws, which command the profound respect of all following generations. Newton's laws of motion together with his law of gravitation are one such an eminence. Newton's work makes it possible to unravel all the phenomena associated with mechanical motions. After Newton's day, a knowledge of physics which did not include an understanding of Newton's work was inconceivable.

Maxwell's equations are for electric and magnetic phenomena what Newton's laws are for mechanical phenomena. While later advances such as relativity and quantum mechanics have followed, an understanding of this newer knowledge of the universe presupposes an understanding of Newton's laws and of Maxwell's equations. Maxwell's equations are fundamental not only to electronics but to all of physics. To anyone who is motivated by anything beyond the most narrowly practical, it is worth while to understand Maxwell's equations simply for the good of his soul.

Those who work in electronics have to understand Maxwell's equations to some degree, for these equations govern the behavior of electric and magnetic fields. Sometimes the understanding appears in a rather specialized form, as in certain particular rules which govern the behavior of coils and condensers in radio circuits. All of these particular rules stem from Maxwell's equations.

It was with some trepidation that I tackled the problem of explaining Maxwell's equations in this book. I have several thick reference books which deal with nothing but Maxwell's equations and examples of their application in various practical problems.

Each book is longer than this book, and each is much tougher reading.

Usually the student is brought to some understanding of Maxwell's equations by easy stages, through dealing first with certain simple and specialized behavior of electric and magnetic fields, including the role of charges in producing electric fields and that of currents in producing magnetic fields. Then Maxwell's equations are presented as a synthesis of this behavior. There follows a mathematical study of the equations, by means of which certain general forms of behavior of fields are deduced as mathematical theorems. Maxwell's equations are then used to solve particular problems involving electric and magnetic fields.

There is just not space here for that sort of thing, nor can the reader be presumed to have the time or the mathematics to wade through it.

Oliver Heaviside was an important and eccentric physicist and electrical engineer of the latter part of the last century and the early part of this. In his book on electricity and magnetism, he simply stated Maxwell's equations. He then applied them to explain the behavior of a particularly simple phenomenon, a plane electromagnetic wave. He turned to more complicated problems later. We will follow a similar course, except that we cannot apply the equations to as many problems as Heaviside did in writing for experts in his field.

Fortunately for this approach, we already have the necessary notions of electric and magnetic fields and of their representation by lines of force. We should remember that the lines of force show the direction of the field and that the density or closeness of the lines of force indicates the strength of the field. Because a field is a vector, which has a magnitude and a direction (the direction of the lines of force), we can resolve the field into components, and we can speak of the component of the field in any direction we choose. Thus, in FIG. 6.1 the line with the two arrowheads is a chosen direction and the vector E is the electric field. To find the component E_p parallel to the chosen direction we draw two vectors, E_p parallel to the direction and E_n normal to the direction, such that the vector sum of E_p and E_n is equal to E. Then E_p is the component of field in the chosen direction and E_n is the component normal to that direction.

In order to understand Maxwell's equations in the simplest possible terms, it is helpful to become familiar with two important quantities called *electric flux* and *magnetic flux*. The electric and magnetic fluxes are quantities which can be expressed in terms of

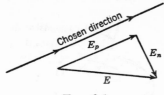

FIG. 6.1

the electric and magnetic fields. They are useful quantities. They enter into Maxwell's equations in a particular way which we shall see. We should not, however, look for some mysterious meaning of these quantities. They are just what we define them to be. We should ask, then, how are these fluxes defined?

Imagine that we have an electric field of strength E perpendicular to a small flat area A. Then the electric flux, which I will call ϕ (phi), is a constant ϵ times the field strength, E, times the area, A.

$$\phi = \epsilon E A$$

ϵ (epsilon) is called the dielectric constant of space. Similarly, for a magnetic field of strength H normal to the area A, the magnetic flux ψ (psi) is given by

$$\psi = \mu H A$$

where μ (mu) is called the permitivity of space.

Because the strength of a field is proportional to the density of lines of force, the flux through an area is proportional to the number of lines of force crossing that area.

Suppose we want to calculate the flux across an area which is not normal to the electric or magnetic field. To do this, we draw a line normal to the area and multiply the area by the component of field which is parallel to this line. We call this normal component

E_n or H_n. Thus, we should really write for electric flux ϕ and magnetic flux ψ

$$\phi = \epsilon E_n A$$

$$\psi = \mu H_n A$$

Suppose that we have a cap-shaped surface as shown in FIG. 6.2. The particular shape of the surface doesn't matter; what will be

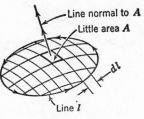

FIG. 6.2

said is true of any surface, and I have chosen this shape merely because it is easy to draw. I have divided this surface into little areas; one of these I have labeled A. I have drawn a line normal or perpendicular to this area A, and I have indicated a direction on it by means of arrowheads. We get the flux through this little area A by taking the component of field parallel to this line and in the direction indicated and by multiplying the field by the area. This flux may thus be positive or negative, depending on whether the component of field is in the direction of the arrowheads or in the opposite direction. We can get the total flux through the whole surface bounded by the line l, which runs around the perimeter of the surface, by adding together the fluxes for all the little areas into which the surface has been divided.

Once we have clearly in our mind what electric and magnetic flux are—that is, what we have defined them to be—it is easy to understand Maxwell's equations. We can write them in the following form:

$$\oint H_l \, dl = \frac{\partial \phi}{\partial t} + I_c$$

$$\oint E_l \, dl = - \frac{\partial \psi}{\partial t}$$

The *line integral signs* on the left may appear cabalistic to those who have not encountered them before. Their meaning is simple, however. In FIG. 6.2 we may note that arrowheads indicate a direction on the line *l* which runs around the boundary of the surface. Moreover, a little length *dl* of the boundary has been indicated. Suppose that we take the component of magnetic field H_l parallel to this little line *dl* and in the direction of the arrowheads. Let us multiply this component H_l by the length *dl*, and then do this for all other little lengths, once around the perimeter, and finally add up all the products. This sum is what we mean by the *line integral*

$$\oint H_l \, dl$$

What do we mean by $\partial\phi/\partial t$? This means the rate at which the electric flux changes with time. $\partial\psi/\partial t$ is the rate at which magnetic flux changes with time. These symbols mean the amount the flux changes in an extremely short period of time divided by the length of the period of time, measured in seconds.

I_c stands for the total current carried by charged particles flowing across the total area bounded by *l*, the flow in the direction of the arrowheads on the line normal to the surface. Of course, this current may be positive or negative, depending on which way the current flows with respect to the arrowheads on the line.

We notice that in the first of Maxwell's equations the quantity $\partial\phi/\partial t$ is added to the current I_c. As we noted in Chapter IV, an electric current—that is, a flow of electric charges—produces a magnetic field. Maxwell was the first to recognize that a change in electric flux acts just as does a flow of charges in producing a magnetic field. Because $\partial\phi/\partial t$ behaves like a flow of charges, $\partial\phi/\partial t$ is reckoned as part of the total electric current. It is called *displacement current* (there are historical reasons for the word *displacement* which need not concern us). To distinguish the part of the current I_c which is due to the flow of charges, I_c is called *convection current*. We may add these two parts of the current together to get the total current, *I*:

$$I = \frac{\partial\phi}{\partial t} + I_c$$

Although the quantity $\partial\psi/\partial t$, which appears in the second of Maxwell's equations, has no name, we may if we wish call it *magnetic displacement current*. Because there are no free magnetic poles, there is no such thing as magnetic convection current.

We are now in a position to state Maxwell's equations in words. The first equation says that if, with due regard for sign and direction, we go once around the boundary of a region, multiply each element of the length of the boundary by the component of magnetic field in the direction of the boundary, and add all these products up, then the total is equal to the total current, convection current and displacement current, flowing through the boundary. Or, mathematically, the line integral of the magnetic field around the boundary is equal to the total current through the boundary. This equation has to do with the production of magnetic fields by the flow of charges and by displacement current—that is, by changes in electric fields.

Maxwell's second equation says that the line integral of the electric field around the boundary is equal to the negative of the rate of change of magnetic flux through the boundary; that is, to the negative of the magnetic displacement current through the boundary. This equation has to do with the production of electric fields by changes in magnetic fields.

In interpreting this second equation, we should remember that the work done on a moving charge is the magnitude of the charge times the component of electric field in the direction of motion times the distance moved. Thus, if we moved an electric charge around the line l of Fig. 6.2 fast enough so that the field did not change appreciably while we moved the charge, the work done on the charge would be just the charge times the line integral of the electric field—that is, times the left-hand side of Maxwell's second equation. Magnetic fields cannot do work on electric charges, but changing magnetic fields produce electric fields which can do work on moving electric charges.

Indeed, this is the principle of the betatron. The betatron is an electron accelerator. It is used to produce very fast electrons. The first betatrons were used in experiments in nuclear physics. Nowadays the fast electrons from betatrons are often used to produce very penetrating X rays which can be used to make X ray photographs of heavy steel parts, and which have been used in treating cancer.

Electron velocity, and hence the kinetic energy of electrons, is often specified in *electron volts* or simply *volts*. This means the voltage which would be necessary to accelerate an electron to a particular velocity and kinetic energy. Betatrons give electrons energies of tens of millions of electron volts. Betatrons are huge, heavy beasts, consisting principally of an electromagnet whose iron core and copper coils weigh many tons. A glass, doughnut-shaped, evacuated tube is placed between the poles of the magnet, and the electrons which are to be accelerated travel around and around in circles inside of the doughnut. The magnet is so designed that the magnetic flux through the circle of the electron path is twice what it would be if the magnetic field had the same strength over all of the area of the circle that it has at the electron path itself.

The magnetic field serves two purposes. It bends the electrons in their paths so that they can circle around inside of the doughnut. Then, as the electrons circle around, the magnetic field is made to increase in strength. According to Maxwell's second equation, this produces an electric field along the circular electron path, in such a direction as to increase the speed of the electrons. It is this field that accelerates the electrons in their paths until they have tens of millions of volts energy. If the magnetic flux through the circular path is adjusted as stated above, the diameter of the circular electron path will remain constant as the electrons are accelerated.

The example of the betatron shows one application of Maxwell's second equation. Another is the case in which a wire or a coil of wire which is part of an electric circuit moves physically through a magnetic field so that the magnetic flux through the complete circuit changes. In one type of microphone for picking up sound waves, a moving diaphragm moves a coil of wire in a magnetic field so as to produce an electric field which is a representation of the sound wave. Electric generators also work in this manner. Many other things, simple and complicated, can be understood if once we become familiar with Maxwell's equations and learn to remember the meaning of the quantities that appear in them. In fact, they tell what there is to be known about the behavior of electric and magnetic fields.

They tell their full story, however, only to those who are able to extract information from them by means of mathematical transformations and manipulations. Here we must content ourselves with a few simple examples. I trust, however, that even some of these may prove a little startling as well as important and interesting.

It is very hard even for the mathematically expert to find combinations of changing electric and magnetic fields which are solutions of Maxwell's equations. We can, however, test any proposed electric and magnetic fields. If they do not satisfy Maxwell's equations the proposed fields cannot represent real physical phenomena. Conversely, if in some way we find electric and magnetic fields which do satisfy Maxwell's equations, these fields do represent possible physical phenomena, things which could take place and be observed in the world about us. Let us now consider one simple, possible combination of electric and magnetic fields—that which Oliver Heaviside placed at the beginning of his book, the plane electromagnetic wave.

By *plane* wave we mean one which does not expand in circles as it travels, as do the ripples from a stone in a pond, but one which travels everywhere in one direction. Strictly speaking, one cannot produce plane electromagnetic waves of the sort we shall discuss. However, suppose that an electromagnetic wave travels out radially from a source such as a radio antenna. Very far from the antenna, a wave crest will be spherical in form. When the sphere is large enough, the wave is nearly plane, and just as the surface of the earth can be regarded as plane for many purposes, we can in our considerations regard such a wave crest as lying in a plane.

FIG. 6.3 is intended to illustrate a portion of a plane wave. The rightmost part of the wave is called the *wave front;* this lies in a plane normal to the direction of propagation and, in the figure, normal to the plane of the paper. To the left of the wave front there is a uniform magnetic field of strength *H,* directed upward, and a uniform electric field of strength *E* points straight into the plane of the paper, away from us. To the right of the wave front there is no electric or magnetic field. The wave travels through air or vacuum, where there are no electric charges, so there is no convection current. The wave front travels to the right with a velocity v.

As our line l we will take a square of length L on a side, with its surface parallel to the magnetic field and perpendicular to the

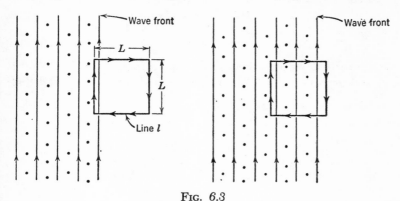

FIG. 6.3

electric field. We will consider conditions at two succeeding times; just after the wave front has barely passed the left-hand side of the square, and just before it reaches the right-hand side of the square.

In each case, there is no component of magnetic field along the top or the bottom of the square, and the field has not yet reached the right-hand side of the square. Thus, there is a component of magnetic field along the left-hand side of the square only, and the line integral around the square is simply

$$\oint H_l \, dl = HL$$

The wave takes a time T to cross the square of width L, where T is given by

$$T = \frac{L}{v}$$

At the start of this time, the electric flux through the square is zero; at the end of the time T it is

$$\phi = \epsilon E L^2$$

The rate of change of the flux is this total change of flux divided by the time, T, or

$$\frac{\partial \phi}{\partial t} = \frac{\phi}{T} = \epsilon E L \frac{L}{T} = \epsilon E L v$$

According to Maxwell's first equation,

$$HL = \frac{\partial \phi}{\partial t} = \epsilon L v$$

$$H = \epsilon E v$$

Suppose that we now consider a square parallel to the electric field and perpendicular to the magnetic field. We easily find that:

$$\oint E_l \, dl = EL$$

$$\psi = -\mu H L^2$$

$$\frac{\partial \psi}{\partial t} = \frac{\psi}{T} = -\mu H L \frac{L}{T} = -\mu H L v$$

The sign is negative because of the direction of the field with respect to the directions indicated in Fig. 6.2.

According to Maxwell's second equation,

$$EL = -\frac{\partial \psi}{\partial t} = \mu H L v$$

$$E = \mu H v$$

We now have both this and the earlier relation between E and H to work with, that is,

$$H = \epsilon E v$$

If we multiply the two relations between E and H together, we obtain

$$EH = \mu \epsilon E H v^2$$

This gives

$$v^2 = \frac{1}{\mu \epsilon}$$

$$v = \frac{1}{\sqrt{\mu \epsilon}}$$

If we put in the numerical values of μ and ϵ given in the appendix we find that $v = 3 \times 10^8$ meters per second. This is just the velocity of light. When Maxwell first deduced electromagnetic waves from his equations, it was this fact that led him to believe, correctly, that light is simply electromagnetic waves.

We can divide the two relations for E and H and obtain

$$\frac{H}{E} = \frac{\epsilon}{\mu} \frac{E}{H}$$

$$\frac{E}{H} = \sqrt{\frac{\mu}{\epsilon}} = 377$$

This is a relation that is very important to those who work with electromagnetic waves. It holds true for all plane electromagnetic waves, whether they vary with distance in the direction of motion in the abrupt manner of the wave which we have just considered or vary sinusoidally with time and distance.

When waves vary sinusoidally with time, the electric and magnetic fields are perpendicular to one another and normal to the direction of travel, just as in the wave described above. As the wave moves past a point, the electric field and the magnetic field at the point rise and fall in intensity. The magnetic field is at its peak at the same time that the electric field is at its peak.

Imagine that we turn the drawing of FIG. 6.3 around so that the bottom becomes the top. The electric field still points away from us. The magnetic field, which formerly pointed up, now points down. And the wave now travels to the left instead of to the right.

I have tried to illustrate this in FIG. 6.4. To the right of the heavy vertical line A–A', the electric field E is away from us, the magnetic field H is upward, and the wave travels to the right. To the left of line A–A', the electric field is away from us, the magnetic field is downward, and the wave travels to the left.

Can we have a situation of this kind? I have shown a rectangle of height h and very narrow width which just encloses the dividing line A–A'. We see that the line integral of H around this path is

$$\oint H = -2Hh$$

According to Maxwell's first equation, this must be equal to the sum of the displacement current plus the convection current through the rectangle. If we make the rectangle very, very narrow, the electric flux through it must be negligibly small. Thus, we must have

$$-2Hh = I_c$$

This means that the condition we have imagined can exist if along the line A–A' a convection current, a current of moving charges, flows through the rectangle, normal to the plane of the

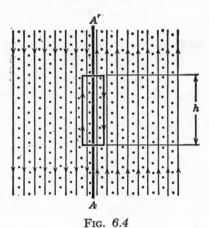

FIG. 6.4

paper. The current per unit distance along the line A–A' must be such that $2H$ amperes flow for each meter of distance along A–A'. The positive direction has been taken as the direction into the plane of the paper, the direction of the electric field. As the above relation says that the current must be negative, the direction of current flow will be opposite to the direction of the electric field—that is, out of the plane of the paper. If the current consisted of negative electrons, the electrons would flow into the plane of the paper, in the same direction as the electric field.

The electric force on a charged particle is the charge times the field. As the charge of the electron is negative, the force on the electrons constituting the current will be up from the plane of the paper, against their motion. Thus, to make them move in the direction necessary to produce the electromagnetic waves which go off to the left and right, we must push the electrons constituting the current in the direction of motion; we must do work on them. To cause the current to flow, work must be done, and power, the rate at which this work is done, must be supplied. This power flows away to the left and to the right in the form of the electromagnetic power of the waves, which the flowing current generates.

Radio waves of the broadcast band are sent out by tall towers, hundreds of feet high. Such a tower is approximately a quarter wave length long, and a powerful radio transmitter maintains a standing wave of current along it. As the current oscillates sinusoidally with time, it sends out radio waves. As the waves travel away from the tower, in the part of the waves near to the ground the magnetic lines of force of the waves are circles around the tower, and the electric lines of force are vertical, parallel to the tower. Farther above the ground, the electric lines of force arch along a dome centered on the tower. The waves travel out radially from the tower, and near the ground the waves spread out in circles, like the ripples caused by a stone dropped in a pond.

Antennas for FM and TV are more complicated, but the principles are the same. Broadcast-band waves have the electric field vertical and the magnetic field horizontal; we say that they are *vertically polarized.* This is convenient for relatively long waves such as broadcast waves, for tall towers about a quarter wave length long form convenient and efficient antennas. In this country, FM and TV antennas are so oriented as to produce waves with a horizontal electric field and a vertical magnetic field. We call such waves *horizontally polarized* waves. In England, however, TV waves are vertically polarized.

One wishes not only to send electromagnetic waves through space from a transmitting antenna to a receiving antenna; one wishes to guide them by means of wires or conductors. Any two parallel conductors close to one another form a *transmission line.* Fig. 6.5 shows the electric lines of force (solid) and the magnetic lines of force (dashed) for two common types of transmission line, shown end-on. That to the left consists of two parallel wires, and is called a *two-wire line* or a *parallel-wire line.* That to the right consists of a tube with a wire at the center; it is called a *coaxial line.*

We can see in FIG. 6.5 that near the surface of the conductors (wires, tubes) the electric field is everywhere normal to the surface and the magnetic field is everywhere parallel to the surface. This is true for all microwave fields near the surface of conductors, and

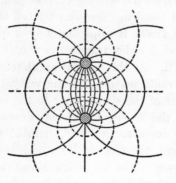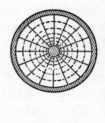

FIG. 6.5

neither electric nor magnetic fields are present inside of conductors. At the surface there is just enough electric charge where the electric lines of force end to satisfy Maxwell's equations in the form of Gauss's law, which we will discuss a little later. Just such currents flow parallel to the surface of conductors at the surface as will allow Maxwell's second equation to be satisfied with a magnetic field parallel to the surface outside of the surface and no magnetic field inside of the surface.

Electric fields cannot exist in conductors at all, except, as explained in Chapter III, the very weak fields associated with the flow of electric current. Steady or very slowly varying magnetic fields can exist inside a conductor. If the magnetic fields vary rapidly, however, they produce electric fields which are sufficient to cause currents to flow, and these currents will reduce the magnetic field practically to zero.

The work of Southworth and Barrow has shown us that electromagnetic waves which are short enough will go through a metal pipe or tube called a wave guide. Usually, less power is lost because of electrical resistance in a wave guide than in a transmission line of the same length. However, waves have to be short compared with the diameter of the tube to go through a wave guide. Wave guides are usually either rectangular or round in cross section. Wave guides are used extensively in radar and in microwave communication systems.

For instance, in the transcontinental radio relay system which sends telephone and television signals across the country, the antennas are located on the tops of towers, some of them over a hundred feet high, while the transmitters and receivers are located on the ground. Long rectangular metal tubes or wave guides carry the signals from the transmitter to the transmitting antenna and from the receiving antenna to the receiver with little loss.

Maxwell's equations cover not merely electromagnetic waves but all phenomena involving electric and magnetic fields. One can gain a general insight into the behavior of electric and magnetic fields by studying them.

For instance, imagine the surface discussed in connection with Fig. 6.2 to swell out into a balloon, with the line l bounding a hole in the balloon. Let us now make the perimeter l shorter and shorter, so that finally its length becomes zero and the hole in the surface vanishes. As we do this, the line integral around l becomes smaller and smaller so that finally

$$\oint H_l \, dl = 0$$

$$\oint E_l \, dl = 0$$

We now have a *closed surface* enclosing a volume of space. What do Maxwell's equations say about such a closed surface?

The first equation says that:

$$\frac{\partial \phi}{\partial t} + I_e = 0$$

$$\frac{\partial \phi}{\partial t} = -I_e$$

This means that the total current flow, displacement plus convection current, into or out of any volume is always zero.

Imagine that we start out with no current, no electric field, and no flux. We then let a convection current, a current of charges, flow into the volume through the surface enclosing it. If the flow consists of positive charges, this will constitute a negative convection current, for the direction is opposite to that of the line normal to the surface, which points outward. The negative convection current is the rate at which positive charge crosses the surface and enters the enclosed volume; it is the rate of change of charge in the volume. $\partial\phi/\partial t$ is the rate of change of flux crossing the surface. Because, according to Maxwell's equations, the two rates must be equal, by the time a total electric charge Q has flowed through the surface and into the volume, we will find that the total electric flux outward is always

$$\phi = Q$$

This is shown as Gauss's law. It was known in Maxwell's time, and, like much earlier knowledge, it is embedded in Maxwell's equations. It tells how electric fields are associated with charges.

Sometimes we deal with *static* electric and magnetic fields—that is, with fields which do not change with time. For such fields, $\partial\phi/\partial t$ and $\partial\psi/\partial t$ are zero. When ϕ and ψ do not change, the only electric fields are those associated with charges, according to Gauss's law (that is, according to Maxwell's equations).

We can deduce the inverse-square law of force between fixed charges from Maxwell's equations. Imagine a single charge Q, located in the center of a spherical surface of radius r. The electric field will have a constant strength E_1 over the surface of the sphere and will everywhere point outward. Thus, the electric flux ϕ across the surface of the sphere will be ϵE_1 times the area of the surface, or

$$\phi = 4\pi r^2 \epsilon E_1$$

According to Gauss's law

$$4\pi r^2 \epsilon E_1 = Q_1$$

$$E_1 = \frac{Q_1}{4\pi \epsilon r^2}$$

Imagine another charge of charge Q_2 to be at a distance r from the first charge. The force f exerted on Q_2 by Q_1 will be the field E_1 due to Q_1 times Q_2; thus,

$$f = \frac{Q_1 Q_2}{4 \pi \epsilon r^2}$$

Thus, we have obtained the inverse-square law of force between two charges from Maxwell's equations. Like charges are repelled; unlike charges are attracted.

We can also apply Maxwell's equations to the production of a magnetic field by a current, as discussed in connection with

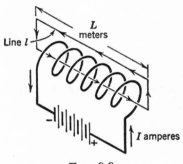

FIG. 6.6

FIG. 4.1 of Chapter IV. This figure has been redrawn in FIG. 6.6, and a closed line l has been drawn through the solenoid for a length L and back on the outside.

The wire carries a steady convection current of I amperes. If the coil has n turns per meter, the current flows through the boundary l a total of nL times. According to Maxwell's first equation, then,

$$\oint H_l \, dl = nLI$$

Now, the magnetic field has a nearly constant value H inside the solenoid and a very small value outside of the solenoid. Hence, the line integral is simply HL, and we have

$$HL = nLI$$
$$H = nI$$

This is the expression for the magnetic field inside a long solenoid. The strength of the field is equal to the *ampere turns per meter*.

In FIG. 6.6 the battery is necessary simply to cause the electric current to persist in spite of the electrical resistance of the wire, which causes electric energy to be turned into heat just as mechanical friction turns the kinetic energy of motion into heat. Suppose, now, that we try to change the amount of current flowing through the coil of FIG. 6.6, say, by changing the voltage of the battery. As the current changes, the magnetic flux must change. But, according to Maxwell's second equation, a changing magnetic flux causes an electric field. It turns out that this additional electric field is in such a direction as to oppose whatever change in battery voltage we made in trying to change the current. If we suddenly change the battery voltage, the current at first does not change at all. Gradually it will assume a new value because of the effects of the resistance of the wire.

Thus, it follows from Maxwell's equations that currents in wires tend to persist. This is analogous to Newton's law that motion tends to persist. The effect is strongest when the wire is wound in a coil of many turns, so that the current produces a strong magnetic flux. We may liken the flow of current through such a coil to the sliding of a mass on a slippery surface, and the electrical resistance of the coil to the friction of the sliding mass.

Coils, or *inductors* or *inductances* are one of the building blocks of radio. Another building block is what is called a *capacitor* or a *condenser*. This is just two metal plates very close together, separated either by air or by an insulating solid material. FIG. 6.7 shows two such metal plates connected by a battery, which produces an electric field and an electric flux between them.[1] By Gauss's law, this flux is associated with charges on the surfaces of the conductors. If the total flux is ϕ, there is a charge $Q = +\phi$ on the positive plate of the condenser and a charge $Q = -\phi$ on the negative plate of the condenser. The voltage V across the condenser is related to the electric field E between the plates. If the field is constant between

[1] In this figure the arrowheads are drawn in the direction of the electric field, and not in the direction of the force on an electron, as in Chapter III.

the plates and if the distance between the plates is l, then

$$V = El$$

For a given condenser, the charge Q is proportional to the voltage V; that is, Q is equal to V multiplied by a constant C:

$$Q = CV$$

The constant C is called the *capacitance* of the condenser. We note that if we make no electrical connections to the plates of a condenser, so that the charge Q cannot flow away but must remain

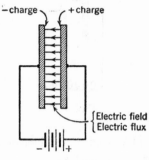

FIG. 6.7

constant, then V will vary if C varies. We can change the capacitance C by changing the distance l between the plates. This is the principle of the condenser microphone. In this device, a thin stretched piece of metal foil is placed very close to a solid metal plate and a charge is put on the resulting condenser. Sound waves cause the thin foil to vibrate. This changes the voltage across the condenser, producing an electric signal which corresponds to the sound wave striking the foil.

Usually, condensers or capacitors have unmoving plates and constant capacitances. Usually they are used for other purposes. Consider, for instance, what would happen if we removed the battery of FIG. 6.7 and connected the plates of the same condenser together by means of a wire, as shown in FIG. 6.8. A current would tend to flow from the positive plate to the negative plate. Suppose, however, that the wire was coiled, to form an inductance. It would take some time for the current to start flowing. Further, once the current got started in the coil, it would be hard to stop. As a matter of fact, the current would oscillate back and forth sinusoidally in the coil, alternately charging the plates of the condenser minus and plus, and then, later, plus and minus. The behavior of the current is like the oscillations of a mass supported by a spring. The capacitor is analogous to the spring.

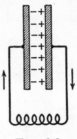

FIG. 6.8

This behavior is also like that of an electromagnetic wave trapped in a closed box or resonator, that is, a standing wave, as discussed in Chapter V. It should be, for both are governed by the same laws—that is, Maxwell's equations.

As we noted in connection with waves in Chapter V, the phenomenon of standing waves can be used to select, to allow to pass, a narrow range of frequencies. In microwave radio we use for this purpose a small closed box or resonator with holes to let waves in and out, and the signal to and from the resonator travels as electromagnetic waves in tubes or wave guides. At lower frequencies it is more convenient to send signals along wires, or transmission lines, and to obtain a behavior analogous to that of the resonator by use of circuits made up of coils and condensers. Thus, when you turn the dial of your radio, the "resonator" which is adjusted actually consists of a coil and a condenser. Usually, it is the condenser which is adjusted. This condenser consists of interleaved metal plates with an air space between, and the degree of interleaving is changed as the knob turns the shaft. This changes the *resonant frequency* of the electrical *circuit* consisting of the coil and condenser.

There are many other important applications of electromagnetic waves. For instance, in *transformers* which are used to change the voltage in alternating-current electric systems, a coil of wire is used to produce a magnetic flux which varies sinusoidally with time. This magnetic flux passes through another coil of wire. As the flux changes, it produces an electric field between the ends of the wire of the coil—or, we can say, it produces a voltage between the ends of the wires.

We have not yet covered all the simple illustrations of Maxwell's equations, nor will we be able to cover them all. We have not discussed one very important matter which we cannot afford to pass over: that is, that the constants ϵ and μ are different for different substances.

ϵ is greater for glass, mica or other solid dielectrics than it is for air. Thus, the application of a given voltage across a given thickness and area of mica produces more electric flux than does the application of the same voltage across the same area and thickness of air. The change of the voltage produces more displacement current in the case of mica than in the case of air. For a given spacing between plates of a given size, a capacitor using mica as a dielectric will have more capacitance than a capacitor using air as a dielectric.

μ is much greater for iron than for air. Thus, a current through a coil surrounded by iron produces more magnetic flux than if the same coil were surrounded by air. This is why iron cores are used in electromagnets and in transformers.

The behavior of electric and magnetic fields in spaces partly filled with dielectric materials or partly filled with magnetic materials is quite complicated, and we will consider only one case here. That is the case of lenses made of dielectric substances and surrounded by air.

The velocity of an electromagnetic wave is $1/\sqrt{\mu\epsilon}$. Thus, light waves or radio waves travel slower in a dielectric substance such as glass than they do in air or in vacuum. We have seen in Chapter

V that lenses focus waves by means of such a difference in wave velocity. A lens for focusing electromagnetic waves is an example of the utility of partly filling a space in which waves travel with a material having a dielectric constant different from that of air or vacuum.

Actually, saying that ϵ or μ is different for some substance than it is for vacuum is only a sort of average way of talking about the substance. All matter is mostly vacuum, thinly populated with minute particles such as electrons and protons. Some of these particles inherently have magnetic and electric fields associated with them. Electrons have an electric field associated with them, and they produce magnetic fields as they move within atoms.

When an electromagnetic wave travels through a substance, it moves or it changes the motions of the particles in the atoms, or of atoms or molecules themselves. Thus it affects the electric and magnetic fields of the particles or of the atoms or molecules. When the waves are long and smooth compared with the spacings between the particles, atoms, or molecules, we can take these effects into account by assigning to the substance a value of ϵ or μ different from ϵ or μ for the vacuum of which the solid is largely composed.

Microwave radio offers a beautiful analogy to such behavior. When we shoot a radio wave through a regularly spaced array of metal disks or strips, spaced close together compared with the wave length, the wave is not reflected or scattered. Instead, it behaves just as if it were passing through a substance with a value of ϵ higher than that for air or vacuum. In this case, the fields of the wave move charges about on the metal disks or strips, and the fields of these moving charges mimic on a large scale the behavior of the submicroscopic molecules of glass when a light wave passes through the glass. The transcontinental microwave radio relay system uses in its antennas huge ten-foot by ten-foot lenses made up of metal strips separated by Polyfoam (a bubbly dielectric much like sponge rubber, but stiff).

The physicist or electrical engineer wants to pursue the study of Maxwell's equations much further than we have here. He must proceed by rewriting these equations in various ways suited to particular mathematical manipulations. For instance, here are Maxwell's equations in the differential form in rectangular co-ordinates.

$$\frac{\partial E_z}{\partial y} - \frac{\partial E_y}{\partial z} = -j\omega\mu H_x \qquad \frac{\partial H_z}{\partial y} - \frac{\partial H_y}{\partial z} = j\omega\epsilon E_x + J_x$$

$$\frac{\partial E_x}{\partial z} - \frac{\partial E_z}{\partial x} = -j\omega\mu H_y \qquad \frac{\partial H_x}{\partial z} - \frac{\partial H_z}{\partial x} = j\omega\epsilon E_y + J_y$$

$$\frac{\partial E_y}{\partial x} - \frac{\partial E_x}{\partial y} = -j\omega\mu H_z \qquad \frac{\partial H_y}{\partial x} - \frac{\partial H_x}{\partial y} = j\omega\epsilon E_z + J_z$$

Here the professional worker with electricity and magnetism must take over, and we must regretfully take leave of Maxwell's wonderful equations.

CHAPTER VII

Some Vacuum-Tube Amplifiers

THE whole of our complicated electronic art of
communication, control, and computation is completely dependent
on the existence of amplifiers which, with almost unthinkable rapid-
ity and with sufficient fidelity, can control large amounts of power
in a manner dictated by a weaker input or control signal. The
nature of any amplifier is summed up in the simple drawing of FIG.
7.1. The amplifier, somewhere inside the box labeled *amplifier,*

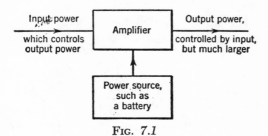

FIG. *7.1*

does not produce power; it controls it. Thus, the amplifier must
be provided with a *power source,* from which it can draw power.
An *input signal* of small power goes into the amplifier. The amplifier supplies at the *output* an *output signal* which is to some degree
a replica of the input signal, but an amplified replica with greater
power. The output signal may in actual cases have two times the
power of the input signal, or ten times, or 100 times, or 10,000 times
or more the power of the input signal, but the power must be greater
than that of the input signal for the device to be an amplifier.

Amplifiers are needed in long-distance telephony. Before amplifiers were available, long-distance calls were weak and uncertain.

Nowadays, in its travel across the country a long-distance telephone call is amplified every five to thirty miles (depending on just how it is sent). You hear a person in a coast-to-coast call perhaps better than you hear a man in a nearby suburb. All long-distance calls are amplified.

In order to control electronically complicated machines such as lathes, steel mills, chemical plants, or airplanes, weak control signals must be amplified so that they can operate machinery.

In complex electronic computers, the output of one part of the equipment must control the operation of other parts, and amplification is necessary for this.

In order to produce the electrical oscillations which are radiated as radio waves, an oscillator is needed. Suppose we connect the output of an amplifier back to the input through a resonator or resonant circuit tuned to a particular frequency. Initially, there will always be some small disturbance called *noise* present (see Chapter IX), and this will be amplified. The greater power of the output will again be amplified, and the signal will build up to some final value. The device *oscillates*, producing a sinusoidal signal which can be used in a radio transmitter, or for many other purposes.

Before the invention of the transistor, a few years ago, vacuum tubes were, if not the only amplifiers available, at least the only versatile amplifiers which could make possible a diverse and effective electronic art. For many purposes, vacuum tubes are still irreplaceable. While transistors are as yet relatively low-power devices, vacuum tubes supply steady powers of hundreds of thousands of watts and peak powers of tens of millions of watts. While transistors act as effective amplifiers up to frequencies of only a few hundreds of megacycles, vacuum tubes have been built which amplify effectively at frequencies of around 50,000 megacycles.

It is not only our technology which is dependent upon vacuum tubes. Fundamental scientific investigations would be sorely handicapped without them. Without vacuum tubes we would not have the powerful accelerators, such as cyclotrons, synchrotrons, and linear accelerators, which physicists use in investigating the nature of the atomic nucleus. Neither would we have radiation detectors, amplifiers, and counters to observe nuclear reactions. Without vacuum tubes we would not have microwave spectroscopy, or nuclear resonance measurements, which help to unravel the detailed structure of compounds and of atoms themselves. Without vacuum tubes we would not have radio astronomy, which adds to the knowledge which we obtain from the light of the stars other and distinct information carried to us by the radio waves that the stars and the dust and gas scattered through the universe emit. Without vacuum tubes, biologists and physiologists would be deprived of delicate instruments—but there is almost no end to the uses of vacuum tubes, both in science and in industry.

The advance in the whole electronic art has followed advances in the vacuum tubes on which it has been based. As vacuum tubes which have higher powers have become available, as amplifiers which have less noise have become available, as we have succeeded in making amplifiers which amplify higher frequencies, the electronic art has advanced to take advantage of these improved properties and ranges of operation. We have gone from radar using waves of several meters length, which give broad beams and poor discrimination of angle, to 10- and 3-centimeter-wave-length radars with narrower beams and, so to speak, acuter vision, and finally for some purposes to millimeter-wave radars with needle-sharp beams. We have gone from early radio-telegraph signals of thousands of meters' wave length to short-wave radio signals of ten to twenty meters' wave length, which span the world carrying both code and voice, though sometimes with much static and distortion. We have gone further, to signals of 7.5 centimeters' wave length sent across the country in hops between relay stations thirty miles apart; such signals carry even television with little distortion. All of these advances could be made only when vacuum tubes with new capabilities became available.

Vacuum tubes do marvelous things. They offer us almost unlimited amplification. But they have inherent limitations as well. The usable gain is limited by noise, which we will discuss in Chapter IX. Most vacuum tubes will amplify a limited range or band of frequencies only. While the frequency of operation of vacuum tubes is continually pushed up, so that some vacuum tubes have been made which will amplify waves whose wavelength is only a quarter of an inch and whose frequency is 50,000,000,000 cycles per second, there are certain inherent limitations which make it difficult to make satisfactory vacuum tubes for extremely high frequencies. To understand the inherent limitations of vacuum tubes is to understand the limitations of the whole electronic art, for the limitations of amplifiers limit what we can do electronically.

We cannot understand the limitations of vacuum tubes without understanding how they operate. Here, it is best to start with the very first of vacuum tube amplifiers, the one Lee de Forest invented in the first decade of this century and called the *audion*. We now call it the *triode*.

The triode has numerous close relatives, such as the *tetrode, pentode,* and others. This family of tubes constitute by far the most versatile of vacuum tubes. These are the tubes of your radio or TV receiver. Over a wide range of frequencies they will do almost anything, and that is what they are called on to do.

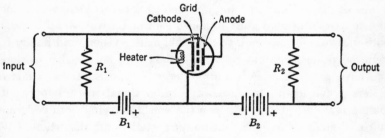

FIG. 7.2

FIG. 7.2 shows schematically the parts of a triode. These are an electron-emitting cathode (heated by an electric heater), a *grid* which is an array of fine parallel wires close to the cathode, and an anode to which the electrons from the cathode flow. All of these electrodes are of course enclosed in a glass or metal *envelope* which is evacuated to a high degree.

In operation, the anode is held positive with respect to the cathode, by means of a battery B_2 or another sort of electric source. The anode produces an electric field which tends to draw electrons to it from the cathode, just as in the diode described in Chapter IV.

The grid, however, is held negative with respect to the cathode, by battery B_1 or by some other electric source. Thus, the grid produces an electric field which tends to keep electrons from leaving the cathode. Because the grid is closer to the cathode than the anode is, and because the effect of the anode in producing a field at the cathode is reduced by the presence of the grid, the grid has a much more powerful effect in controlling the current of electrons leaving the cathode than does the anode. Thus, a change in the grid voltage (the voltage supplied by the battery B_1 in the picture) produces as much change in anode current as does a change perhaps ten to 100 times as great in anode voltage. This is why the triode can act as a very effective amplifier.

In using the tube as an amplifier, a resistance or resistor R_2 is connected between the anode and the anode voltage supply (the battery B_2 in this case). We should remember from Chapter III that a resistor is simply a poor conductor of electricity. It may be a film of carbon or a coil of poorly conducting wire. When a voltage is applied to a resistor, it sets up an electric field along this poorly conducting path, and the field causes current to flow. The current through the resistor and the voltage across the resistor are related by Ohm's law:

$$V = IR$$

Here V is the voltage across the resistor, R is the resistance of the resistor (measured in ohms) and I is the current through the resistor (measured in amperes). Ohm's law says that if a current I flows through a resistor of resistance R it will cause a voltage V to appear across the resistor.

In Fig. 7.2 the current of electrons which flows from the cathode to the anode passes through the resistor R_2, which is connected between the anode voltage supply and the anode. According to Ohm's law, this current produces a voltage across R_2. Now, the anode current of the triode can be changed by changing the voltage of the grid. Thus, changing the voltage of the grid changes the voltage appearing across the resistor R_2.

Let us now consider a circuit in which two triodes are connected together as shown in FIG. 7.3. The voltage across the resistor R_2 of FIG. 7.2 now appears as part of the voltage on the grid of a second triode and controls the current through the resistor R_3 connected to the anode of this second triode.

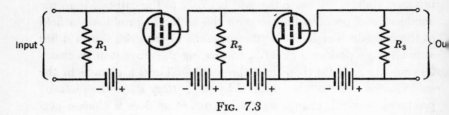

FIG. 7.3

We will find that, as the voltage across R_1 changes, the voltage across R_2 is changed even more (say, 10 times as much). This change in voltage across R_2 will produce an even greater change in voltage across R_3 (perhaps 100 times the change across R_1). The circuit of FIG. 7.3 is a *two-stage* amplifier. By adding more tubes, we could get even more amplification.

Electric power is voltage times current. If P stands for power, from Ohm's law we see that when the current flows through a resistor

$$P = IV = I^2R = \frac{V^2}{R}$$

A gain of 10 times in current or voltage means a gain of 100 times in power.

Multi-stage amplifiers are the heart of radio, television, and almost all electronic equipment. The circuits used are of course more complicated than that shown in FIG. 7.3. They have several additional features of great practical importance. Some of the most important features are illustrated in FIG. 7.4.

In FIG. 7.4, for instance, we show for supplying electric power two *power supplies*, S_1 and S_2, rather than batteries. These power supplies produce steady, constant voltages and supply steady currents—*direct current*—from the *alternating current* of the usual electric supply. This is usually accomplished by means of diodes such as described in Chapter III. A diode will conduct current in

one direction only. By means of a diode one can obtain from an
alternating voltage a series of pulses of current, all in the same
direction. We remember that condensers store electric charge,

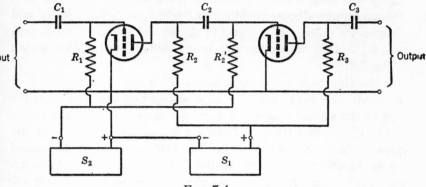

FIG. 7.4

and that electric current tends to persist at a constant value in
inductors. If, as shown in FIG. 7.5, the current from the diode is
passed through a network made up of condensers, C, and inductors,

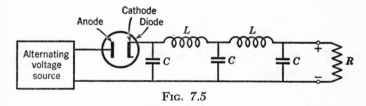

FIG. 7.5

L, the pulsating current from the diode can be so stored and
smoothed as to flow steadily and constantly through the resistance,
R, for instance, or into an amplifier as from the power supplies in
FIG. 7.4.

The use of power supplies rather than batteries is one practical
feature of the amplifier of FIG. 7.4. There is another important
feature. The plate of the first tube is not connected directly to the
grid of the second. Instead, a capacitor or condenser, C_2, is placed
between the two. A resistor, R_2, supplies current to the anode of
the first tube; a resistor, R_2', holds the grid of the second tube at
the right average voltage.

Because of the voltages of S_1 and S_2, an electric field and an electric flux appear between the electrodes of capacitor C_2. This does not constitute an electric current. However, if the voltage across R_2 changes, the flux between the electrodes of C_2 changes. This constitutes displacement current, which flows through R_2' and changes the voltage of the grid of the second tube. Other capacitors, C_1 and C_3, whose function is similar to that of C_2, are shown in Fig. 7.4.

If the change in the voltage across R_2 is fast enough, the effect of the displacement current is so powerful that the voltage of the grid of the second triode will vary just as does the voltage of the anode of the first triode. Thus, for signals of high enough frequency, the capacitor C_2 in effect connects the grid of the second triode directly to the anode of the first triode. At how high frequencies? At any frequencies we choose! The higher is the capacitance of capacitor C_2, the lower is the frequency at which the amplifier will amplify. The capacitance is simply the electric flux produced divided by the voltage across the capacitor. From Chapter VI we remember that the capacitance, C, is given by

$$C = \frac{\phi}{V}$$

By Gauss's law, the charge, Q, on the electrodes is equal to the electric flux ϕ, so that

$$C = \frac{Q}{V}$$

Of course, actual amplifier circuits are somewhat more complicated than that shown in Fig. 7.4, but the principles on which they operate are the same.

The final triode of the amplifier might not supply current to a resistor R_3; it might supply current to the towering antenna of a broadcast transmitter. In this case the vacuum tube would be a tubular structure several feet long, operating at tens of thousands of volts and with an electron current of many amperes flowing to the anode, so that the anode must be cooled by a water jacket. Or the triode might be a metal-and-glass affair a little larger than a walnut, supplying about a half watt of power to the microwave antenna of a transcontinental radio-relay-system transmitter, at a frequency of 4,000,000,000 cycles per second and operating at 150 volts and 40 milliamperes. Or the triode might be a glass tube that you see in your radio or TV set, operating at a few hundred volts and a few milliamperes. Or it might be a similar tube in an electronic computer.

Triodes suffer from several defects, some of them remediable and some of them unavoidable.

A remediable defect is overcome in the pentode, shown in Fig. 7.6. In the triode, variation in the anode voltage does affect the elec-

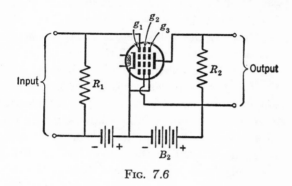

FIG. 7.6

tron flow somewhat, and in a way which reduces gain. Much worse than this, at high frequencies the electric fields between the plate and the grid cause a displacement current to flow from the output (anode) to the input (grid) of the amplifier. This adversely affects the performance of the amplifier and may cause it to oscillate.

In the pentode of Fig. 7.6 a *screen grid*, g_2, is placed between the *control grid*, g_1, and the anode. This screen grid is held positive by battery B_2; it acts to draw electrons from the cathode no matter what the voltage of the anode may be. As in the case of the electron gun, most of the electrons which reach g_2 pass right through it; in this case they go to the anode.

A *suppressor grid*, g_3, is put between the screen grid, g_2, and the anode. This is a very open grid and is connected to the cathode, so that it is negative with respect to the anode. When electrons strike an electrode, *secondary electrons* are knocked out. When the anode is negative with respect to the screen grid, g_2, these secondary electrons would leave the anode and go to the screen were it not for the field produced near the anode by the suppressor grid, g_3.

Pentodes give higher gains than triodes, and they are easier to use in circuits because little displacement current flows from the anode back to the grid. Most of the tubes in your radio or TV set are pentodes. The tubes which supply several watts of audio power to the speaker will be pentodes.

What about unavoidable defects of triodes and pentodes? Consider the pentode of Fig. 7.6. When this tube amplifies a fluctuating signal, the electric fields between the anode and the suppressor and screen grids—and the fields between the anode and various metal parts surrounding it—change. This change in field and hence in flux constitutes a displacement current. Where does this current come from? It comes from variations in the electron convection current reaching the anode. Thus, not all of the electron current reaching the anode goes through the resistor R_2. As we raise the frequency of the signal, less and less of the fluctuating current which constitutes the signal goes through the resistor R_2. By Ohm's law, the fluctuating-signal voltage across R_2 is reduced. The gain of the amplifier decreases as the frequency is increased.

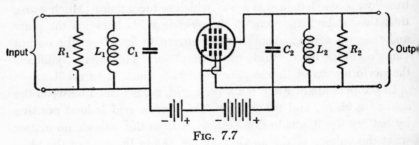

Fig. 7.7

Can anything be done about this? In a way, something can, as shown in Fig. 7.7. In Fig. 7.7, C_1 and C_2 do not represent capacitors connected to the pentode; they represent symbolically and with quantitative accuracy the effect of the electric flux from the control grid and from the anode of the tube. We can say that the grid and anode *act* as capacitors, and C_1 and C_2 symbolize this behavior.

If we connect inductors L_1 and L_2 as shown in Fig. 7.7, R_1, L_1, and C_1 and R_2, L_2 and C_2 constitute resonant circuits, or resonators. By properly adjusting L_1 and L_2, the resonant frequencies of both of these circuits can be made equal to the frequency of a signal that one desires to amplify. When this is done, the pentode can give a high amplification at a very high frequency.

However, while the circuit of Fig. 7.7 gives a high gain at a particular frequency to which the resonant circuits are adjusted, the gain falls if we raise the signal frequency above or lower it below this particular frequency. We find that by making R_1 and R_2 resistors of large resistance we can get a high gain over a narrow range of frequencies, while by giving R_1 and R_2 low resistances we can get a lower gain over a broader range or band of frequencies, but we cannot amplify a very broad band of frequencies and have high gain at the same time. This is a fundamental defect of triodes and pentodes.

Another defect hinges on size. When a triode is operated at very high frequencies an appreciable part of a cycle of variation of the electric fields within the tube may take place during the passage of electrons from the cathode past the control grid of the tube. This can interfere with the effective operation of the tube. If we want to avoid such an effect, we have merely to halve the size of the tube each time we double the frequency of operation. Then, if we keep the current and the voltage constant, the tube will operate just as efficiently at the higher frequency.

This procedure of scaling down the tube size has one obvious disadvantage; the tube tends to disappear! One can't build microscopic vacuum tubes. Even if one could, the tiny cathodes could not supply the required current and the tiny anodes could not dissipate the required power.

A typical tube for operation at a microwave frequency of 4,000 megacycles—that is, at a wave length of 7.5 centimeters, or 3 inches —will have a grid consisting of 1,000 wires per inch, each wire about ⅓ of a thousandth of an inch in diameter. This is about a tenth the diameter of a human hair. The grid will be about ½ a

thousandth of an inch from the cathode, which is a flat disk about
$3/16$ inches in diameter.

Such a tube is an effective microwave amplifier in a microwave
radio-relay system. It will give about a watt of power. Since large
antennas are used in such a system, such a tube can send a television signal 20 to 40 miles. This, however, is about as well as we
can do with triodes. Fortunately, there are other types of microwave tubes which can deliver kilowatts of power continuously and
megawatts of power in pulses at microwave frequencies.

Back in the late 1930's the Varian brothers startled the world of
electronics with a wonderful new microwave amplifier and oscillator
called the *klystron*. Two things were involved in the klystron; a
new way of acting on and controlling the electron flow and a
new electrical circuit for producing the electric fields to act on
the electron flow.

The new circuit was named the *rhumbatron*, but the name didn't
stick. Actually, it was just our friend, the resonator; a closed (or
almost closed) metal box with an electromagnetic wave trapped
inside of it.

FIG. 7.8 shows such a resonator in cross section. It is a shell of
metal with a more or less doughnut shape, but there is a thin slit
or gap extending around the inside of the hole of the doughnut. It
is chiefly across this gap that the electric field of the electromagnetic
wave appears, as indicated by the lines of force with arrowheads.
The magnetic lines of force are closed circles winding around inside
of the doughnut. In the figure we see them pointed toward us in
the upper part of the cross section and away from us in the lower
part. On the inside surface of the walls a current flows, as indicated. There are of course no electric or magnetic fields inside of
the metal of the resonator.

Both the electric and the magnetic fields vary sinusoidally with
time. The change in the magnetic field produces the electric field,
and the change in the electric field produces the magnetic field, in
accord with Maxwell's equations. Thus, when the strength of the
magnetic field is least, when it is changing most rapidly in passing
from negative to positive, the electric field is greatest. When the
change in electric field is greatest, when the electric field is passing

from negative to positive and is zero, the magnetic field is greatest. This is characteristic of the standing wave in a resonator and different from a wave traveling through space. We may remember that in a plane electromagnetic wave the electric field is greatest when the magnetic field is greatest, while we see that in the resonator the electric field is greatest when the magnetic field is zero.

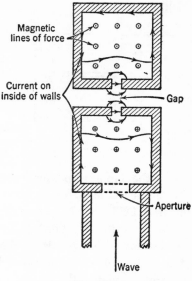

FIG. 7.8

A trapped wave dies out as it oscillates unless power is supplied continually. In FIG. 7.8 the power is supplied as a wave traveling through a metal pipe or wave guide and is admitted to the resonator through a small aperture. In the resonators of vacuum tubes the inside of the resonator may be evacuated, and the aperture may be covered with glass, mica, or ceramic.

FIG. 7.9 shows a klystron amplifier using two resonators. An electron gun is used to produce an electron beam which is shot through the input resonator, travels on for a distance, then passes through the output resonator, and is finally collected on a collector electrode. Often, as we noted in Chapter IV, a strong uniform magnetic field in the direction of the electron beam is used to assure that the electrons travel in nearly straight paths. Otherwise the electric fields produced by the electrons would cause the beam to widen as it traveled.

In the operation of the klystron of FIG. 7.9 an input signal traveling to the input resonator through a wave guide sets up electric

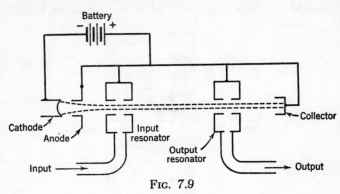

FIG. 7.9

and magnetic fields in the input resonator. As the electric field across the gap of the input resonator varies sinusoidally with time, changing from a negative field (a field in one direction) to a positive field (a field in the opposite direction) and back again repeatedly, it alternately slows down and speeds up the electrons passing through the resonator. While the electrons travel between the input resonator and the output resonator, the slowed-down electrons are overtaken by electrons which left later but which were speeded up by the varying electric field. Thus, the even flow of electrons entering the input resonator becomes bunched following the action of the input resonator in speeding up and slowing down (*velocity modulating*) the electrons of the electron stream.

The bunched electron stream constitutes a fluctuating current of electrons, an alternating current, whose frequency is the same as the frequency of the input signal. When this current flows across the gap of the output resonator, it sets up a strong electromagnetic oscillation inside of the output resonator. Power leaks out of the output resonator through an aperture into the output wave guide, constituting an output signal considerably stronger than the input signal supplied to the input wave guides.

What is the advantage of the klystron over the triode or pentode? Chiefly, it is that for a given frequency of operation the klystron is bigger. This is very important, because triodes for microwave frequencies are so small that they are hard to build, so small that they can not be operated at high powers. A microwave klystron may be four feet long and may give a peak power of 30 million watts.

How is it that the klystron can be so much larger than the triode? In the triode, the signal acts on the electrons near the cathode, where the electrons are moving very slowly. Yet the electrons must get past the grid and to the anode in a fraction of a cycle of the amplified signal. This means that, in the microwave triode, the cathode, grid, and anode must be put very close together.

In the klystron the electrons are acted on by the input resonator after they have been accelerated to from one twentieth to one half the speed of light. Thus, they can travel much farther in a fraction of a cycle of change of field. The length of the field across the gap of the input resonator can be far, far greater than the cathode-to-grid spacing in a microwave triode, and still the electrons can traverse this field in a small part of a cycle, in a time which—for instance, at a frequency of 3,000,000,000 cycles per second (a wave length of 10 centimeters, or 4 inches)—must be small compared with a third of a billionth of a second.

Klystron amplifiers have been made for a wide range of wave lengths, from perhaps 50 centimeters to around 1 centimeter, and for a wide range of powers, from a few watts up. Klystrons made at Stanford University for use in a billion-volt electron accelerator give peak powers of tens of millions of watts. Klystrons delivering 15 kilowatts at frequencies ranging from 500 to 800 megacycles have been built to serve as amplifiers in ultra-high-frequency television transmitters.

If one used highly directive antennas, the power of present day klystrons would be more than sufficient to send television signals to the moon or to telephone to Mars if people and apparatus could be sent to those remote places. Using the 250-foot antenna under construction at Jodrell Bank in England, it will be possible to get radar echoes from Mars and Venus, as we shall see in Chapter XI.

A klystron can be made to serve as an oscillator by connecting the output to the input. However, most klystrons used as oscillators are of a type called the *reflex klystron*.

A reflex klystron uses only one resonator, as shown in FIG. *7.10*. After the electrons traverse the resonator once, their direction of motion is reversed by the field of a repeller electrode which is held negative with respect to the cathode. Thus, the bunched beam

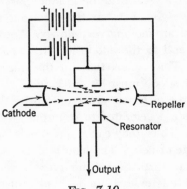

FIG. *7.10*

returns to the input resonator and maintains the oscillating field in it. Power leaks out through an aperture into a wave guide and is carried off to be used. In the reflex klystron, the beam travels only a short distance. Moreover, the field of the concave repeller exerts a focusing action on the electrons of the beam. No magnetic field is needed. Thus, the reflex klystron can be a very small, light device, perhaps 1¼ inches in diameter and 3 inches long. All radar receivers used in World War II were of the superheterodyne or double-detection type (this will be explained in Chapter VIII). Such receivers make use of an oscillator. In World War II radar receivers, these oscillators were reflex klystrons.

The reader may wonder what happens to the electrons in a reflex klystron after they have crossed the resonator twice and are headed back toward the cathode. If they get near to the cathode they cause a sort of misbehavior called *hysteresis;* the frequency does not change smoothly with repeller voltage. The discovery of this effect just when a tube was about to go into production caused the author (and a number of others) some very uneasy weeks during World War II. The defect was remedied by modifying the focusing effect of the repeller so that most of the electrons were caught on the edge of an aperture after traversing the resonator twice and before reaching the cathode.

Klystrons overcome many of the limitations of triodes. It is not too much to say that a whole microwave art could be based on klystrons alone, an art comparable to the lower-frequency art which has been based on triodes, tetrodes and pentodes. It would not be true, however, to say that the whole microwave art has been based on klystrons. For instance, the American Telephone and Telegraph Company's coast-to-coast microwave radio-relay system makes use of microwave triodes rather than klystrons as amplifiers.

Perhaps even more important, the powerful microwave radar pulses which seek out enemy planes and ships are usually produced by a kind of tube called a magnetron. Magnetrons are very efficient oscillators and are relatively small and light for the powers they produce. There is a possibility, however, that some future radar transmitters will make use of klystrons rather than magnetrons. Higher power has been produced by means of klystrons than by means of magnetrons.

While klystron amplifiers function effectively at higher frequencies than do triodes, both klystrons and triodes suffer from a particular inherent defect. Resonant circuits, or resonators, must be used with both types of tubes. The frequency of operation can be changed by adjusting or tuning these resonators or resonant circuits, but a broad band of frequencies cannot be amplified simultaneously by such tubes. Since the war this limitation on band width has been overcome in a newer type of tube called a traveling-wave tube. The importance of band width, and how the traveling-wave tube manages to operate without any resonant circuit which would limit the band, will be discussed in the following chapter.

CHAPTER VIII

Signals, Band Width, Traveling-Wave Tubes, and Millimeter Waves

So FAR we have talked about waves which vary sinusoidally with time and with distance. We have seen that the velocity is the wave length times the frequency. We have considered standing waves in resonators or resonant circuits, in which the fields, the voltage, and the current vary sinusoidally with time.

Sinusoidal waves, waves with a single frequency, can be transmitted, received, and amplified. They are, however, rather uninteresting. Unlike the sorts of signals which we actually send by TV or radio or hear over the telephone, sine waves are endlessly repetitious. A single sine wave can never tell us anything new. In terms of communication theory, which we shall discuss in Chapters XIV and XV, a sine wave conveys no information.

Sine waves are important because, as we have noted, sine waves preserve their shape, their unique sort of variation with time, in passing through any linear system. If this were the only property of sine waves, they would perhaps be mere mathematical curiosities. Sine waves have another very important property, however, which was clearly demonstrated by Fourier, an early-nineteenth-century mathematician and physicist. Any reasonable physical curve, any reasonable variation of a field, a voltage, a current, with time, can be represented as a sum of sine waves! And, by *reasonable*, I merely exclude certain pathological mathematical specimens, largely invented to show that Fourier's efforts to reduce everything to a sum of sine waves can be frustrated by one sufficiently ingenious.

The representation of any electrical signal as a combination of sine waves by *Fourier series* and *Fourier integrals*, as these representations are called, has a profound importance in electronics. The behavior of a linear circuit, such as a resonator, a capacitor, an inductor, a resistor, or a complicated combination of these elements, can be easily calculated if the applied signal is a sine wave. If the input signal to any linear circuit or amplifier is a combination of sine waves of various frequencies, the output will be a combination of sine waves of the same frequencies. In dealing with the total signal, each *sinusoidal component* of the signal can be treated separately.

The representation of signals by sine waves of several frequencies is so important, so fundamental to the electronic art, that we must have some understanding of it. Such understanding can be achieved most easily by considering a few simple examples. For instance, FIG. *8.1* shows at the top two sine waves of slightly differ-

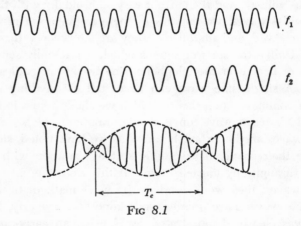

FIG 8.1

ent frequencies, f_1 and f_2, and at the bottom the sum of the two sine waves. The signal at the bottom is a signal which has components of two frequencies only. In general appearance it is a wavy signal whose amplitude varies with time. A dotted line has been drawn outlining this combined signal; this is called the *envelope* of the signal. The envelope rises from zero to a greatest value and falls to zero again in some time T_e which is indicated in the figure, and this rise and fall is repeated with a frequency, f_e, given by

$$f_e = \frac{1}{T_e}$$

Always,

$$f_e = f_1 - f_2$$

That is, the frequency with which the envelope rises and falls is the difference between the frequencies of the two sine waves of which the signal is made up, the greater frequency minus the lesser frequency.

The signal shown at the bottom of FIG. 8.1 resembles somewhat the sort of signal sent out by an AM, that is, *amplitude modulation* radio transmitter (a broadcast transmitter for instance), but it is really not the same.   Let us try to understand the slightly more complicated nature of a broadcast or *amplitude modulation* signal. Let us choose a very simple case, that in which we want to send by amplitude modulation of a radio signal a sine wave of audio frequency, say, 500 cycles per second.   Suppose that the frequency of the radio wave we use to transmit the signal is 1,000,000 cycles.

At the broadcast transmitter, the sine wave of 1,000,000 cycles frequency is put into a device called a *modulator*.   By means of the modulator, the 500-cycle sine wave controls the amplitude or envelope of the 1,000,000-cycle sine wave, so that the envelope is itself a 500-cycle sine wave, as shown in FIG. 8.2.   (Here the frequency of the radio-frequency wave is not to scale.)

When we receive such a signal with a radio receiver, we can recover the 500-cycle sine wave by means of a *detector*.   A detector is a rectifier such as our diode of Chapter III, a device which passes current in only one direction.   If we put the AM signal of FIG. 8.2 through such a rectifier followed by a filter which will pass audio frequencies only, we will get out a unidirectional current of varying strength.   In fact, the strength of this current will vary just as does the sinusoidal envelope of the AM signal.

While we can think of an AM signal such as that shown in FIG. 8.2 as a sine wave with a varying amplitude, strictly speaking a sine wave can be a sine wave only if it has a constant amplitude. If the amplitude varies, several frequencies must be present. As a matter of fact, when we modulate a sine wave of frequency f so as to obtain a signal with a sinusoidal envelope of some frequency f_e, we

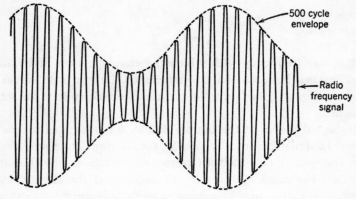

FIG. 8.2

find that the signal we get contains not only a component of frequency f called the *carrier* but also two *sidebands* having frequencies $f + f_e$ and $f - f_e$.

In general, the signals we want to transmit by radio are not sine waves; they are combinations of sine waves of many frequencies. A telephone signal contains frequencies lying between 200 and 3,500 cycles. A high fidelity *audio* or sound signal may embrace a band of frequencies of perhaps twenty to 20,000 cycles. A TV signal requires a band of about four megacycles. In general, if we amplitude-modulate a sinusoidal signal of frequency f with a band of frequencies lying between 0 and B, the modulated signal will contain sideband frequencies covering a range from $f - B$ to $f + B$.

In FM, or *frequency modulation*, the frequency rather than the amplitude of the transmitted signal is varied in modulating the radio-frequency wave. In order to recover the modulation in an FM receiver, the signal can be passed through an electrical filter whose output varies with input frequency. This causes the amplitude of the output to vary as the frequency of the received signal varies. The output can then be rectified just as in an AM receiver.

and so the modulation can be recovered.   There are other ways of recovering the modulation from an FM signal.

In amplitude-modulating a signal, there is a limit to the allowable degree of modulation.   If we increase the strength of the modulating signal, eventually a level of modulation of the radio-frequency sine wave will be reached such that the amplitude of the radio frequency signal will at some time fall to zero.   If we try to modulate the sine wave more strongly than this, the envelope will no longer accurately reproduce the modulating signal.   Hence, at the radio receiver, the modulating signal cannot be accurately reproduced.

There is no similar limitation in FM, but increasing the strength of the modulation does have an effect.   Suppose that the carrier frequency is f and the modulating signal is a sine wave of frequency f_e.   If the modulation is weak, it can be shown that the only new frequencies produced are sidebands of frequencies $f - f_e$ and $f + f_e$.   If the modulation is stronger, however, one finds that other frequencies, such as $f - 3f_e$, $f - 2f_e$, $f + 2f_e$, $f + 3f_e$ are produced.   An FM signal may cover a very broad band of frequencies, much broader than the band of frequencies of the modulating signal.

We should take note of one feature which is common to the fluctuation of the envelope of two sine waves, as shown in FIG. 8.1; to the AM signal of FIG. 8.2; and to the FM signal as well.   Regardless of the actual frequencies involved, it is the difference of frequencies, the band of frequencies, which determines the fluctuation of the envelope, and which is determined by the modulating signal applied to the radio-frequency signal in AM and FM.   In fact, the frequencies comprising a signal can be shifted, all by a constant amount, and the important features of the signal will be preserved in the process.

In a sense, this is what is done in radio and TV broadcasting. Each radio program starts out as audio frequencies lying in the same frequency range.   Different radio stations send these signals to us by means of radio waves of different frequencies.   The radio antenna picks up all the different radio programs, but, as different programs have been sent as radio waves of different frequencies, electrical filters in the radio set can select the radio frequencies corresponding to one program and reject the frequencies corresponding to other programs.

AM (amplitude modulation) and FM (frequency modulation) are two rather specialized ways by means of which a signal of one frequency (an audio signal) can be represented by a signal of another frequency (a radio signal). In AM, if the audio signal is a 500-cycle sine wave, the radio signal which represents it will comprise a signal of carrier frequency and two sidebands having frequencies 500 cycles above and below the carrier frequency. An FM signal may be even more complicated.

However, in representing a signal of one frequency by a signal of another, it is possible simply to shift the frequency of the original signal, so that for each frequency in the original signal there is just one frequency in the signal which represents it. This is important for several purposes. Much as in radio and TV broadcasting, the frequencies of signals may be shifted so that several different signals can be sent without confusion along one transmission line, or through one broad-band amplifier, each having been shifted to a different band of frequencies. There are other uses for frequency shifting, however. For instance, it is often desirable to change the frequency of a signal for greater convenience in amplifying it; we will come to this use of frequency shifting in due time.

We cannot go into all the details of frequency shifting, but I believe that a simple case will illustrate the phenomenon involved. Suppose that we add to a weak signal of frequency f_1 (a of FIG. 8.3) a strong signal of frequency f_2 (b of FIG. 8.3). The combined signal (c of FIG. 8.3) superficially resembles an amplitude-modulation signal. The frequency of the envelope (shown dashed in FIG. 8.3) is $f_2 - f_1$. This frequency is not present in the simple sum of the two signals, c of FIG. 8.3, but if we put this combined signal through a non-linear device called a *mixer*, or a *frequency converter*, or a *modulator*, the frequency of the envelope, $f_2 - f_1$, will appear in the output and can be filtered out. The process is analogous to the detection of an AM signal, which we discussed earlier. If f_1 is greater than f_2, we still get the difference frequency, which is $f_1 - f_2$. This overall process is sometimes called *beating* the two signals, and the frequency $f_1 - f_2$ (or $f_2 - f_1$) is called the *beat frequency.*

When a weak and a much stronger signal are passed through a non-linear device (mixer, frequency converter, modulator), the amplitude of the difference frequency signal in the output of the

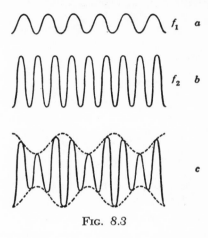

FIG. 8.3

mixer will be proportional to the amplitude of the weak signal; the frequency converter is in this sense a linear device. Because of this linearity, when the weak signal consists, not of a single frequency component, but of many frequency components, each component is separately shifted in frequency by a constant amount, and the relative amplitudes of the various frequency components are preserved in the process. Thus, we obtain an accurate representation of the weak signal, but one shifted in frequency.

This process of signal shifting is more complicated than FIG. 8.3 and the simple argument given above disclose. Actually, when we put a weak signal of frequency f_1 and a strong signal of frequency f_2 into a non-linear mixer, we obtain at the output both the *difference frequency* $f_2 - f_1$ and *sum frequency* $f_1 + f_2$. This means that we can add to the frequency of a signal as well as subtract from it. We can shift the frequency of a signal up as well as down.

The principle of frequency shifting is used in a sort of radio receiver called the *double-detection* or *superheterodyne* receiver, which is used in AM, in FM and in microwave radio.

Fig. 8.4 shows the parts of a superheterodyne receiver which might be used, for instance, in receiving an AM broadcast signal. It might be tuned to receive a signal transmitted by amplitude modulating a 770-kilocycle sinusoidal wave. The received signal

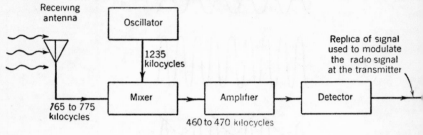

Fig. *8.4*

might contain frequencies lying in the 10-kilocycle band between 765 kilocycles and 775 kilocycles. If we put this received signal into a non-linear mixer (frequency converter, modulator) together with a strong signal having a frequency of 1,235 kilocycles, we will get out a signal lying in the range 460 kilocycles to 470 kilocycles, and a signal lying in the range 2,000 kilocycles to 2,010 kilocycles. We can select the former signal by means of an electrical filter which will pass frequencies lying in the range 460–470 kilocycles. The tuned circuits in an amplifier called an *intermediate-frequency* (or IF) amplifier can in fact constitute the filter required. We can amplify these frequencies with an amplifier using pentodes. Then, by means of a diode, the amplified signal can be detected to recover the modulation—that is, the audio signal which was used to modulate the original radio-frequency signal at the transmitter.

Superheterodyne receivers can equally well be used as microwave receivers in radio and communication, and they are. In communication systems it is sometimes desired to amplify a microwave signal and send it on again at a microwave frequency with increased power. Suppose that we shift the frequency of a signal lying in the band from 4,000 to 4,020 megacycles to a band lying between 60 and 80 megacycles and amplify it. We can then put this amplified signal into a non-linear device, a modulator, together with a stronger signal of microwave frequency: for instance, a signal of frequency 4,020 megacycles. We will get out two signals: a signal lying in the band 3,980 to 4,000 megacycles and a signal lying in the band 4,080 to 4,100 megacycles. We can if we wish select the latter signal by means of a filter. This signal can be amplified and radiated from a microwave antenna.

In the case described, the weak received signal occupied a band of from 4,000 to 4,020 megacycles, while the strong microwave signal sent out occupied a band from 4,080 to 4,100 megacycles. The purpose of such a shift in frequency is to avoid having the output signal picked up at the input and amplified repeatedly; this would cause distortion of the signal and could result in oscillation.

In the superheterodyne receiver the signal is shifted in frequency for convenience in amplifying it. The frequency of a signal may, as we have said, be shifted for another sort of reason. For instance, a microwave radio relay system is capable of carrying hundreds of telephone conversations at once. A single telephone signal occupies a band or *channel* of frequencies from approximately 200 cycles to 3,500 cycles. By frequency-shifting each telephone signal so that different telephone signals occupy different bands of frequencies (just as different broadcast stations use different bands of frequencies), a large number of telephone channels can be stacked one above another in frequency. In one typical case, a group of twelve channels is stacked into a band lying from 60,000 cycles to 108,000 cycles. Then five of these groups are shifted in frequency; and stacked above one another to occupy a band from 312,000 to 552,000 cycles; they form what is called a *super-group*, embracing a total of sixty channels. Finally, ten super-groups, totaling 600 channels, are stacked one above another in the frequency range of 64,000 to 2,788,000 cycles, to form the combined signal of 600 telephone channels, for transmission by microwave radio relay (or by other means).

Transmission systems such as this, in which many messages are sent simultaneously over different frequencies, are called *carrier* systems. All long-distance telephony, whether over open wires, over multiconductor cables, or over coaxial cables, makes use of carrier systems of one form or another. Some carrier systems accommodate only two or four channels, some a dozen, and the L-3 coaxial-cable-carrier system can transmit somewhat more than 1,800 telephone channels simultaneously. Always, if more channels are to be transmitted, more band width is required, for each original signal must be shifted to some range of frequencies different from that used for any other signal.

We see that band width, the range of frequencies occupied by a signal, is a very important and, we might say, a very persistent property of the signal. When the frequency is shifted, band width is preserved. The band width of a wire or a coaxial cable or a microwave system measures how many telephone channels can be transmitted over the system. In actually considering what a signal can be used for, the band width is more important than the frequency, for the frequency can be shifted. So far we have considered band width in connection with radio and TV signals, but band width is equally important in other sorts of signals as well. In radar, for instance, the signals used are pulses, which rise and fall in amplitude over a short time. Fig. 8.5 illustrates a pulse.

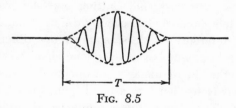

FIG. 8.5

The radar sends out a series of such pulses in searching for planes or ships. The pulses are reflected back by the object sought, and the distance of the object can be measured by measuring the time it takes a pulse to go out and return.

There is a fundamental law which has to do with the *duration,* or *length* (of time), of such pulses. In Fig. 8.5 the length of the pulse is indicated by the time interval T during which the pulse is greater than some small fraction of its maximum amplitude. The general rule is that this pulse length cannot be less than the reciprocal of the range, or band, of frequencies making up the pulse. For instance, if we use frequencies lying in the range between frequency

f_1 and frequency f_2, then the band, B, of frequency used is

$$B = f_1 - f_2$$

In this case, the least length, T, that the pulse can have is

$$T = \frac{1}{B} \text{ seconds}$$

As this rule has been illustrated and stated it is, of course, approximate, but it can be formulated more exactly in mathematical terms.

This relation between pulse length and band width is vitally important in radar. A radio wave travels with a velocity of 3×10^8 meters per second, or, very nearly, 1,000 feet in a microsecond, that is, a millionth of a second. Thus, a radar pulse whose duration is one microsecond is about 1,000 feet long as it travels through the air as a microwave radar wave. Early radars used pulses of about this duration. According to our formula, such a pulse includes a range of frequencies of about 1,000,000 cycles, or 1 megacycle, and we must amplify a range of frequencies this wide in receiving such a pulse.

A pulse 1,000 feet long is a dull tool to use if we wish to sort out planes flying in close formation and to measure their distances precisely. Some modern radars use pulses having lengths of a tenth of a microsecond or less. To amplify a pulse a tenth of a microsecond long requires a ten-megacycle band width.

In experimental microwave work, pulses having lengths of five thousandths of a microsecond or less have been used. Such pulses are only about 5 feet long. What have they been used for? They have been sent down wave guides to find electrical imperfections such as bad joints and dents. Perhaps someday they will be used in very precise radar.

A pulse five thousandths of a microsecond long embraces a band of frequencies at least 200 megacycles wide. Let us consider what this means. We have seen that, the greater the band width, the greater the number of signals, telephone, radio, or TV, that can be sent using the band width. The entire broadcast range of frequencies is only about 1 megacycle wide; it extends from about .5 megacycles to 1.5 megacycles. Above this frequency lie various police and assorted communication bands. Between 10 and 30 megacycles lie all the short-wave frequencies on which transoceanic communication, both telegraph and telephone, depend. Around 50 megacycles are TV channels; a little above 100 megacycles are all our FM broadcast channels, and the rest of the TV channels, except for ultrahigh-frequency TV, extend little above 200 megacycles. If we are to amplify a pulse five thousandths of a microsecond long, we must amplify simultaneously a band of frequencies great enough to send all our broadcast, short wave, FM and most of our TV channels, along with assorted other bands, military as well as civilian. And yet, bands of frequencies ten times broader than this, bands 2,000 megacycles wide and more, can be amplified by a particular type of amplifier called a traveling-wave tube. Such bands could in principle be used to transmit hundreds of thousands of telephone channels and a great many TV channels at once.

Besides its intellectual interest and its social importance, there is a good deal of personal glamor connected with science, although I have tried to keep away from it in this book. About the origin of the traveling-wave tube, I will say only that it was invented in England during the war by an Austrian architect, Rudolph Kompfner, who had always wanted to be a physicist. He had an opportunity to improve his knowledge of physics during his internment in the early part of the war. During the later part of the war he was released from internment and worked on microwave tubes for the Admiralty. After the war he received a doctor's degree in physics from Oxford. Now he is in this country.

Perhaps it took the fresh look of a man from another field of work to remove the band-width limitation of amplifiers. Kompfner did this simply by building an effective amplifier with no resonant circuit.

In an ordinary amplifier, the resonant circuit plays the very important part of allowing a small input power to produce a large electric field to control the electron flow. We can see how the resonator can give us a large field or a small power in several ways.

In the last chapter we noted that the power dissipated in a resistor is given by

$$P = \frac{V^2}{R}$$

We can rewrite this

$$V = \sqrt{RP}$$

For a given power, the voltage will be greater if we make the resistance of the resistor greater.   When the resistance is a part of the resonant circuit of an amplifier, consisting of a capacitor, an inductor, and a resistor connected together as in Fig. 7.7, making the resistance of the resistor larger narrows the band of frequencies which the amplifier will amplify.

We can also liken the behavior of a resonator to that of a heavy pendulum swinging with little friction.   By pushing the pendulum slightly each time it swings by, we can make it oscillate with a large amplitude even if we push lightly and supply very little power.   It is very hard to make it swing at any other rate, however. To move it back and forth at any other frequency than its natural frequency of oscillation requires very strong pushes indeed.   Such a pendulum with little friction is like an electrical resonant circuit with a high resistance.   It is hard to produce a high voltage and electric field in such a circuit at any frequency very far removed from the resonant frequency.

If the electric field produced by the input signal is not to be made large by use of a high-resistance, narrow-band resonator, some other means must be found for the input signal to produce a strong effect on the electrons of an electron beam.   Kompfner solved this problem by using a traveling wave to influence the electrons.   He produced a wave with an electric field in the direction of motion of the electrons.   He arranged matters so that the wave traveled with the same speed as the electrons in the electron beam.   For instance, 1,500-volt electrons (electrons accelerated by 1,500 volts) travel with one thirteenth the speed of light.   Using such electrons, Kompfner would provide a circuit around the beam which could guide an electromagnetic wave along the electron stream with one thirteenth the speed of light, and he would apply the input power to this circuit.   Thus, an electron which entered the circuit when the field was accelerating would continue to be in an accelerating field as both the electron and the wave traveled along, and an electron which entered the circuit when the field was retarding would continue to find itself in a retarding field.

This will be made clearer in examining the actual structure of a traveling-wave tube, as shown in Fɪɢ. 8.6. To the left we see an electron gun consisting of a cathode and an anode. To the far right is a collector to collect the spent electrons. A longitudinal magnetic field, not shown, confines the electron flow to a narrow beam, as explained in Chapter IV. In between, the electrons travel through a *helix*—that is, a long coil of wire like a stretched door spring. All of these parts are enclosed in an evacuated glass envelope.

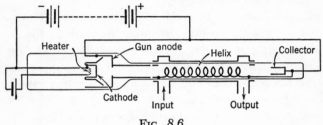

Fɪɢ. 8.6

It is the helix which carries the slow electromagnetic wave. It is found that an electromagnetic wave tends to follow the wire of the helix with about the speed of light. Thus, if the wire which is wound up to form the helix is about thirteen times as long as the helix it forms, the wave will travel along the length of the helix with about one thirteenth the speed of light. An input wave guide at the left end of the helix launches the wave, and the wave flows away from the right end of the helix into an output wave guide.

Kompfner showed mathematically, and found experimentally, that the strong cumulative influence of the electric field of the traveling electromagnetic wave does more than strongly bunch the electrons of the electron stream. The bunched electrons act to increase the amplitude of the electromagnetic wave. In fact, in a typical traveling-wave tube for operation at a frequency of 4,000 megacycles (a wave length of 7.5 cm), for which the helix is perhaps 8 inches long, the wave power may increase by five to ten times in each inch of travel along the helix. Single traveling-wave tubes have given as much as 1,000,000 times power gain.

While traveling-wave tubes give astonishingly high gains, their most amazing feature is the broad band width over which they amplify signals. The helix will carry waves over an extremely broad band of frequencies. Traveling-wave tubes have been made which amplify frequencies over a five-to-one range, and which amplify bands of frequencies several thousands of megacycles wide. In principle, such band widths could be used to carry tremendous numbers of telephone and television channels. They could be used to amplify pulses of extreme shortness. So far, they have not been used for such purposes.

For once it appears that tube performance has outstripped the rest of the electronic art. Traveling-wave tubes have been used experimentally to produce and amplify pulses five billionths of a second long, and this is far short of their capabilities. Traveling-wave tubes have been used in microwave radio-relay systems for television transmission in England and Japan, but to transmit only one television channel at a time. Traveling-wave tubes have various military potentialities. However, the full potentialities of traveling-wave tubes, including their incredible band width, have not yet been exploited. Perhaps the rest of the art will catch up with the capabilities of traveling-wave tubes. What this may result in we cannot completely foresee.

Even so, traveling-wave tubes have many uses and potentialities in the present art. It seems possible that traveling-wave tubes will rival klystrons in power output; pulsed powers of several hundreds of thousands of watts have already been attained. Traveling-wave tubes have been made which in amplifying introduce less noise than does any other sort of microwave tube; this will be discussed in the following chapter. Traveling-wave tubes have also proved useful in a forefront of the microwave art, that of millimeter waves, or waves whose wave lengths are less than 1 centimeter (10 millimeters, 0.4 inches) and whose frequencies are correspondingly higher than 30,000 megacycles.

It is obvious that the range of frequencies encompassed by the wave lengths between 5 millimeters and 10 millimeters is as great as that of all longer waves. The entire broadcast and short-wave-radio ranges comprise a band width of 30 megacycles. The wave-length range between 1 centimeter and .999 centimeters spans a frequency range of 30 megacycles. Millimeter waves offer band width in almost inexhaustible quantities. We may expect that the almost unlimited resource of band width provided by millimeter waves will become increasingly important as communication expands, and especially as television finds new group-to-group and perhaps person-to-person uses.

We may also remember in connection with millimeter waves that shorter waves allow narrower microwave beams, and thus millimeter-wave radars can be used to locate objects very precisely.

While millimeter waves have many advantages, their use is beset by inherent difficulties. Because of their short wave length, millimeter waves are strongly scattered by rain. This limits the use of millimeter waves in radar and makes them unsuited for open-air communication over long paths or with great reliability. However, millimeter waves may someday be used to send television and telephone signals through circular metal wave guides clear across the country.

Another serious difficulty in exploiting millimeter waves is that it is hard to build satisfactory tubes for millimeter waves. Millimeter-wave magnetrons have been made which give pulses of tens of thousands of watts. These magnetrons may be useful in certain types of radars. Reflex klystrons have been made which give a few thousandths of a watt down to wave lengths of around 5 millimeters. These may be used in radar and in other receivers. However, the electron tubes which appear to hold the most promise in the millimeter range of wave lengths are traveling-wave tubes and relatives of traveling-wave tubes.

As we noted in the last chapter, a vacuum tube can be made to operate effectively at a higher frequency simply by making it smaller in proportion to the wave length. This has been done with traveling-wave tubes. A traveling-wave tube has been made with a helix fifteen thousandths of an inch in inside diameter—that is, about three times the diameter of a human hair. It has been possible to shoot an electron beam of several thousandths of an ampere through such a helix, and power gains of from ten to 100 times have been attained at wave lengths of around 6 millimeters.

It is also possible to use circuits other than, and more rugged than, a helix to carry slow waves. Such circuits may consist of a

series of slots about a quarter wave length deep—that is, perhaps
$\frac{1}{16}$ inch deep—in the edge of a strip of metal. They may consist
of a grid of wires wound over a slot about a half wave length,
perhaps $\frac{1}{8}$ inch, wide. Millimeter-wave amplifiers have been made
with a variety of circuits. The important thing is, it has proved
possible to make traveling-wave tube amplifiers for wave lengths
down to about 5 millimeters.

We have noted that any amplifier can be made to oscillate by
connecting the output to the input. As a matter of convenience,
however, it is often better to use a special device as an oscillator
rather than to make all oscillators by using tubes designed essentially as amplifiers. This is particularly true in the millimeter range
of wave lengths. The special device which has proved valuable as
an oscillator is a relative of the traveling-wave tube. In this
country, it is generally called the *backward-wave oscillator,* and in
France a *carcinotron*. The backward-wave oscillator is peculiar
in that, unlike other oscillators, it has no resonator or resonant
circuit. The frequency of oscillation is changed simply by changing
the voltage which controls the velocity of the electrons. This is
particularly important at millimeter wave lengths, for it is hard to
make minute mechanical adjustments of the tiny parts of millimeter-
wave tubes.

In the traveling-wave tube there is a cumulative action on the
electrons by the electric field of a slow electromagnetic wave which
travels with the same speed as the electrons. In the backward-wave

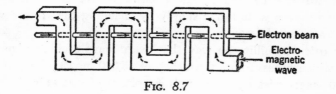

FIG. 8.7

oscillator there is a cumulative action on the electrons by a wave
which travels in the *opposite* direction from the electrons. How
is this possible?

FIG. 8.7 shows one form of backward-wave oscillator. Imagine
that an electromagnetic wave is present in the circuit, as there is

when the tube is oscillating. The electromagnetic wave travels in a general right-to-left direction through a tube or wave guide bent in a serpentine form. The electron beam travels through this wave guide repeatedly, passing through a series of holes in the serpentine structure.

Suppose, now, that when an electron crosses the wave guide for the first time, it encounters a crest of the wave, which accelerates it. Suppose, further, that the electron and wave velocities, the wave length, and the distance between crossings are so related that the electron encounters the subsequent wave trough on its next crossing of the guide; if this is so, it will be further accelerated. It will encounter a crest at the next crossing, and it will be accelerated at this and at all subsequent crossings of the wave guide. When this is so, the wave bunches the electrons more and more as they travel to the right. In turn, the bunched electron beam sets up the wave which travels to the left and bunches the electrons. The tube automatically produces microwave power which travels out of the left end of the wave guide.

What happens if we change the speed of the electrons by changing the voltage which accelerates them? At the old frequency, the relation between the electron velocity, the wave length, and the wave velocity is not just right for the sort of cumulative interaction between wave and electrons that I have described. What happens is that the frequency of oscillation changes, so that the cumulative interaction does take place. Thus, the frequency of the waves generated by the backward-wave oscillator can be changed over a wide range simply by changing the voltage which accelerates the electrons.

A particular millimeter-wave backward-wave oscillator has been built which tunes from a frequency of 45,000 megacycles to one of 63,000 megacycles by changing the voltage of operation from 700 volts to 2,400 volts.

For somewhat longer wave lengths, a backward-wave oscillator has been made which tunes over a five-to-one frequency range, from 2,700 megacycles to 13,500 megacycles, by changing the voltage from 40 volts to 2,900 volts.

Backward-wave oscillators have been made for longer wave

lengths as well. At wave lengths of around 10 centimeters a power of 100 watts has been produced by a tube essentially like that illustrated in FIG. 8.7. French workers, using a tube embodying some of the features of the magnetron, have produced several hundred watts.

Like the traveling-wave tube, the backward-wave oscillator has potentialities which have not yet been adequately exploited in the microwave art. What they may bring us in the future no one can fully foresee.

CHAPTER IX

Noise

Across the noisy room one can scarcely distinguish a single loud voice; the words are lost in the confused babble of sound waves, they are drowned out by noise. The same voice can be heard clearly when at last the guests leave. On a still night in the open, over water perhaps, the voice will carry much farther. Beyond a certain distance, however, the sound will be so weak that we cannot understand it.

Will it help to pick the sound up with a microphone, to amplify it with a vacuum tube, and to listen to the amplified sound with a telephone receiver? It will help a little, perhaps, but with the amplifier we will hear the weak noises of the still night made large also. Beyond a certain distance, the words cannot be distinguished, no matter how powerful an amplifier we may use. The words are drowned out by noise.

The case of radio signals is exactly analogous. In listening to stations in the broadcast band during the summer we are often annoyed by the crackle and fry of the static associated with thunderstorms. More distant stations may be drowned out in a steady hiss of noise, even in clear winter weather. The pictures from distant TV stations are obscured by an appearance of *snow,* a fine-grained, fluctuating pattern which is the counterpart of the hiss of noise in the radio receiver. This pattern too, and the electrical signal producing it, are called *noise* by engineers and physicists. To an electronics engineer, the currents and voltages in the circuit of a radio receiver, a TV set, or any other electrical circuit constitute either a signal—that is, something put there purposefully—or noise—that is, something that gets there in spite of the engineer's efforts to exclude it. Noise is something which tends to obscure the signal and render it unintelligible.

Radio receivers receive noise as well as signals. Radio receivers also produce noise themselves. We can use low-power transmitters to send radio signals short distances. Because of noise, we must use transmitters of higher power to send signals longer distances. Increasing the amplification of the receiver is not enough to enable us to hear a weak transmitter if it is very far away. As we increase the amplification beyond a certain point, we will merely hear, or see, an intense noise.

Is noise really a fundamental limitation on radio communication? As some locations and some times are quieter in the everyday sense, as a stilly night is quieter than a noisy room, so, too, some times and some places are quieter than others in an electrical sense. Short-wave radio transmission, which provides the majority of our transoceanic telephony, is much quieter in the tropical regions than it is near the North Pole. You are more apt to get a good, quiet connection in phoning all the way to Hawaii than you are in a call to London. Calls to northern Europe are better in winter than in summer, and they are better in periods of low sunspot activity than in periods of high sunspot activity. Radio communication may be very noisy if not altogether impossible during the magnetic storms caused when bursts of charged particles reach us from the sun.

In the early, long-wave days of radio, various forms of strong *static* picked up by the antenna dominated and obscured other forms of noise. However, as higher and higher frequencies were exploited it was found that, as the frequency is increased, noise becomes less variable and less intense. In the broadcast band (around 1 megacycle) we are much troubled by summer thunderstorms. FM and TV (around 100 megacycles) are less troubled by such static, but we are apt to hear or see on FM or TV the noise generated by the ignition systems of passing cars, the noise from the sparks of the spark plugs. The sorts of noise which are generated by thunderstorms and accidently by man-made devices tend to disappear at high-enough frequencies.

This does not mean that all noise disappears at high frequencies. By 1928, working at a frequency of 20 megacycles, Friis had constructed a radio receiver so sensitive that a fundamental, unavoidable noise in its input called *Johnson noise* or *thermal noise* could be detected. It was, in fact, this unprecedentedly sensitive radio receiver which enabled Jansky to discover cosmic radio noise, and so to take the first crucial step into that revolutionary new field, radio astronomy.

At still higher frequencies, in the microwave range (thousands of megacycles) neither storms nor electrical machinery produce appreciable noise. The noise reaching the receiver antenna has fallen to the level of Johnson noise, a noise which is associated with all the objects in the universe. Johnson noise is the low-frequency portion of the electromagnetic radiation sent out by all hot bodies and, indeed, by any bodies which have a temperature above absolute zero.

Heat is merely a form of motion, a tiny, chaotic motion, and the temperature of an object tells us how intense the agitation of its molecules is. When water reaches the boiling point, the motion of its molecules becomes so intense that the molecules no longer stick together as a liquid. When water is cooled, the motion becomes less intense, and finally, at the freezing point, the motion of the molecules becomes small enough so that the forces between the molecules can consolidate the substance into a solid that is ice. The molecules of ice still move, but they move only by vibrating, by oscillating about their mean positions. In fact, we can regard the vibration which is heat in solids, such as ice, as chaotic sound waves traveling in all directions, much like the sound in a noisy room, but less intense and of an amplitude determined entirely by the temperature of the solid substance.

We can, indeed, sometimes observe the motions of particles which constitutes heat. When the English botanist Brown looked at tiny particles of pollen under a microscope, he saw them move jumpily about. Such motion has since then been called *Brownian motion*. It is simply a manifestation of the thermal motions of the molecules of the liquid which surrounds the particles. The agitated molecules hit the tiny visible particles and cause the particles to jump about. Motions due to thermal vibration can also be observed in the erratic rotation of objects suspended from very fine fibers of quartz.

The mirrors of sensitive galvanometers swing erratically with thermal motions, for instance.

Molecules of various substances are made up of atoms. All atoms contain electrons and protons, which are charged particles. As the atoms of a substance vibrate with the motion which is heat, they send out chaotic electromagnetic waves of all frequencies. It is these waves which form the ultimate, unavoidable electrical noise from which we suffer in the electronic art, even at microwave frequencies.

The emission of electromagnetic radiation by hot substances is of fundamental physical importance. It is the means by which energy gets to us from the sun, as well as being a plague to microwave communication. Such thermal radiation of electromagnetic waves deserves the careful attention of anyone interested in physics.

The simplest way of understanding something of how thermal radiation is emitted and absorbed by hot bodies is to consider what happens in a collection of various bodies, a collection which may include pieces of opaque material, bright or black, as well as pieces of almost perfectly transparent material which absorb only a little of what radiation falls on them and allow the rest to pass through.

When bodies in a collection are all at the same temperature, they are said to be in *thermal equilibrium*. Imagine a space in which there is thermal equilibrium, a space which contains both various solid objects and air. On the average—that is, if we watch it over a long time—we will find that each molecule of air has a certain kinetic energy characteristic of the temperature. All the solid bodies have energies of vibration characteristic of the temperature. In solids which are conductors and contain free electrons—that is, electrons which are not bound to the atoms but are free to move about—the electrons will have chaotic motions characteristic of the temperature. And the space, the space inside solid bodies as well as the space between them, is filled with electromagnetic waves of various frequencies, including radio waves, heat waves, and light waves. The average power of these waves in a particular range of frequencies is also fixed by the temperature. There is a continual transfer of energy back and forth among the molecular motion in the gas, the motions of free electrons, the vibrations of the solids, and the chaotic electromagnetic waves of various frequencies. On the average, however, each of these maintains its characteristic energy for the particular temperature involved.

Actual physical systems are never quite in thermal equilibrium, for they are always surrounded by bodies at somewhat different temperatures. Things inside a closed container, a box, which is itself held at a constant temperature are very nearly in equilibrium. In fact, it was by speculating about the electromagnetic energy in such a box containing no air, no solids, but only electromagnetic waves, that Max Planck was led to lay the foundations of quantum theory. That is a subject which we cannot explore here.

Imagine that we examined the electromagnetic radiation inside a box held at constant temperature. We would find electromagnetic radiation emerging from the surface of each solid body in the box, and we would find that electromagnetic radiation from other bodies fell on the surface of each body. When such a collection of bodies are in thermal equilibrium, there is an astonishingly simple fact or law of nature concerning the rate at which radiation leaves each elementary area of the surface of each body and the rate at which radiation falls on the same little part of the surface. Regardless of the physical nature of the body, the rate at which radiation leaves a given area is equal to the rate at which radiation falls on the same area. And the rate is the same for an equal area of any body regardless of the nature of the body. The rate depends only on the temperature.

If we consider a highly transparent body, we will see that most of the radiation leaving a particular square millimeter of the surface is radiation which fell on the opposite side of the body and was transmitted through it. If we consider a highly reflecting body, we will see that most of the radiation which leaves a given square millimeter of the surface is simply the radiation which reaches that part of the surface from other bodies and is reflected directly back again. If we consider a black object which absorbs radiation perfectly, the radiation which reaches it from other bodies is neither reflected nor transmitted: it is absorbed. In this case, all the radiation leaving a given square millimeter of surface is due to the thermal agitation of the charged particles near the surface.

Because no objects are perfectly transparent or perfectly reflecting, some of the radiation leaving any object, transparent or reflecting, will always have originated within the object, from the thermal motion of charged particles. And, of course, some of the radiation reaching any imperfectly transmitting or reflecting object will always be absorbed into molecular motion. Since a body must always retain the same energy, reflection or transparency and absorption go hand in hand. A body which at a given temperature absorbs only a tenth of the electromagnetic energy falling on it will at the same temperature radiate only a tenth as much as a perfectly absorbing body; the rest of the quota of radiation leaving it will be transmitted or reflected radiation.

Usually, we do not deal with systems of bodies which are in thermal equilibrium. Usually, we see objects surrounded by other objects at different temperatures. In this case we can easily distinguish transparent objects, reflecting objects, and objects which absorb (and emit) radiation completely. Perfectly absorbing objects are perfectly black.

Suppose, for instance, that we have a microwave receiver so sensitive that it can measure the intensity of radio waves coming from objects at ordinary temperatures. By a sort of trick, such a sensitivity can be attained. Suppose that we point the antenna of the receiver out at the world at large. The antenna will receive thermal radiation—that is, Johnson noise—from various objects. These will not necessarily be the objects at which the antenna is pointed. For instance, if we point the antenna at a mirror, the signal will actually come largely from whatever is reflected in the mirror. Because the mirror is not perfectly reflecting, however, some signal will come directly from the mirror. If a piece of glass is put in front of the antenna, the noise will largely come from objects seen through the glass, though a small part of the noise will come from the glass. We will usually receive radiation indirectly as well as directly, from an assortment of objects at different temperatures.

Some objects, such as steel wool or a bubbly dielectric called Polyfoam to which a small amount of a conducting substance such as carbon has been added, and broken-up objects such as trees and bushes, are almost completely absorbing to microwaves; they are "black" as far as microwaves are concerned. If we point our antenna at such objects, we receive from them microwave radiation or noise of an intensity which depends only on the temperature of the object and not on the temperature of its surroundings. How powerful is such noise radiation?

The power of the electrical noise received depends not only on the temperature of the object from which the noise comes but also on the width of the band of frequencies which the receiver accepts. In fact, the Johnson noise power, P, can be written

$$P = kTB \quad \text{watts}$$

$$P = 1.37 \times 10^{-23}TB \quad \text{watts}$$

Here k is a constant called the *Boltzmann constant*. T is temperature in *degrees Kelvin*—that is, temperature reckoned from a temperature called absolute zero. Absolute zero is a temperature at which the random motions which we call heat would cease. On the centigrade scale of temperature, water's freezing temperature is zero degrees centigrade and its boiling temperature is 100 degrees centigrade. Absolute zero is −273 degrees centigrade, and zero degrees centigrade is 273 degrees Kelvin.

How large is the power of Johnson noise in actual meaningful cases? Suppose that we have a microwave receiver with an antenna which is very highly directive, so that we can point it at individual objects, celestial and terrestrial. Let us say that this microwave receiver has a band width of 20 megacycles, or 2×10^7 cycles per second; that is about the band width of many radar receivers and of microwave systems used to transmit television. Were we to point the antenna toward the night sky we would measure noise corresponding to a temperature of less than 10 degrees Kelvin, that is, a power of 2.74×10^{-15} watts. Were we to point the antenna at a clump of trees at a temperature of 293 degrees Kelvin (20 degrees centigrade, 68 degrees Fahrenheit) we would receive a noise power of about 8×10^{-13} watts. Should we point the antenna at the sun, we would receive a noise power of about 1.6×10^{-11} watts, which is characteristic of a temperature of 6,000 degrees Kelvin. This is the temperature we observe the sun to have by microwave measurements and, indeed, by visual measurements.

If, however, we used a 100-megacycle receiver we would receive a noise signal from the sun corresponding to a temperature of about 1,000,000 degrees Kelvin. How can this be? The sun is surrounded by a mantle of extremely hot gas, the corona. The corona is almost transparent to light waves and to microwaves; it scarcely absorbs or emits them at all. It is opaque to radio waves of longer wave lengths however, so that it both absorbs and emits such waves. One of the greatest mysteries about the sun is how the corona can be so much hotter than the surface under it.

The noise powers we have listed above, and even the microwave noise power from the sun, are very minute. Yet the noise of which we have been speaking is simply electromagnetic waves emitted from a hot body, and that is just what the strong light and intense heat which we receive from the sun are. The noise received by the microwave receiver is so small partly because the band width which we have considered, which is a large band width by radio standards, is truly minuscule compared with the band width of the electromagnetic spectrum that constitutes heat and light. In fact, visible light alone is a band of electromagnetic waves about 2.5×10^8 megacycles wide, or over ten million times as broad as the band width of the microwave receiver we have discussed. This does not tell the whole story in comparing Johnson noise with light and heat. We cannot apply our formula for Johnson noise in the cases of heat and light, because the formula is in error at extremely high frequencies and extremely short wave lengths. The error arises because the formula does not take into account certain fine details of physical behavior which are not observed at radio frequencies. These fine details are the province of quantum mechanics, and Max Planck was the first to see these clearly in the case of electromagnetic radiation. Quantum effects are very important in the behavior of electromagnetic waves as short as waves of light. Here we are concerned with microwave radio waves, and in connection with these the effects peculiar to quantum mechanics are so small as to be unobservable.

Let us return to the question of the magnitude of Johnson-noise power. Suppose, for instance, that we want to receive a microwave signal with a 20-megacycle band width. Suppose that the microwave transmitter is located amid surroundings at a temperature of 20° centigrade (293 degrees Kelvin). Then, if we point our receiving antenna at the transmitter we will receive not only part of the transmitted power but Johnson-noise power as well. We have seen that in a band width of 20 megacycles we will receive about 8×10^{-13} watts, or roughly 10^{-12} watts. Suppose we want the received signal power to be a million times (10^6 times) as great as the received noise power. If this is to be so, we must receive from the transmitter a total power of 10^{-6} watts. If the total transmitted power is, for instance, one watt, we need receive only a millionth of the transmitted power in order for the received signal power to be a million times greater than the received noise power.

Unfortunately, the total noise that troubles us in microwave communication is not entirely Johnson noise received from the vicinity of the transmitter. In fact, in microwave communication and in radar most of the noise is generated in the receiver itself, and one problem of microwave research is to make less noisy microwave receivers. In order to judge microwave receivers, the total noise in the signal received is compared with the noise which would be present if the only noise were Johnson noise for a temperature of 293° Kelvin mixed with the input signal. In the very best microwave receivers, the total noise is about three times as great as amplified Johnson noise alone. Two parts of the noise are generated in the receiver and one part is Johnson noise amplified by the receiver. This best receiver is a special low-noise traveling-wave tube operating at a wave length of 10 centimeters or a frequency of 3,000 megacycles. Microwave receivers commonly used give a noise of ten to 100 times amplified Johnson noise.

How does one go about making better microwave receivers? There are different kinds of microwave receivers. Some use a microwave amplifier, such as a traveling-wave tube, connected directly to the antennas. Others make use of frequency changing, which we discussed in Chapter VIII, to change the frequency of the signal to some lower frequency, at which it can be amplified by pentodes.

Even if we restricted ourselves to one type of receiver, it would be hopeless to try to tell in full how one goes about reducing noise.

The account could well fill an entire technical book and still not be complete. Even such a book would leave out a great deal of the human difficulty, the frustration, and the pleasure of some measure of success which characterize electronics research.

It is perhaps good to say a little about these things at some point in this book. They can be conveyed, if at all, only in a very personal sort of account. Because I am writing the account, the search for a low-noise traveling-wave tube is an excellent subject, for I have followed it closely. I hope that in telling about it I can indicate what happens over a period of years in such an endeavor, how typical people engaged in electronics research spend their time. In order to do this, I must write about the individual people who did the work I will describe, men whose work is neither better nor worse than that of others whose names I have not mentioned in connection with subjects discussed in other chapters.

Vacuum tubes are noisy because an electric current is not a smooth, uniform flow of electric charge. Examined on a fine-enough scale, the flow of electricity from the cathode of a vacuum tube is a flow of individual electrons; it is more like a pattering rain than a steady stream of water. Moreover, as the individual electrons are "boiled off" the hot cathode, they leave with different velocities. Both the granular nature of the flow of electrons and the fluctuating patterns of velocities with which they leave contribute to noise in microwave tubes. Such fluctuations are necessarily present in electron flow. The problem of reducing noise is to make the output of the tube as strongly dependent as possible on the electromagnetic signal input and as little influenced as possible by fluctuations in the electron stream. It is a problem on which a considerable number of people have worked for a considerable number of years.

Kompfner, who invented the traveling-wave tube toward the end of the war, was in his work actually searching for a low-noise amplifier. The tube he built was very unstable. He used a low-loss helix, and thus, if the amplified wave was partly reflected at the output, it could travel back to the input and cause the tube to oscillate. Nonetheless, he did get gain, and his measurements of the noise of the tube indicated better performance than was attained for years afterwards. However, because of the instability of Kompfner's early tubes, they did not seem very promising in the press of wartime work, and the matter of low noise was not immediately pursued. However, work was eventually carried out in England by Kompfner and F. N. H. Robinson which led to a tube with a noise only about twelve times amplified Johnson noise.

When I first worked on traveling-wave tubes in this country, I was most impressed by their great band width. Above all, I wanted to make a broad-band tube that would amplify stably. This took several years. How was the time spent? Even at the fastest, it usually takes many months to construct an entirely new type of vacuum tube. The first tubes I designed were all wrong. In those days one could make only the most rudimentary sort of calculations concerning traveling-wave tubes. I started out to make a tube to operate at a very low voltage. This proved to be hard to do, and I abandoned the effort. The first tube that was made operated feebly and at entirely the wrong voltage.   I had made a mistake in my calculations. Even after this mistake had been corrected I didn't know how to get the waves on and off the helix in a satisfactory manner, and it took time to solve that problem. I did not know how to focus the electron beam effectively, and about half of the current hit the helix instead of going on the collector.

Also, I knew that I should put loss on the helix to keep the tube from oscillating, but I did not know how to do this. Resistance wire wasn't "lossy" enough. I tried iron wire. It was lossy enough, but it changed the focusing effect of the magnetic field. The electrons hit the iron wire and heated it. The wire got hot enough to be non-magnetic, and the focusing changed so that less current hit the wire. The wire alternately heated up and cooled down.

Nonetheless, by June of 1946, L. M. Field and I had a tube we felt we could talk about, and we talked about it at an Institute of Radio Engineers Conference. Over a year of work had gone into a tube that essentially showed little beyond the fact that a traveling-wave tube would function as a broad-band amplifier. Work went on, but not without distractions.

In 1946 Les Field and I discovered that the traveling-wave tube often made hash of the signal it amplified. The tube was oscillating at a comparatively low frequency because of the presence of positive ions—that is, gas molecules from which the electrons of the beam had knocked out an electron. Over a year was spent in diverse inventing before it was discovered that the condition could be avoided by baking the tube properly during its evacuation.

Of course, during all this period, progress was made. A theory of operation of the traveling-wave tube was worked out. An approximate theory of the electromagnetic waves which travel on a helix was also worked out. The focusing of electron beams was studied. This was all to the good, but distractions occurred as well.

For instance, in 1946 Les Field, who had worked with me, went to Stanford University to become a professor. At this time W. B. Hebenstreit and I were working on the problem of reducing noise in traveling-wave tubes. The theory of noise in the usual type of traveling-wave tube indicated that one should use a very low voltage and a very small gain to make a low-noise tube. Bill Hebenstreit started work on an altered form of traveling-wave tube which I will identify merely by calling it a transverse-field tube. Hebenstreit made elaborate calculations and started to build a tube. In the meantime, he and I were distracted. While trying to make calculations concerning noise, we thought of something called the double-stream amplifier (it appears that A. V. Haeff, then of the Naval Research Laboratory, thought of it about the same time). The double-stream amplifier looked wonderful then, and we just had to work on it. Now, its good points, if any, seem small, but it took years of hard work to find this out. While he was in the midst of work on both the low-noise tube and the double-stream amplifier, Bill left for California, and work on his transverse field low-noise tube was interrupted. It is still a good idea, and I hope that we can do more about it sometime.

The double-stream amplifier wasn't the only distraction. From the very first, in 1945, I had felt that a magnetron amplifier, a sort of cross between a magnetron and a traveling-wave tube, would be advantageous. While we were trying to make traveling-wave tubes, two men worked to make a magnetron amplifier. One of the men went to Illinois. The work had to be dropped. It became apparent that the traveling-wave tube wasn't as simple as it had looked and that we couldn't afford effort on two things at once. Later, workers in Paris made successful magnetron amplifiers.

By this time it was 1949. We had traveling-wave tubes, but none of them were low-noise tubes. The theory of traveling-wave tubes had been well enough worked out, however, so that a new approach could be used in calculating noise. The old theory had said that noise could be made low only by making the voltage low and the gain low. The new theory said that voltage should have nothing to do with noise and that the gain should be high for low noise. (1955 theory says the gain doesn't matter.)

The theory also said that if one observed the noise along an electron beam he should see it as a standing-wave pattern. I for one didn't know whether to believe this or not. By this time, however, Les Field had sent one of his students, C. F. Quate, back to work at the Bell Laboratories. He went to work with C. C. Cutler. Chape Cutler and Cal Quate set out to look for noise waves on an electron stream. By 1950 they had found them. The new theory of noise appeared to be true. In fact, Cutler and Quate made a tube with an unprecedentedly low noise.

At this time, Dean Watkins and Ping King Tien were working with Field at Stanford. In 1950 Watkins had an idea which proved to be a real key to lower noise figure. It was based on the new theory of noise, the theory based on noise standing-waves. It involved accelerating the electrons to their final velocity in two steps, and is called *velocity jump*. By 1951 this was thoroughly understood in terms of another idea of Tien, Field, and Watkins, called space-charge-wave deamplification (and amplification). It looked as if one could reduce the noise of an electron beam almost without limit. By 1952 Watkins had got the noise down to ten times Johnson noise, and soon R. W. Peter of R.C.A. had pushed it down to around nine times. It seemed almost as if noise were on its way out.

Efforts to reduce noise further by space-charge-wave deamplification proved futile. People looked around for a reason. I remember that in 1952 one visitor showed me a chart which purported to prove that there was something in the old theory that low voltage was necessary for low noise (one can prove anything with charts).

In 1953 I succeeded in proving a theorem which showed that in fact the noise in an electron beam really cannot be reduced at all, it can only be rearranged, so to speak, so that the tube as a whole is not so noisy. In fact, it seemed that in an ordinary traveling-wave tube the noise could not be made less than about four times Johnson noise.

A number of other people seem to have been working along the same lines: R. W. Peter, S. Bloom and J. A. Ruet, at R.C.A.; H. Haus, at the Massachusetts Institute of Technology; and F. N. H. Robinson, at Oxford University in England, published similar work.

Almost as soon as the minimum noisiness of four times Johnson noise had been proposed, G. E. St. John and C. R. Moster, of the Bell Laboratories, succeeded in getting the noise down to three times Johnson noise. Something was wrong with the theorem! It was, however, essentially a detail, which lowered the number but did not affect the general conclusion.

How was the noise to be reduced further? Not in an ordinary traveling-wave tube. Could some invention, some trick do it? We were working on one such trick. But late in 1954 Robinson and Haus working together proved conclusively that tricks were not enough, that the lower-limiting noise figure held not only for traveling-wave tubes, but also for all conceivable microwave tubes of a very broad class. Ingenious ideas were swept away at one stroke. It was now clear, however, what general sorts of things could possibly reduce noise further and what could not.

The reader will no doubt find this summary bewildering. For those who followed the work in detail, ten years somehow slipped by. Much of the time was spent in a bewilderment more detailed but quite as complete as the reader's can be. Much time was spent in building the wrong things. Much time was spent in building things the wrong way. Much time was spent in pursuing ideas which had nothing to do with noise. Everything I have mentioned, and much that I have not, consumed time in thinking, time in building, time in testing. Somehow out of all this came low-noise tubes and a new understanding. But, how can it have taken a lot of intelligent people ten years to do this one, rather narrow thing? Only people who have done similar work can really understand this.

CHAPTER X

Radiation

WE HAVE SEEN that the Johnson noise which a microwave antenna picks up from a hot body is merely a minuscule fraction of total, chaotic electromagnetic energy which the agitated particles in the body radiate. To a designer of microwave systems this tiny fraction of the radiation may seem the most important part, but to mankind at large this is scarcely so. We would all freeze if it were not for the electromagnetic radiation we receive from the sun.

Indeed, the radiation of heat is important even to the electronics engineer. Vacuum tubes contain hot cathodes. Much of the energy required to heat the cathode is lost through radiation; the rest leaks off by conduction of heat through the wires attached to the cathode and to the internal electric-heater coil which heats the cathode. Most of the transfer of heat from the internal heater to the cathode which surrounds it takes place by means of radiation. Further, various electrodes in vacuum tubes depend on radiation to keep them sufficiently cool. Thus, the designer of vacuum tubes has to understand about the radiation of heat in order to design heaters, cathodes, and other electrodes. It would be foolish to pretend to the reader, however, that this chapter is included because of the importance of the radiation of heat in connection with vacuum tubes. That is how I came to learn what I know about radiation, but the contents of this chapter give rather an outward view from electronics, a view of some fascinating facts about radiation—on earth and in the solar system, in burning glasses and in cameras.

If you touch a steam radiator, your hand is heated by *conduction*. If you hold your hand in the hot air rising from a hot air register, your hand is heated by *convection*. If you hold your hand in the beam of heat from a reflector-type electric heater, your hand is heated by *radiation;* it is warmed despite the fact that the air surrounding it is cool.

Conduction and convection are complicated processes, difficult to describe quantitatively. Radiation is simpler. While it has complexities, we can find out many interesting things about radiation without dealing with these. For the effort of understanding, I think one can get more out of a consideration of radiation than of almost any other scientific subject.

One of the aspects of radiation which need concern us little is the question of the frequency or wave length of the electromagnetic energy radiated by a hot body. At any temperature a body radiates energy over a broad band of frequencies. The radiation is most intense at some frequency which depends on the temperature of the body, and it is less intense at higher and lower frequencies. As we gradually raise the temperature of a body, it passes from a dull red to orange and on to yellow. The sun is hot enough to radiate white light; that is, the radiation is fairly constant over the range of frequencies which constitute visible light. Hotter stars than the sun radiate most of their energy at frequencies above those of visible light, and the radiation is more intense at the higher frequencies which constitute blue light than it is at the lower frequencies which constitute red light.

We will think of the total electromagnetic energy which a body radiates as constituting heat radiation, whatever the frequency of the radiation. The law for the total radiation from a hot body is simple. The power, P, in watts leaving a part of the surface of an area of A square meters is

$$P = 5.73 \times 10^{-8} eT^4 A \text{ watts}$$

Here T is temperature in degrees Kelvin. The factor e is called the *emissivity*. If a body is perfectly absorbing, that is, if a body is perfectly black, then $e = 1$. For other bodies, e varies somewhat with temperature, because, actually, e is different for the different frequencies constituting the radiation. The calculations presented later will be somewhat in error because we disregard this variation

of emissivity with temperature, but we can show the main effects
of radiation by means of this simple law.

How shall we use this important law of radiation? If we tackle
problems near at hand, our conclusions will be in error, for we have
to contend with the transfer of heat by air currents—that is, by convection—and by conduction, as well as by radiation. Even in
vacuum tubes we have to take into account transfer of heat by conduction through various solid supports. The logical place to begin
would seem to be in interstellar or interplanetary space, and that
is just what we will do. To make matters as simple as possible, we
will start out far, far from the sun and its heat, with a man cast
adrift in a space suit. Will he freeze, or will he fry?

We will simplify the space suit to a can 1½ feet in diameter and
6 feet long; the area of the surface of the can is about 3 square
meters. Suppose that the can is at body temperature, which is 310
degrees Kelvin. What is the heat loss?

The heat loss will depend on the emissivity, e. For a shiny
aluminum surface this will be small; perhaps around 0.1. For a
black surface, e is 1. For these two emissivities the heat losses are:

Emissivity e	Heat loss, watts
0.1	160
1.0	1,600

The human body just in living produces heat at a rate of 150
watts. Thus, if the can, the space suit, is nice and shiny, the man
inside will just about stay warm, but in a black space suit he will
cool down in a hurry. This fact should be noted by the authors
of space operas. They should never distinguish their villains by
means of black space suits unless those villains can do their das-
tardly deeds truly in cold blood.

The heating of a space suit by the occupant inside may be mar-
ginal however, for the space suit may have to be considerably
larger than we have assumed in order to contain food, water, and
air tanks. Can the man still keep warm, using just his body heat?
Nothing is simpler. All we have to do is to surround the shiny can

with a second shiny can, called a *heat shield*. The two can be spaced very close together and supported one from the other in such a manner as to allow negligible conduction of heat. I have illustrated these inner and outer cans schematically in Fig. *10.1*.

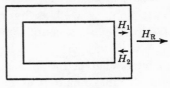

FIG. *10.1*

If the man produces heat at a rate of 150 watts, this is the rate at which heat must leave the outer wall of the outer can; I have used an arrow marked H_R to indicate this 150 watts. Between the space suit and the heat shield I have shown two arrows, H_1 and H_2. H_1 is the rate at which heat flows from the space suit to the heat shield. H_2 is the rate at which heat flows from the heat shield back to the space suit. Because heat doesn't accumulate in the heat shield, we see at once that

$$H_R + H_2 = H_1$$

That is, the total rate at which heat leaves the heat shield is equal to the rate at which heat arrives at the heat shield.

We must know something else, as well. H_2 must consist of two parts. First, if the inside and the outside of the heat shield are equally shiny, an amount of heat, H_R, will be radiated inward as well as outward. Secondly, an object which emits only 0.1 as much radiation as a black body also absorbs only 0.1 as much radiation as a black body, and so it reflects 0.9 of the radiation striking it. Thus, 0.9 of the heat H_1 striking the heat shield is reflected to form a part of H_2. Summing up, we have

$$H_2 = H_R + 0.9\,H_1$$

We need to know still more. Consider the outside surface of the can-shaped suit itself. Suppose that if it were not surrounded by the heat shield it would radiate heat at a rate H_o. The heat flow H_1 from it must be this heat plus whatever part of the heat

H_2 going toward it is reflected. If it is as shiny as the heat shield, so that it reflects 0.9 of H_2, we will have

$$H_1 = H_o + 0.9H_2$$

Those skilled in algebra will be able to deduce from these three equations the relation between H_o, H_R, H_1 and H_2. I did, and found, remembering that $H_R = 150$ watts,

$$H_o = 2.9H_R = \quad 435 \text{ watts}$$
$$H_1 = 20 \;\; H_R = 3{,}000 \text{ watts}$$
$$H_2 = 19 \;\; H_R = 2{,}850 \text{ watts}$$

If the reader is skeptical he can check these values in the three equations.

The moral of this exercise lies in the fact that an object which itself would radiate heat at a rate of 435 watts will lose heat at a rate of only 150 watts if it is surrounded by a shiny heat shield. Further, if we regard the inner object and its shield as one unit and add another shield outside, the radiation will be cut down by a further factor of $1/2.9$, to 52 watts. With three heat shields the radiation would be only 18 watts instead of the original 435 watts for the unshielded object.

In mundane affairs, this is the secret of home insulation consisting of several separated layers of aluminum foil. The space between the layers is so broken up that the enclosed air cannot circulate freely to carry heat away by convection. The layers of foil are so supported that conduction is small. The shiny layers of foil act as heat shields against radiation. They are somewhat more effective than the foregoing calculations might indicate, for the emissivity, e, of shiny aluminum is less than 0.1 for the low-frequency electromagnetic waves which predominate in radiation from objects at room temperature.

In returning to the empyrean, we conclude that there just isn't any problem at all in keeping warm in interstellar space. If we used enough heat shields, body warmth would keep a whole space ship at habitable temperature; even a candle would heat it. In interstellar space, far from the sun, there isn't too much trouble keeping cool, either, for a black drum a foot and a half in diameter by 6 feet long radiates at a rate of over 1,000 watts at body temperature.

Within the confines of the solar system, the presence of our sun makes a profound difference. We can easily see just what this difference is. We have seen that the radiation from an area A of a hot body is

$$P = 5.73 \times 10^{-8} eT^4 A \text{ watts}$$

This is, for instance, the electromagnetic radiation from an area A of the sun's surface. To get the total radiation leaving the sun, we use as the area A the area of the whole surface of the sun. This is $4\pi r_s^2$, where r_s is the radius of the sun. At some greater distance r from the center of the sun this radiation passes through a spherical surface of area $4\pi r^2$. The fraction of the total radiation that will fall on an area A at a distance r will be $A/4\pi r^2$; we see that this will be a power, P, given by

$$P = 5.73 \times 10^{-8} eT^4 (r_s/r)^2 A$$

The power received by an object varies directly as the area, A, and inversely as the square of the distance, r, from the center of the sun.

What temperature would a spherical object attain at various distances from the sun, assuming the object to be a good enough conductor of heat so as to be all at the same temperature? Suppose the body has an emissivity e_o, a radius a, and a temperature T_o. The area of the surface is $4\pi a^2$, and the power, P_o, which the object radiates will be

$$P_o = 5.73 \times 10^{-8} e_o T_o^4 (4\pi a^2)$$

The sun radiates about as if it were black, with emissivity $e = 1$ and at a temperature of 6000 degrees Kelvin. The power of the sun's radiation which is absorbed is the power intercepted by the cross-sectional area of the sphere, the area of the disk, πa^2, times e_o (the rest of the radiation from the sun is reflected). We see that this power is

$$P = 5.73 \times 10^{-8} (6000)^4 (r_s/r)^2 (\pi a^2) e_o$$

This must be equal to the power, P_o, radiated by the spherical object, and this fact enables us to find the temperature, T_o, of the spherical object. We see that

$$T_o = 6000\sqrt{r_s/2r} \quad \text{degrees Kelvin}$$

The temperature does not depend on the emissivity, e_o, of the object. A shiny object absorbs less radiation than a dark object, but it also radiates less.

The radius of the sun is 0.438 million miles. I have tabulated below the distances of various planets from the sun and I have tabulated calculated values of T_o in degrees Kelvin for objects at these distances. I have also given the temperature in degrees Fahrenheit.

Planet	Distance from Sun, Millions of Miles	Temperature Degrees Kelvin	Temperature Degrees Fahrenheit
Mercury	36.0	467	381
Venus	67.2	342	156
Earth	93.0	291	64
Mars	141.5	235	− 36
Jupiter	483	127	−231
Saturn	886	94	−289
Uranus	1,783	67	−340
Neptune	2,793	53	−363
Pluto	3,666	46	−375

We see that to be maintained at a pleasant temperature by radiation from the sun, a spherical object must be about as far from the sun as the earth is.

While the temperature attained does not depend on the emissivity, e_o, of the object if the emissivity is the same for the side toward the sun as it is for the side away from the sun, non-uniform objects would attain other temperatures. If the object were shiny on the side toward the sun and dark on the side away from the sun, it would be cooler than if it were uniform, and it would be hotter if it were dark on the side toward the sun and shiny on the side away from the sun.

It is perhaps surprising how nearly the temperature we have calculated for a uniform sphere as far away from the sun as is the earth—that is, 64 degrees Fahrenheit—is to the temperatures we experience on earth. This gives us confidence in the belief that Venus will be almost intolerably hot, Mars almost intolerably cold, and the rest of the planets impossibly extreme in temperature.

Such a calculation is, of course, so simplified as to omit from consideration some very important factors governing the temperatures of the planets. Mercury, which turns the same hemisphere always to the sun, conducts heat poorly enough so that the dark side is much cooler than the light side. Planets which, like the earth, have night and day experience diurnal changes in temperature. Moreover, the planets receive energy from the sun as electromagnetic waves of comparatively high frequency, because the sun is so hot. A planet loses heat by radiating waves of comparatively low frequency, because the temperature of the planet is so low. The emissivity may be different for the two sorts of waves. As a matter of fact, the earth's atmosphere, which is quite transparent to sunlight, is almost opaque to many of the longer wave lengths which the solid portion of the earth itself radiates. Thus, the earth's atmosphere tends to trap the heat received from the sun.

Such simple calculations can give real scientific substance to speculations about space travel, and indeed have. For instance, extensive calculations have been made concerning solar power plants for space ships, in which water is boiled by the heat of the sun in order to run steam turbines.

Such proposed power plants, like similar solar steam-power plants for the deserts of the earth, make use of mirrors or lenses to concentrate the radiation received from the sun on an area smaller than that on which it would otherwise have fallen.

Burning glasses are familiar to all boys, and they date from an early period of our history. There are stories that Archimedes used huge mirrors to set fire to Roman ships. What should we believe about such tales? We could never hope to decide unequivocally by means of historical records, for even the most detailed and convincing records may be untruthful. We can, however, tell simply from the law of radiation what things Archimedes could and could not have done.

To gain some insight into the action of burning glasses and burn-

ing mirrors it is best to start rather indirectly by restating in a
slightly different form the law governing radiation from the sun.
The drawing of FIG. *10.2* will help us to do this. This figure shows
the sun, centered at *a*, and a point *b* a distance *r* from the center of
the sun. We draw a line from *b* which is just tangent to the sun,

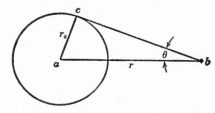

FIG. *10.2*

that is, which just touches it at one point, at *c*. From *c* we draw a
radial line of length r_s to the center of the sun. Simple geometry
tells us that the radius *a–c* and the tangent *c–b* will always be at
right angles.

The triangle *a–b–c* is a right triangle. Mathematically, the ratio
r_s/r is called the sine of the angle θ between *a–b* and *b–c*. This is
written

$$\frac{r_s}{r} = \text{sine } \theta$$

We see from our expression for the power *P* of radiation falling on
an area *A* at point *b*

$$P = 5.73 \times 10^{-8} eT^4 (\text{sine } \theta)^2 A$$

Now it is a law of radiation that the surface of a body looks just
as hot through a perfectly transparent lens or in a perfectly reflecting mirror as it does when seen directly. If we look at the sun
through a lens so that the sun appears to be larger, we will receive
more power from it per unit area. FIG. *10.3* illustrates this. Above
we see light reaching a point directly from the sun; the radiation
reaches the point within a narrow cone of peak angle $2\theta_1$. Below,
the radiation collected by a burning glass reaches the point *b* in a
cone of much larger angle $2\theta_2$, and is thus much more intense.

If we assume that a burning glass is perfectly transparent or a burning mirror is perfectly reflecting, the intensity of the radiation from it depends only on how broad a cone of rays falls from it. A narrow, distant lens gives a low intensity of radiation; a nearby broad lens gives a high intensity of radiation.

For the sun as seen from the earth, approximately

$$\text{sine } \theta = 5 \times 10^{-3}$$

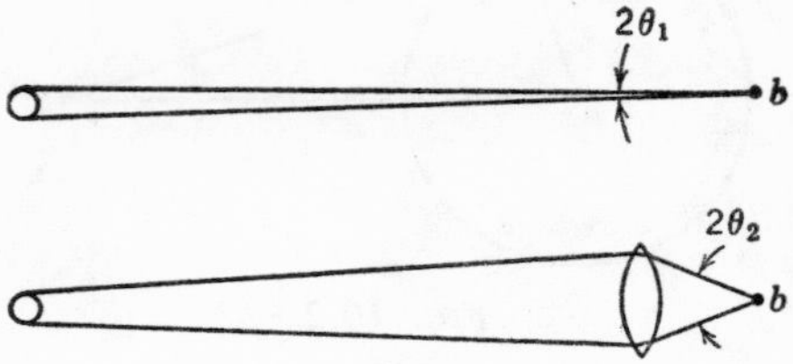

FIG. *10.3*

To give radiation a hundred times as intense as the direct radiation of the sun, we would have to have a mirror or lens for which

$$\text{sine } \theta = 5 \times 10^{-2}$$

This is true for a mirror ten feet in diameter at a distance of 100 feet. Archimedes could conceivably have set a ship on fire at such a distance with such a mirror, but burning mirrors could not work at great distances. At a distance of 1,000 feet the radiation from a 10-foot mirror could have only the intensity of direct sunlight.

Men sometimes make solar furnaces which heat objects to extremely high temperatures without contamination. The secret of reaching such high temperatures is of course to have the rays of the sun reach the object to be heated from as many directions as possible. In a solar furnace built at the California Institute of Technology, several lenses were used, with mirrors to direct the sun's rays on the object to be heated somewhat as shown at the left in FIG. *10.4*. Other solar furnaces make use of a deep parabolic reflector, as in the right of FIG. *10.4*. I believe that an extremely good solar furnace could be made by giving all the spectators in a football bowl squares of cardboard covered with aluminum foil. If all the spectators reflected the sun's rays to one spot in the field, they could literally burn the referee up.

While all the light of day comes from the sun, we see much of it
indirectly, reflected from the moon and planets and from the objects
about us on earth.   These objects are bright or dark as they reflect
more or less of the sun's rays.

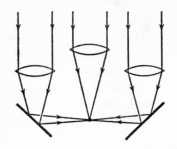

FIG. *10.4*

We use lenses as burning glasses to focus the sun's rays.   We also
use lenses in cameras to focus the light from various objects on the
film in the cameras.   The same law which governs the intensity of
radiation from a burning glass governs the amount of light falling
on the film of the camera.

In the law for radiation from the burning glass, which is

$$P = 5.73 \times 10^{-8}eT^4(\text{sine }\theta)^2A$$

the quantity

$$5.73 \times 10^{-8}eT^4$$

is the brightness of the surface of the sun.   It is the power of the
radiation leaving each square meter of the surface of the sun.   In
the same way, if we divide the power, P, by the area, A, on which
it falls, the quantity P/A is the brightness of the radiation produced
at the focus of the burning glass.   It is the power per square meter
in the image of the sun which the burning glass produces.

Thus, if we wish, we can rewrite our law as follows:

$$B_i = B(\text{sine }\theta)^2$$

Here B is the brightness of an object (the sun, in the cases we have
considered), B_i is the brightness of the image of the object produced by a lens, and 2θ is the peak angle of a cone drawn from a
point of the image back to the lens producing the image.

If, in a camera, d is the diameter of the lens and l is the distance from the lens to the film, the exact expression for $(\text{sine } \theta)^2$ is

$$(\text{sine } \theta)^2 = \frac{(d/2)^2}{l^2 + (d/2)^2} = \frac{1}{4(l/d)^2 + 1}$$

The greatest value sine θ can have is 1, and we can approach this value only if the lens diameter is extremely large compared with the distance from lens to image. Thus, the brightness of the image is always less than the brightness of the object imaged.

The quantity sine θ is called the numerical aperture of a lens. Photographers use another quantity, called the f number, which is the ratio of the distance from the lens to the image to the diameter of the lens. The f number is thus

$$f = \frac{l}{d}$$

We see that

$$(\text{sine } \theta)^2 = \frac{1}{4f^2 + 1}$$

It may be interesting to know the ratio of the brightness of the image in the camera to the brightness of the scene before it, that is, B_i/B, for several common f numbers:

f	B_i/B
1.5	0.1
2.8	0.03
3.5	0.02
4.5	0.012
8	0.004

The smaller the f number, the brighter the image, and hence the shorter the exposure time which need be used. Thus, lenses with small f numbers are called *fast* lenses. To produce fast lenses which give sharp images is one of the chief problems of lens design. An f-1.5 lens is a very fast lens indeed. Yet, an f-1.5 lens gives an image only a tenth as bright as the object imaged. However, to attain an image of brightness equal to the brightness of the object imaged one would have to use a lens of infinite diameter.

The eye is a camera, and binoculars merely provide auxiliary lenses for the camera which is the eye. It follows that binoculars cannot increase the brightness of objects seen; they can merely make them larger. Binoculars with lenses which are too narrow can, however, decrease the brightness of objects. If a binocular or telescope magnifies N diameters (makes things appear N times broader) the lens should be at least N times as broad as the pupil of the eye if the brightness is not to be diminished. The pupil of the eye, when it is opened wide in dim light, is about a tenth of an inch in diameter.

We have already explored in Chapter V, Waves, the relation between lens diameter and resolving power, that is, the sharpness of detail which can be seen with a telescope or a microscope. Now we have added to this our understanding of the limitation on the brightness of images. These are two fundamental physical limitations on the performance of all optical devices. The fact that light comes in little indivisible packets called quanta imposes another sort of fundamental, unavoidable limitation. Beyond these basic limitations, there are plenty of practical limitations in the design and fabrication of lenses, but these are subject to improvement. The limitations on brightness and resolving power can never be evaded, nor can the fact that light arrives unevenly as a stream of quanta.

Led by the realization that the electromagnetic radiation from hot bodies which constitutes Johnson noise is but a part of the total electromagnetic radiation from bodies, we have considered the temperatures of space suits and planets, the limitations of burning glasses, cameras, and telescopes. All of these matters are related through the science of physics. This is one sort of relation which we see everywhere about us.

Things can be related in another way; they can be related because they are all a part of some system or device used for some particular purpose. This is the sort of relation which we find in technology, in which the knowledge gained from various branches of science is brought together to solve some overall problem.

CHAPTER XI

Microwave Systems

OUT OF microwave bits and pieces and out of microwave theory and art, men have put together microwave systems. These men comprise systems-planning engineers, who lay out general requirements and the general form of a system, and system development engineers, who give the system its concrete and final form. Sometimes systems men have other titles, and, indeed, good systems work has been done by research workers. Whatever we call men who work with systems (we may as well call them systems engineers despite their different organizational titles), they are men with overall problems. The problem may be to transmit a television signal a few miles, from a race track or a ball field, to a studio. The problem may be to carry operating instructions and emergency signals between the pumping stations along a pipeline a thousand miles long. The problem may be to transmit telephone and television signals across the continent, interconnecting all the large cities on the way. The problem may be to detect enemy aircraft or to guide missiles. Someday the problem may be to communicate with ships in space, with the moon, or with planets.

To carry out these tasks, the systems engineer has available as tools the theoretical understanding, the art of microwaves. He also has available klystrons, traveling-wave tubes, and magnetrons. He has available non-linear silicon diodes or crystals by means of which he can change the frequency of signals. He has triodes and pentodes to amplify signals of lower than microwave frequencies. He has coaxial lines and wave guides to carry microwave signals, resonators and filters to pass microwave signals of one band of frequencies and reject or divert microwave signals of other bands of frequencies. He has antennas to radiate and to receive micro-wave signals. He has a knowledge of the propagation of micro-waves. He understands how they can be modulated so as to carry messages of various sorts.

Out of his knowledge and experience, the systems engineer must somehow combine these components and techniques to achieve his overall purpose.

Because the primary purpose is the sending out and receiving of some sort of message by means of microwaves, the systems engi-neer's primary concern must be with the properties of the signal and with the behavior of microwaves and of microwave compo-nents. He must study the signal he is to send. He must know its band width. He must know how much noise can be tolerated, and what sort of noise. Perhaps noise of high frequencies is less objec-tionable than noise of low frequencies (this is true in television, for instance). If this is so, the fact may be taken into account by using a greater fraction of the power to transmit the lower frequencies.

Because of the non-linear behavior of vacuum-tube amplifiers, a defect which cannot be altogether avoided, frequencies in the signal will combine and give rise to other frequencies; this is one sort of distortion of a signal. Because the resonators, filters and other cir-cuits give only approximately the behavior that the engineer would like, the microwave system will distort the signal in transmission in another way.

Distortion tends to make a signal less recognizable, less intelli-gible, and in this way it is much like noise. It is equally important to the systems engineer, and it is much harder to predict. Because of distortion, some frequency components of a signal may arrive too strong and others too weak. Some frequency components may be shifted in phase, so that the sine waves reach their peak ampli-tudes at the wrong times. In TV, distortion may result in blurring, or in bright or dark lines along the edges of objects, or in displaced images called echoes. In color TV, distortion may cause wrong or less vivid colors. In transmitting many telephone conversa-tions, distortion may result in *cross talk*, so that one subscriber hears a gabbling sound or a noiselike sound when other subscribers talk over the same system.

The systems engineer must keep all of these things in mind as he designs a system. He must think of many other things as well. He must think of how to hold parts together physically. He must decide whether to use standard panels and chassis which will fit on a standard *relay rack* (a tall structure about 2 feet wide, with two separated vertical steel supports to which panels can be bolted), or to build special cabinets or other structures. He must think of blowers and ducts for cooling. He must think of power supplies, and of gasoline-driven generators for stand-by power. He must think how antennas and towers can be built most cheaply. He must consider the problem of access roads. He must think of alarm circuits. He must think of test procedures for detecting trouble and of maintenance procedures for correcting trouble.

Systems engineering is an extremely broad and complex art. Those responsible for systems planning and development must think of a tremendous variety of things all at once. Often a decision on one point may affect another matter that might at first seem unrelated. Always keeping reliability, ease of maintenance, and cost in mind, the systems engineers must somehow juggle, discard, and combine until they arrive at something which can be recognized as a well-planned, well-engineered system.

Systems planning and development in all its ramifications is much too strong meat for either me or the reader. With due humility, however, let us look at some of the narrowly microwave aspects of microwave systems. We cannot consider the all-important matters of the detailed nature of signals and of distortion, and the effects of distortion on signals; these subjects are too complicated. We can, however, consider matters of power, noise, antennas, and microwave transmission. Dealing with these only, we can gain a good deal of insight into some of the limitations and possibilities of microwave systems.

The microwave-system designer starts out with a set of requirements and ends up with a system. This is only logical, but it will be much better for us to start out with a system and see what sort of performance the designer has built into it to accomplish his purpose.

The American Telephone and Telegraph Company's TD-2 (this

is merely a model number and means nothing more) radio-relay system spans the country in a series of 107 hops each about 30 miles long.   The transmitting and receiving antennas must be high, so as to allow a line-of-sight path between them, and at 108 locations, starting in New York and ending in Los Angeles, these antennas are mounted on the tops of city buildings, on the peaks of mountains, and on 200-foot towers rising above the midwestern plains.   At each intermediate point there is a microwave *repeater*, which picks up the microwave signal from the preceding repeater, amplifies it, and sends it on to the next repeater at a slightly different frequency.   The coast-to-coast TR-2 system was installed in 1951.   Since then many more routes have been added, as we can see from the map of FIG. *11.1*, which was published in the Bell

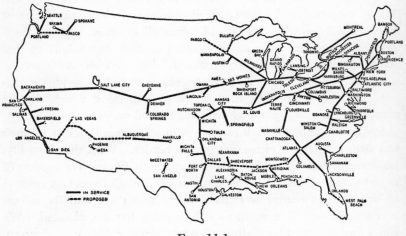

FIG. *11.1*

Laboratories *Record* in November 1954.   Since then the network has been considerably expanded.   TD-2 microwave radio relay carries not only TV programs in black-and-white and color, but a great many telephone conversations as well.

The TD-2 system is really a number of microwave channels running in parallel, using the same sites and antennas and operating on slightly different frequencies.   All the frequencies lie in a band from 3,800 to 4,300 megacycles, corresponding to a wave-length range of 7.9 to 7.0 centimeters. In making calculations we will assume a wave length of 7.5 centimeters, 3 inches, or $\frac{1}{4}$ feet.

Each microwave transmitter and receiver uses an antenna 10 feet square. The effective area of these antennas is about one half of the geometrical area. Each transmitter radiates a power of about $\frac{1}{2}$ watt, which must carry an FM signal of a band width of 20 megacycles an average distance of 30 miles. How much of the power arrives?

In Chapter V, which deals with waves, the ratio of received power, P_R, to transmitted power, P_T, is given as

$$\frac{P_R}{P_T} = \frac{A_R A_T}{\lambda^2 L^2}$$

Here A_R is the area of the receiving antenna, A_T is the area of the transmitting antenna, λ is the wave length, and L the distance between transmitter and receiver. In our case, L is around 30 miles, or 150,000 feet. A_T and A_R are each 50 square feet, and λ is $\frac{1}{4}$ feet. We obtain

$$\frac{P_R}{P_T} = 1.8 \times 10^{-6}$$

Because the transmitter power is about $\frac{1}{2}$ watt, the received power is very nearly 10^{-6} watts, that is, a millionth of a watt.

When the signal arrives at the receiver it is mixed with Johnson noise of power

$$P = 1.37 \times 10^{-23} TB \text{ watts}$$

We take T as 293 degrees Kelvin and B as 20 megacycles, that is 2×10^7 cycles, so that the Johnson noise power, P, is

$$P = 8 \times 10^{-14} \text{ watts}$$

The receiver is not perfect but itself produces noise, so that the total noise in the amplified signal is perhaps thirty times Johnson noise. This means that the total noise is equivalent to receiving a noise power of roughly $30 \times 8 \times 10^{-14}$ or 2.4×10^{-12} watts. As the received signal is 10^{-6} watts, the ratio of signal to noise is about 4×10^5; the signal is four hundred thousand times as strong as the noise.

This is not the whole story however, for the signal must be amplified approximately a hundred times in traveling from coast to coast. An equal amount of noise is introduced at each amplification, so that the total accumulated noise is a hundred times as great as the noise introduced at one repeater. This means that the final ratio of microwave signal power to noise power is not 4×10^5 but only a hundredth of this, or 4×10^3. The power is sufficient to provide telephone and television transmission of adequate quality; that is, it is sufficient most of the time.

Everyone who has watched coast-to-coast TV shows has on rare occasions seen the picture dissolve into a flurry of "snow." Such behavior, when it is not merely due to failure or malfunctioning of apparatus, is caused by *fading* of the microwave signal on some one of the 107 30-mile links which it must traverse. Fading is an atmospheric effect; on an airless world like the moon there would be no fading. In the summertime, layers of varying density may form in the still air; these may bend toward the receiver a part of the microwave signal which would ordinarily miss it. Thus, during periods of fading, signals arrive at the receiver from two directions. If these signals add *in phase*—that is, if the crest of one wave arrives at the same time as the crest of the other—the received signal is strengthened, but if the crest of one wave arrives along with the trough of the other wave, and if the waves have nearly equal amplitudes, the waves nearly cancel and the received signal almost disappears. The receiver tries to correct for this by means of an *automatic gain control* which increases the amplification when the signal level is low, but what comes out of the receiver during a fade is mostly amplified noise, noise which appears on the TV screen as snow.

Microwave links spanning water or the salt flats of Utah may be troubled by another sort of fading, due to the simultaneous reception of a signal reflected from the water or land and a signal received directly without reflection. As the density of the air changes, the times taken to traverse the two paths change slightly, and this can cause fading. In order to overcome this sort of fading, one antenna, the receiving antenna or the transmitting antenna, is put up very high and the other is put close to the surface, so the length and height of the reflected path is almost the same as that of the direct path.

The study of the *propagation* of microwaves is an extremely difficult aspect of the art. Not only are microwave signals bent by stratifications in the atmosphere; they are scattered by the uneven, gusty nature of the air. Such scattered signals can be received weakly at distances of hundreds of miles, far beyond the horizon that we can reach by waves traveling directly in a line-of-sight path. In the future, by using very high power transmitters, it may be possible to send microwave signals and signals of somewhat longer wave lengths across sizeable bodies of water. The American Telephone and Telegraph Company has already been granted permission to transmit from Florida to Cuba by scatter propagation, using a frequency a little below 1,000 megacycles.

The atmosphere proves useful in signaling beyond the horizon by means other than scatter propagation. Reflection by the ionized layers, or ionosphere, of the upper atmosphere makes possible all of our long-distance, short-wave radio transmission. Thus, the earth's atmosphere is not an unmitigated nuisance. Sometimes, however, it seems so to the microwave systems engineer. To transmit a signal over a distance of 3,000 miles he has to pick it up and relay it one hundred times in order not to exceed the line-of-sight-path length of around 30 miles which the earth's curvature allows. And over each of these short paths he has to cope not only with fading but also, in the case of short microwaves, with the scattering of the waves by rain drops, a scattering which can considerably add to the path loss during heavy rain.

How much simpler it would be to transmit microwave messages from the earth to the moon, or even to the planets. There is a clear, direct path all the way. The total amount of air that the waves would have to traverse going vertically through the atmosphere is equivalent to only about 5 miles of air at sea-level pressure. It can't be far through the rain looking straight up. The stratified layers are horizontal, and would little affect waves going straight through them. In sending messages to the moon, to space ships, or to the planets, the systems engineer would have nothing to fight but sheer distance. How serious is that?

Suppose that men someday reach the moon and want to communicate with us across the 240,000 miles of empty space between the earth and the moon. How powerful will their transmitters have to be? Roughly, the path from the earth to the moon is 10,000, or 10^4, times as long as the path from one microwave radio relay station to another. Our formula, based on the inverse-square falling of signal power with distance, tells us that, for a given power and for given antennas, the signal received at the moon will be 10^{-8} times as powerful as that received over a 24-mile path on earth. The signal-to-noise ratio for a single hop of the TD-2 system is about 4×10^5 times; for the same transmitter on earth and the same receiver on the moon, the signal-to-noise ratio would be 4×10^5 times 10^{-8}, or 4×10^{-3} times. Something would have to be done to make the signal stronger.

The antenna which will be used at Jodrell Bank in England for radio astronomy will be 250 feet in diameter. Imagine if you can an antenna having an area of an acre, mounted so that it can be tilted in any direction. I have difficulty in doing so, but I know that such an antenna is being built. Suppose that we used such an antenna for transmitting or receiving on earth, and used our modest 10-foot antenna on the moon. The area of the transmitting antenna would thus be increased by about 400 times (the Jodrell Bank antenna is circular) so this alone would raise the signal-to-noise ratio to 4×10^{-3} times 400, or to 1.6 times.

Suppose that we used 1,000 watts' transmitter power instead of ½ watt. This would raise the signal-to-noise ratio to about 3,200 times, which should be quite good enough to transmit a TV channel or hundreds of telephone channels from earth to the moon. The equipment we would need for this would be simply a regular TD-2 receiver on the moon, and a TD-2 transmitter plus a 1,000-watt power amplifier feeding into a 250-foot diameter antenna on earth. All these could be provided. The only problem would be to get the receiver to the moon!

What about communication with Mars? At its closest Mars is about 140 times as far away as the moon, so that the signal would be 1 over 140 squared, or only about 5×10^{-5} as strong at Mars as it would be at the moon. If we used a 250-foot round antenna at Mars instead of a 10-foot square antenna, this would bring the received signal up to 2×10^{-2} times its strength at the moon. The TD-2 receiver introduces a noise of perhaps thirty times Johnson noise, while it is possible by careful design to make a receiver with a noise of only around six times Johnson noise; this would give us a factor of 5, so that with a 250-foot antenna and the improved receiver the signal-to-noise ratio would be 2×10^{-2} times 5, or 0.1 of that for the earth-to-moon ratio. If we raised the power from 1,000 watts to 10,000 watts, we could send TV from earth to Mars at its closest with a signal-to-noise ratio comparable to that of coast-to-coast television.

We should note, however, that even when Mars is closest it will take the signal, which travels with the speed of light, about 3 minutes to go from earth to Mars. Our microwave system could in principle transmit hundreds of telephone conversations, but we could scarcely use the system for telephony; we would have to wait a round-trip time of 6 minutes for a reply to a single remark!

These calculations are so encouraging that one wonders whether or not it may be possible to send messages to the stars. I presume it will be a long time before man will fly to the stars, so it is perhaps legitimate to assume that there will be some startling improvements in the microwave art between now and the time that we wish to send messages there. I will make the following assumptions:

That one can make antennas 500 feet in diameter which will be smooth and accurate enough for use with wave lengths of 1 centimeter.

That one will be able to make receivers which introduce no noise but merely amplify the Johnson noise received by the antenna; we will assume that this noise level corresponds to a temperature of 5 degrees Kelvin, which appears to be the temperature corresponding to radiation coming from interstellar space.

The distance to Alpha Centauri is 4.4 light years, or 8.2×10^{18} feet. The wave length of 1 centimeter is 3.3×10^{-2} feet. The area of a 500-foot-diameter antenna is 2×10^{5} square feet. Accordingly, the ratio of the received power to the transmitted power is

$$\frac{P_R}{P_T} = 5.5 \times 10^{-24}$$

Let us assume a band width of 200 cycles per second. This is a band width sufficient for a teletype message, for instance. For a 200-cycle band and a temperature of 4 degrees Kelvin, Johnson noise is P_J.

$$P_J = 1.1 \times 10^{-20} \text{ watts}$$

Suppose that our received signal must be 100 times as strong as this for a telegraph-type signal. The received power, P_R, must then be

$$P_R = 1.1 \times 10^{-18}$$

Accordingly, the transmitted power, P_T, must be

$$P_T = 500,000 \text{ watts}$$

This is quite a lot of power. Too, to make a receiver which introduces no noise will take some doing, although recent work by C. H. Townes and J. P. Gordon at Columbia University appears to provide a way. I wouldn't wonder a bit if there were even more astonishing developments in microwaves before men reach the stars and need to send messages back.

One doesn't have to swallow interstellar travel or even travel to the moon to find a possible use for extraterrestrial microwave systems. It has been proposed that, long before he reaches the moon, man may send up an artificial satellite to act as a microwave radio relay site for transoceanic communication. A satellite 22,000 miles above the surface at the equator would circle the earth once in 24 hours, and so it would stay above the same spot on the earth's surface as the earth revolves on its axis. Granting that the perturbations of the sun and moon did not cause such a satellite to wander too much, it would always be in view of fixed transmitters and receivers, and it could serve as a radio relay 24 hours a day.

It is easy to show that the antenna size and the power required for such a radio relay would be modest. However, the problems of putting such a satellite in place and of maintaining it in the proper orientation would be great indeed.

If we want to think of extraterrestrial microwave signaling in even less speculative terms, we can consider the problem of receiving radar echoes from Mars or Venus; here we are dealing with a matter which is dependent only on microwave techniques, and not on the possibility of space travel. We may note, in fact, that radar echoes from the moon were received at the Evans Signal Laboratory in 1946.

A radar echo is weak because the transmitted power must make a two-way trip, suffering from the inverse-square law in each direction of travel. We can see just how weak it is by a simple calculation. Suppose that we ask how much radio power, P_P, falls on an entire planet whose disk has an area A_P. Let the power come from a radar antenna of area A_T at a distance L from the planet. We have a formula relating to the received power to the transmitted power P_T; that is,

$$\frac{P_P}{P_T} = \frac{A_T A_P}{\lambda^2 L^2}$$

What happens to this received power? Very nearly at least, it will be scattered equally in all directions, and a distance L from the planet, where the radar transmitter and receiver are located, it will be spread over a sphere of area $4\pi L^2$. Suppose that the radar uses the same antenna, of area A_T, for receiving as for transmitting. This antenna will intercept a fraction, $A_T/4L^2$, of the power falling on the planet. Thus, the ratio of the power P_R received by the radar to the power P_T transmitted will be

$$\frac{P_R}{P_T} = \frac{A_T^2 A_P}{4\pi \lambda^2 L^4}$$

Here A_T is the antenna area, A_P is the area of the disk of the planet, L is the distance from the radar to the planet, and λ is of course the wave length.

What sort of ratio do we get in the case of the earth and Mars? The minimum distance from the earth to Mars is about 35,000,000 miles, or about 1.8×10^{11} feet. The diameter of Mars is about 4,200 miles, or 2.2×10^7 feet, and the area of the disk is $\pi/4$ times the square of this diameter, or 3.8×10^{14} square feet. The area of a 250-foot antenna is about 5×10^4 square feet. Let us consider a wave length of 10 centimeters—4 inches, or $\frac{1}{3}$ feet. We find the ratio of received to transmitted power to be

$$\frac{P_R}{P_T} = 6.5 \times 10^{-22}$$

What shall we use for a transmitter? The big klystrons used with the Stanford linear accelerator give pulsed powers of around 20 megawatts, that is, 2×10^7 watts, but they give such powers as pulses of very short duration. If we transmitted very short pulses, the reflections from various parts of the spherical surface of Mars would come back at very different times compared with the pulse length, and the returning pulse would be so spread out that it would be difficult to detect. A pulse a thousandth of a second long has a length, as it travels, of a million feet, or about 190 miles. If we used a pulse of this length, all the reflections from the central portion of Mars should come back simultaneously. It seems reasonable to me that one could produce a power of at least 2,000,000 watts over a duration of a thousandth of a second. If the transmitted power were 2×10^6 watts, the received power would be

$$P_R = 1.3 \times 10^{-15} \text{ watts}$$

How much noise does the received power have to contend with? This depend on both the band width and the noisiness of the receiver. To receive a pulse one thousandth of a second long, that is, 10^{-3} seconds long, we need a band width of about 1,000 cycles. For a temperature of 293 degrees Kelvin and this band width, the Johnson noise power, P, is

$$P = 4 \times 10^{-18} \text{ watts}$$

A low-noise traveling-wave tube will amplify Johnson noise at 293 degrees Kelvin, and it will itself introduce only about twice as much noise. If the receiving antenna is pointed at Mars, the radiation reaching it, aside from that reflected from Mars, would be merely the radiation coming from interstellar space; Johnson noise will be almost negligible. Thus, the total noise will be equivalent to a received noise power only about twice the Johnson noise for 293 degrees Kelvin, that is, a noise power, P_N, of about

$$P_N = 8 \times 10^{-18} \text{ watts}$$

The ratio of the received power to this noise power will be approximately

$$\frac{P_R}{P_N} = 160$$

This ratio should be great enough to enable one to see the echo despite numerous troubles, including the Doppler shift in frequency of signals reflected from the edges of the planet, an effect due to the rotation of the planet. As a matter of fact, interplanetary radar might settle the question of the period of rotation of Venus.

Will radio astronomers actually go to the trouble of receiving radar echoes from Mars? They certainly will if they can. We have noted that a 10^{-3}-second pulse is about 190 miles long; by measuring the time taken for such a pulse to go out to Mars and return it should be possible to measure the distance to Mars to about that accuracy. An accuracy of 190 miles in a distance of 35,000,000 miles is an accuracy of about one part in about 200,000; this is an accuracy unprecedented in astronomy. While astronomers measure angles and times very accurately and can calculate relative distances with a corresponding precision, their knowledge of distances in actual earthly units such as feet is accurate to only about one part in 10,000. Interplanetary radar will remedy this.

So far we have been led into interesting speculations concerning communication through space, which is as far in the future as space travel. This may be far off indeed. We have considered interplanetary radar, which will be a reality of the very near future. There is much more than this to the future of microwaves, but it is more mundane than celestial.

At present there is a tremendous boom in microwave communication over long distance routes. Not only does the American Telephone and Telegraph Company have a coast-to-coast relay system operating around 4,000 megacycles, but it has systems under development for the frequencies around 6,000 and 11,000 megacycles.

Western Union also uses microwave links in telegraphy. Besides such *common carrier* microwave circuits, which serve whoever wants to rent a TV circuit, make a long-distance telephone call, or send a telegram, there are many private microwave systems paralleling pipelines, or serving electric-power systems, highway authorities, or police systems.

The exploitation of microwaves for such communication started at frequencies around 2,000 and 4,000 megacycles. It will soon extend to frequencies around 11,000 megacycles. Will still higher frequencies be used? At higher and higher frequencies, the transmission loss caused by rain becomes greater and greater. At 11,000 megacycles this may be serious, and it may be impossible to get truly reliable microwave radio communication at frequencies substantially higher than 11,000 megacycles.

Yet the demand for microwave frequencies grows continually. Much of the microwave range is set aside for military uses. There will be increasing competition for the remaining civilian bands. If these are used wisely, they will suffice for longer than if they are used in a haphazard or inefficient manner, but still they will certainly be exhausted if present trends continue. And just over the horizon there is the possibility of an increasing non-broadcast use of television, first for the distant viewing of meetings, surgical operations and conferences, or for banking or industrial control purposes, and perhaps eventually in connection with person-to-person conversations. Where will the band width needed for such uses come from?

Wire transmission preceded radio transmission, and it has developed to a high point for transmission of television as well as telephone. Such transmission began with *open-wire* lines; that is, pairs of wires on telephone poles. It went on to transmission over *twisted pairs* of wires in lead-sheathed cables, at frequencies ranging up to several tens of thousands of cycles. The wires are twisted together in pairs to keep a signal on one pair from getting onto another pair. Finally the *coaxial cable* was developed, with an outer copper conductor a little greater than the diameter of a pencil enclosing a central copper wire. Coaxial cable can be used at frequencies up to several megacycles if the signals are amplified by repeaters every few miles.

The Bell System's L3 coaxial cable system will carry a television signal and hundreds of telephone channels simultaneously in a band of frequencies extending up to 8 megacycles. More messages can be sent by using many coaxial cables. This, however, promises merely to provide more communication, at costs in the same general range as present costs, rather than to provide the very much cheaper sort of broad-band communication which would make a widespread use of non-broadcast television more attractive.

The solution may lie in the use of millimeter waves, perhaps in the range from 4 to 8 millimeters. Such waves cannot be transmitted over long distances in the open; they are absorbed by the oxygen and water vapor of the air, and they are completely blocked by even moderate rainfall. However, they can be transmitted in various field patterns or modes through wave guides filled with nitrogen or some other non-absorbing gas. The loss due to the electrical resistance of the walls of a wave guide is different for different modes, and it increases as the diameter of the wave guide is decreased. For a particular mode called the *circular electric* mode, in which the electric lines of force are circles about the axis of a tubular wave guide, and for a tubular copper wave guide 2 inches in diameter, the power may fall to no less than a millionth of its initial value in a distance of 20 to 30 miles. This is a loss comparable to that in a microwave radio path. Hence, in the future, it may be possible to transmit television and telephone by wave guide, amplifying the signals by means of repeaters spaced 20 to 30 miles apart.

The frequency corresponding to a wavelength of 4 millimeters is 75,000 megacycles; that corresponding to 8 millimeters is 37,500 megacycles. Hence, the frequency band between these two frequencies is 37,500 megacycles, or over 4,000 times the frequency band used in the L3 coaxial system. This does not mean that a wave guide could be used to transmit 4,000 TV channels. The wave guide is a rather imperfect transmission medium. It is not yet clear how many TV channels could be transmitted through one wave guide, but the number would be large.

It seems that there is a real chance that the medium-range future of microwave communications lies in wave-guide transmission. Before this comes we will have more microwave radio communication, and we will probably have interplanetary radar. Further in the future than the time of the wave guide we may perhaps signal across the oceans by means of satellite relay stations. Eventually we may use microwaves to talk to men who have reached the moon or Mars or, perhaps, in some far day, the stars.

CHAPTER XII

Picking Up Television

A MICROWAVE radio link is merely a tool, a tool for sending signals over long distances. The signals themselves are tools, too: tools for reproducing at some distant point a voice or a face, for enabling us to hear and to see almost instantaneously that which happens afar off.

In order to do this one must somehow generate a signal, an electrical description of a sound or a scene, a signal which can be used to recreate a sound or a picture at a distance. I think that the story of sending pictures over a distance, and particularly the story of devices which generate the signals from which pictures can be recreated, is one of the most fascinating in electronics.

The picking up of television pictures is beset by all sorts of practical difficulties of technique. These practical difficulties are complicated matters, which it is hard for one who does not actually work in the field of electronics to appreciate. Perhaps more important, however, is the fact that in picking up television pictures we must cope with fundamental physical limitations. Some of these are inherent in a particular device. Others are inherent in the very process of generating television signals. All, however, are so simple, so clear, that anyone who reads this chapter can understand what they are, how some of them may be overcome, and what truly basic limitations must always remain.

It is much easier to generate a signal for the transmission of sound than for the transmission of a picture. When sound waves strike the eardrum, they cause it to vibrate. If we allow the same sound waves to strike the diaphragm of a microphone instead, they can generate an electric current which varies in exact accord with the sound vibrations. This electrical signal, transmitted to a distant point and amplified, can move the diaphragm of a speaker and so produce a sound wave which mimics the sound that caused the diaphragm of the microphone to vibrate at the sending point.

Why should the reproduction of a picture be more difficult than this? Someone has said that painting a picture should not be hard. All one has to do is to put the right colors in the right places. Color television succeeds moderately well in doing just this. The reader will not find out here how that is done. The process is rather tricky. Here we will consider only black-and-white, or monochrome, TV. We have merely to put light and shade in the right places. This is the heart of the problem of television.

In sending sound we have to send only one signal; a signal to make the diaphragm of the speaker vibrate in accord with the sound wave which is transmitted. In sending a single TV picture we have in effect to send many signals; signals to describe the light or shade of each part of the picture. How is this to be done?

The general scheme which is used in modern television was invented by Paul Gottlieb Nipkow in 1884. Nipkow was unable to achieve television of any sort in his time, chiefly because he did not have amplifiers, but because he lacked other devices as well. He did contribute two things, however; an idea of how a picture can be transmitted electrically, and a conception of devices which could be used for doing this.

How does the picture on your TV screen get there? It is painted on the screen of a picture tube such as was described in Chapter IV by a fine electron beam which scans across the *phosphor* on the inside of the face of the tube. When the electrons strike the phosphor, it glows with a brightness proportional to the rate at which electrons strike the phosphor—that is, to the current of the electron beam. This current is controlled by the TV signal by means of an electrode near the cathode, as described in Chapter III, just as the electron current in a triode is controlled by the voltage on the grid. Thus, as the beam scans a pattern on the phosphor, the picture is repeatedly painted out in light and shade. It is painted out completely 30 times a second.

The nature of the path of the bright spot which the electron

beam produces on the face of the picture tube is shown rather
roughly in Fig. *12.1.* The beam scans across the picture in the
zigzag pattern shown by the solid line. It scans from the left
slanting down toward the right; then it quickly returns to the left

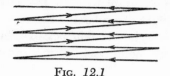

Fig. *12.1*

and scans again to the right, and so on. The rightward motion is
properly called the *scan.* During this motion the beam is turned
on and paints out a line of the picture. The quick leftward motion
is called the *retrace;* during this motion the beam is turned off.

Thus, actual lines of the pattern painted on the face of the picture
tube appear only during the left-to-right scan, as shown in Fig. *12.2.*

Fig. *12.2*

The picture is made up of two interleaved sets of these lines, shown
solid and dotted in Fig. *12.2.* The beam first traces out the solid
lines, starting at the center of the top, and then it returns to the top
and traces out the interleaved dotted lines. After the dotted lines
are traced out, the beam returns to the top and traces out the
solid lines again, and so on. Tracing out the solid lines and tracing
out the dotted lines each takes $\frac{1}{60}$ second, so the whole pattern of
lines is traced out 30 times a second.

In scanning the entire picture area, why is the picture scanned
twice with interleaved lines instead of once, going from one line
directly to the adjacent line? Interleaved scanning is used to avoid
the flicker which would be observed if an appreciable area of the
picture were illuminated only thirty times a second, instead of sixty
times a second as with interleaved scanning.

There are two chief problems associated with the transmission of television. One is that of *synchronization;* this means getting the beam to the right spot on the receiving tube at the right time. It wouldn't do to have the electron beam paint the upper right-hand corner of the transmitted picture on the center of the receiver picture tube. I thought of explaining the features of the television signal which make synchronization possible, but I found some of the details rather confusing myself. I will say only that at the end

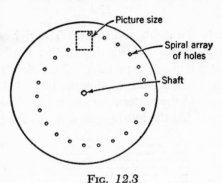

FIG. *12.3*

of each scan from left to right the transmitter emits a special pulse which tells the receiver to return the electron beam to the left-hand side of the picture tube. Another special pulse is sent out at the end of a complete interleaved scan of the entire picture; this tells the receiver when to move the beam from bottom to top.

The more difficult part of television is to generate a signal corresponding to the brightness of the scene to be transmitted. This is difficult chiefly because there are so many little parts of the scene which must be described separately, and because there is so little time to describe each one.

The scanning process divides the picture into a total of 525 lines. As the beam moves along each line, it paints out approximately 500 independent patches of light or shade; each of these is called a *picture element.* In each thirtieth of a second, the television pickup device has to send out signals corresponding to the brightness of about 250,000 different picture elements. At the receiver, the picture tube has to paint in these 250,000 distinct patches of light and shade 30 times a second. The time allowed for each picture element is thus about 10^{-7} second. To evaluate the brightness of an element of a picture in this time is really difficult. How difficult it is we can see by a few simple calculations.

To make any calculations we need to know a little about the nature of the device which picks up television signals. The earliest device proposed for television pickup used the *Nipkow disk,* as shown in Fig. 12.3. This is a thin disk rotating on a shaft. Punched through the disk is a spiral pattern of holes. As the disk rotates, one

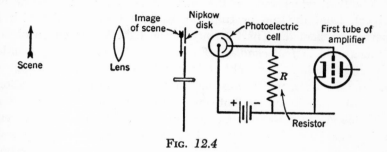

Fig. *12.4*

after another of the holes scans across the picture (the size of the picture is indicated by dotted lines). To scan a picture in an interlaced fashion according to modern TV standards, the disk would have to have 525 holes arranged in two spirals.

Fig. *12.4* shows a television pickup system using a Nipkow disk. It makes use of a lens to produce an image of a scene right on the rotating surface of the Nipkow disk. Thus, the rotating disk lets through light from one little part of the image at a time. This light falls on a *photoelectric cell* which produces an electric current corresponding to the intensity of the light.

A photoelectric cell consists of a sensitive *photocathode,* which emits electrons when light falls on its surface. The current of electrons is picked up by another electrode and flows through a resistor, R; thus it produces a voltage drop across the resistor, R, and this voltage acts as the input to an amplifier, of which the first tube only is indicated in Fig. *12.4*.

We see at once that the signal produced by the current flowing from the photocell through the resistor, R, must compete with

Johnson noise in the resistor. If the current is not large enough, the signal will be lost in the noise. How large is the signal likely to be? To know this, we must understand something of the intensity of ordinary light and something of the sensitivity of photocells.

The current of electrons released from the photocathode of a photoelectric cell depends on the amount of light which falls on the surface per second. This light is measured in *lumens*. As a typical example, a photocathode may emit around 2×10^{-5} amperes per lumen.

The light which reaches the photocell is light which falls on an object, from the sun or from an artificial source, and which is partially reflected. The intensity of the light falling on an object is measured in *foot candles*. For an intensity of one foot candle, the light falling on an object is one lumen per square foot. A *standard candle*, which was once a real standard of illumination, gives an intensity of one foot candle at a distance of one foot. The illumination in a room moderately well lighted with incandescent lights may be 40 foot candles. A room lighted very brilliantly with fluorescent lights may be lighted to an intensity of 100 foot candles. On a cloudy day the outdoor illumination is around 1,000 foot candles, and sunlight gives an illumination as high as 10,000 foot candles.

Let us ask how brightly we must illuminate an object in order to get a picture by means of the Nipkow disk device of Fig. *12.4*. Suppose that we call the illumination of the scene L foot candles. Then L lumens fall on each square foot of the scene. The scene will not reflect all of this light, however. As an estimate, let us say that the scene reflects $.24L$ lumens per square foot.

In Chapter X we saw that the brightness of an image formed by a lens is much less than the brightness of the object which is imaged. For an f-4.5 lens, the image is about $\frac{1}{80}$ as bright as the scene imaged. Hence, if our TV camera uses an f-4.5 lens, the lumens per square foot in the image will be about $3 \times 10^{-3}L$ lumens per square foot.

How big shall we assume the image of the scene to be? A reasonably convenient size would be 3 inches by 4 inches, or $\frac{1}{12}$ square feet. For this area, the number of lumens in the entire image will be about $2.5 \times 10^{-4}L$ lumens.

However, in order to scan over 250,000 separate elements, the holes in the Nipkow disk must let light pass from only 1/250,000 of the picture at a time. Thus, the light falling through the hole in the Nipkow disk is $10^{-9}L$ lumens.

A reasonable value for the electron current emitted by a photocathode is 2×10^{-5} amperes per lumen; thus, the total current through the resistance R will be about $2 \times 10^{-14}L$ amperes.

The power dissipated in the resistance, R, is the square of the current times the resistance R. We want to make this as large as possible. However, we cannot make the resistance very large and still amplify as broad a band of frequencies as necessary in television. A resistance of 2,000 ohms is reasonable. For a resistance of 2,000 ohms, the power dissipated in the resistor because of the photocurrent will be about $8 \times 10^{-25}L^2$ watts. We may compare this with Johnson noise power as given in Chapter IX; this is $1.37 \times 10^{-23}TB$ watts. If the temperature of the resistance, T, is 293 degrees Kelvin, and if the band width, B, is 4×10^6 cycles, which is about the band width needed for television, the Johnson-noise power will be 1.6×10^{-14} watts.

Suppose that we wish the power due to the photocurrent to be 100 times the Johnson-noise power. This would give a somewhat noisy but moderately acceptable signal. To achieve this we would have to have

$$\frac{8 \times 10^{-25}L^2}{1.6 \times 10^{-14}} = 100$$

$$L = 1,400,000 \text{ foot candles}$$

This is over 100 times the illumination of direct sunlight! We easily see one reason why the system of Fig. *12.4* is not used for television pickup. There just isn't enough light in the world!

One of the great problems of the 1930's was to do something about this. One of the persons who tried to do something about it was Philo T. Farnsworth.

The Nipkow disk is clumsy physically. One thing which Farnsworth did was to replace this mechanical system by a purely electronic system. Fig. *12.5* shows the principal parts of the Farnsworth *image dissector* tube.

The TV camera lens illuminates a semitransparent photocathode at the left end of the evacuated tube. The emitted electrons are accelerated by voltages applied to electrodes which are not shown. A longitudinal magnetic field produced by a long focusing coil surrounding the tube focuses the electrons leaving the photocathode, so that an *electron image* of the scene is reproduced at the point indicated in the tube. This electron image is a sharp reproduction

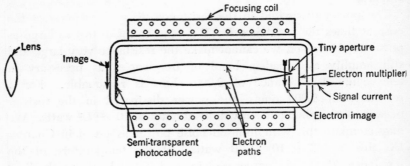

FIG. *12.5*

of the scene; the electron current density is large where the scene is bright and small where the scene is dark. Just as a part of the light image passes through an aperture in the Nipkow disk, so a part of the electron image passes through a tiny aperture in a metal sheet and into a device called an *electron multiplier.*

How is scanning accomplished? In the Nipkow disk, the aperture moved in order to scan the picture. In the image dissector, the entire electron image is shifted past the aperture by means of changing transverse magnetic fields produced by deflecting coils which are not shown in the figure.

Because it involves no mechanical motions, the image dissector is more convenient than the Nipkow disk. However, if we merely collected the current of electrons passing through the tiny aperture and fed it to a vacuum-tube amplifier, the light required by the image dissector would be the same as that required by the Nipkow-disk device of FIG. *12.4*.

The real advantage of the image dissector lies in the little box labeled "electron multiplier." In order to understand this advantage, we must explore the contents of this tiny box.

The operation of the electron multiplier depends on the fact that when an electron strikes a specially treated metal surface it can knock out several electrons called *secondary electrons*. If the electron striking the surface has been accelerated by a voltage of around 100 volts, it may knock out two to four secondary electrons.

The structure of an electron multiplier is illustrated in Fig. *12.6*. The electrons from the tiny aperture of the image dissector strike the first of several specially treated electrodes, which is marked 1 in

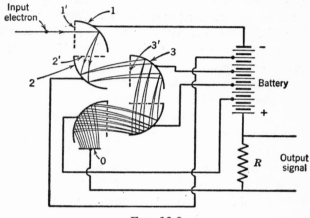

Fig. *12.6*

the figure. The secondary electrons produced are drawn toward a second electrode, 2, by a fine wire mesh, 2′, which is attached to 2. The mesh, 2′, and the second electrode, 2, are held perhaps 100 volts positive with respect to electrode 1 by the battery. The secondary electrons leaving electrode 2 are drawn by the mesh 3′ to electrode 3, where a further multiplication takes place, and so on. The current of electrons from the final multiplying electrode is collected on an output electrode, *O*, and flows through the resistor, *R*, to give an output signal.

By means of an electron multiplier, the output current can be made very much greater than the current which passes through the tiny aperture to form the input to the multiplier. For instance, if each multiplying electrode emits three electrons for every electron that strikes it, and if there are twelve multiplying electrodes, then the output current will be about a million times as great as the input current. Such a current is capable of overriding Johnson noise in the resistance R completely.

At first thought, it might seem that this would solve all our problems, but it does not. What troubles us is the fact that the electron current entering the multiplier consists of tiny but indivisible electrons.

Suppose that, just as before, we assume an illumination of L foot candles, and that a fraction, .24, of the light is reflected, and that we use an f-4.5 lens, and that the image is 3 inches by 4 inches, and that the area of the scanning aperture is 1/250,000 of the area of the image, and that the photocathode emits 2×10^{-5} amperes per lumen. As before, the current will be $2 \times 10^{-14}L$ amperes.

How many electrons per second does this current represent? Current is charge per second. If we divide the current by the charge of the electron, which is 1.6×10^{-19} coulombs (the measure of electric charge), we see that this current constitutes a flow of about $1.2 \times 10^5 L$ electrons per second.

In the scanning process, we look at each of the 250,000 picture elements thirty times per second. Thus, the time that we devote to examining each element is 1/7,500,000 of a second, or about 1.3×10^{-7} seconds. How many electrons flow through the tiny aperture during this time? The number is clearly the number of electrons per second times the time we look at a picture element, and this is about $1.6 \times 10^{-2}L$ electrons per picture element.

If the average number of electrons per picture element were only one half, for instance, sometimes we would by chance get no electrons per picture element, sometimes we would get one, and very infrequently we would get two or three electrons. The signal would be a very poor representation of the brightness of the scene, because from scan to scan it would fluctuate about the true value, and it would never accurately attain the true value. The signal would be very noisy.

To get a really accurate representation of the scene, suitable for commercial television, we would need many more electrons per picture element, perhaps a hundred, so that the different brightnesses of different picture elements could be accurately distinguished by different numbers of electrons. Suppose we were to telecast a scene by direct sunlight, for which L is about 10,000 foot candles. For parts of the picture which reflected the assumed fraction .24 of the incident light, the number of electrons per picture element would be about 160 electrons per picture element.

The image dissector would give a usable picture in direct sunlight. However, we have made no allowances for imperfections, and actual performance might be inferior to what we have calculated. The image dissector is much more sensitive than the Nipkow-disk device, but it is still not good enough for practical TV.

What is the real secret of TV pickup devices? It is something called the *storage principle*, a contribution of Vladimir K. Zworykin. This principle was first used in a device called *iconoscope*. I shall not describe the iconoscope because, although it is a useful commercial device, its operation is inherently complicated and somewhat faulty. Instead, I shall describe the most highly developed of TV pickup tubes: the Image Orthicon.

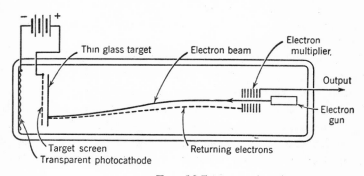

FIG. *12.7*

FIG. *12.7* shows the principal parts of the Image Orthicon. Focusing and deflecting coils and many of the electrodes are omitted in the picture. At the extreme left, the light image falls on a photocathode. The electrons which are emitted are accelerated by a piece of very fine mesh called a *target screen*. Just beyond the target screen is an extremely thin glass target. The electrons from the photocathode are focused on this target.

What happens when the accelerated electrons from the photocathode pass through the target screen and strike the target beyond? They knock out secondary electrons, so that negative electrons leave the target and the target tends to get more positive as time passes. Where the image is bright, more secondaries leave the target; where the image is weak, fewer electrons leave the target.

An electron beam from an electron gun is used to scan the target. This electron beam strikes the opposite (the right-hand) side of the target. The electrons from the gun strike the right-hand side of the target so gently that they do not knock out many secondary electrons. Hence, the electrons of the electron beam tend to stick and make the target negative where the beam strikes it.

The target is extremely thin, and no insulator is perfect. Thus, the target acts just as if both sides were connected electrically. We can say that, at a given point of the target, at a given picture element on the target, the electrons from the photocathode tend to make the target positive, while when the beam scans the target the electrons of the beam tend to make the target negative. Just what does happen when the beam falls on a picture element of the target?

When the beam reaches a picture element, it finds that the picture element has become positive because of electrons from the photocathode. Electrons of the beam strike the picture element and stick, so that the picture element becomes more negative. Finally, the picture element becomes so negative that it repels all further electrons in the beam that try to reach it. In effect, the picture element abstracts a certain number of electrons from the beam while the beam falls on it.

How many electrons does the picture element abstract from the beam? Just as many as were knocked out of the other side of the target by electrons from the photocathode. Hence, the number of electrons that a given element of the target abstracts from the beam is an accurate measure of the brightness of the image on the corresponding portion of the photocathode.

The electrons of the beam that are not abstracted by the target are reflected and go to an electron multiplier; the output current of the multiplier forms the signal output of the Image Orthicon.

Because a bright portion of the image abstracts many electrons from the beam, the output current will be weak for bright portions of the image and strong for dark portions of the image, but in this upside-down fashion the beam current faithfully reproduces the brightness of the image.

Why is the Image Orthicon superior to the image dissector? To find out, we must know how many electrons a given picture element abstracts from the beam. This is a number governed by the number of electrons which fell on the picture element from the target in the whole period of $\frac{1}{30}$ second since the last time the beam scanned the picture element. In effect, each picture element of the target remembers all the electrons which reached it from the photocathode in the $\frac{1}{30}$ second since it was last scanned by the beam. The image dissector used only the electrons emitted by a picture element of the photocathode during the time it is being scanned; this is only 1/250,000 as long as the period between scans.

The limiting sensitivity of the Image Orthicon is governed by the number of electrons leaving a picture element of the photocathode in $\frac{1}{30}$ second. The photocathode is rather small; the total image occupies perhaps 5×10^{-3} square feet, and a picture element occupies 1/250,000 of this, or about 2×10^{-6} square feet. If the illumination is L foot candles, and if a fraction .24 of the light is reflected, the reflected light will be, as before, $.24L$ lumens per square foot. If we use an f-4.5 lens, the illumination at the image will be, as before, $3 \times 10^{-3}L$ lumens per square foot. As the area of the picture element is 2×10^{-6} square feet, the light per picture element will be $6 \times 10^{-9}L$ lumens. If the photocathode gives 2×10^{-5} amperes per lumen, the current per picture element will be $1.2 \times 10^{-13}L$ amperes. As the charge of an electron is 1.6×10^{-19} coulombs, the number of electrons per picture element per second will be $7.5 \times 10^5 L$ electrons per second. The number of electrons which leave an element between scans is $\frac{1}{30}$ of this, or $2.5 \times 10^4 L$ electrons per scan.

If we took this literally, we would believe that an Image Orthicon could pick up a good picture with an illumination of a hundredth of a foot candle—that is, the light provided by a single candle at a distance of 10 feet!

The Image Orthicon is not as good as this; there are sources of noise we have not taken into account. However, it will pick up a fair picture by the illumination of a candle 3 feet away ($\frac{1}{9}$ foot candle), and a recognizable picture can be obtained with an illumination of a few thousandths of a foot candle, by using a somewhat faster lens than the f-4.5 lens we have assumed. Of course, the Image Orthicon is ordinarily used with much higher illuminations to obtain TV pictures of commercial quality.

We have seen in this chapter the inherent limitations of several pickup devices. In the Nipkow-disk device the limitation is Johnson noise in the resistor across the input of the amplifier. In the image dissector the limitation lies in the fact that in order to give a good picture a fair number of electrons must be emitted per picture element *while the picture element is being scanned* (during 1/7,500,000 second). In the Image Orthicon the limitation lies in the fact that a fair number of electrons must be emitted per picture element *in the time between scans* (in $\frac{1}{30}$ second). Is it possible to make a better pickup tube than the Image Orthicon?

Fundamentally, this appears not to be possible. It is possible, however, that certain shortcomings in the performance of the Image Orthicon might be remedied. For instance, we have assumed that the photocathode gives a current of 2×10^{-5} amperes per lumen. Actually, it is conceivable that a photocathode might give a higher current than this. Quantum theory tells us that light comes in little packages of energy called *quanta*. Conceivably, we might get one electron for each quantum, and this would give a current of around 2×10^{-3} amperes per lumen, and so improve the operation of the Image Orthicon by a factor of around 100.

The Image Orthicon is already very good, however. Its sensitivity is comparable to that of the human eye. It represents the culmination of many years of work on television pickup devices, and it does great honor to all who contributed to it.

CHAPTER XIII

About Signals and Noise

In Chapter VIII we saw how a great many telephone conversations can be made into one combined signal, a signal which can be sent through a single amplifier, over a single pair of wires, or over a single microwave channel. We saw that this can be done by shifting in frequency each of the bands of frequencies about 4,000 cycles wide which carry individual voice signals. Thus, these bands of frequencies can be stacked one above another in the combined signal.

If we analyzed the way the voltage of the combined signal varied with time, we would find that it had components of many frequencies. By using a filter which would pass only a particular band of frequencies, we could select the frequencies corresponding to a particular voice signal, and by shifting these frequencies down to their original values we could recover the original voice signal. If, however, we looked at the voltage merely one instant of time, we could only say that this voltage was partly due to each voice signal being transmitted. We would not have enough information to say this part of the voltage belongs to talker A, and that part to talker B, and so on. The various parts of the signal could only be separated by use of filters which passed various bands of frequencies.

It is quite different in the case of the television signal, which we discussed in Chapter XII. In sending a picture by television we have in effect to send many signals, one for each picture element. If we look at the voltage of the signal which represents all these picture elements, we can say the voltage at one particular moment represents the brightness of the 13,878th picture element, and the voltage 1.2×10^{-7} seconds later will represent the brightness of the 13,879th picture element. We can say further that if a particular voltage represents the brightness of the 13,878th picture element, the voltage exactly $\frac{1}{30}$ second later will also represent the brightness of the 13,878th picture element, its new brightness after an interval of $\frac{1}{30}$ second.

In sending the television picture, band width comes in in a different way than in the sending of the voice signals on different bands of frequencies. We have, in effect, to send a distinct pulse representing the brightness of each picture element. As we send 250,000 picture elements thirty times a second, each pulse can be only about 1/7,500,000 seconds long. From Chapter VIII we have the rough rule that the band width must be about 1 over the pulse length. This rule tells us that we should need a band width of about 7,500,000 cycles, 7.5 megacycles, for TV. The rule is an approximate one, which does not distinguish between amplitude-modulated waves (which have two different sideband frequencies for each frequency in the modulating signal) and a modulating signal itself. Actually, a band width of 4 megacycles suffices for television.

In the signal representing many telephone channels, we could separate out a single-component voice signal by means of a filter which would pass or select a certain band of frequencies. In merely looking at the voltage of the combined signal at a given instant of time we could not, however, decide which part belonged to one voice signal and which to another. The television signal also is a composite of many signals, one for each picture element. Yet in the case of the television signal we can look at the voltage at a particular instant and say that it corresponds to the brightness of some particular picture element. However, if we filtered out of the television signal a band of frequencies, we would find in this band of frequencies parts representing the brightnesses of all the picture elements.

It is apparent that there is more than one way to send several separate signals through one amplifier, or over one pair of wires, or over one microwave channel. One way is to assign separate bands of frequencies to different signals. Another is to assign separate, discrete, periodically recurring intervals of time to the different signals. As a matter of fact, it can be shown that there is an infinity of other mixed ways of combining and sorting out signals, but the methods of *frequency division* (assigning separate bands of frequency) and *time division* (assigning separate periodically recurring times) are the two practically important methods.

Which is better, frequency division or time division? In attempting to answer such a question we must know some of the limitations of each. Let us consider the case of time division. Suppose our

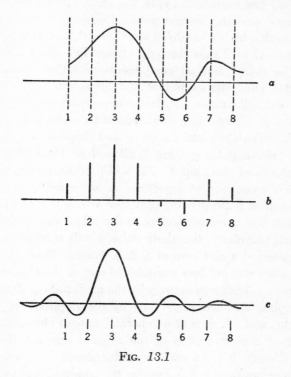

FIG. *13.1*

signal is a voltage that varies with time as in *a* of FIG. *13.1*. Suppose that we want to make measurements on this signal so that a description of it can be sent by time division. The natural thing to do is to measure the voltage at regular intervals of time, at 1, 2, 3, 4, . . . 8, and so on. This is commonly called *sampling* the signal. We could then send these voltages as short pulses of corresponding amplitudes, as shown in *b* of Fig. *13.1*. Such pulses are called *samples* of the signal.

We can easily see that the short pulses or samples of *b* of Fig. *13.1* give some sort of description of the signal *a* of Fig. *13.1*. How can we use such a description in terms of a series of short pulses to reconstruct the original signal? We should remember from Chapter VIII that, to be short, a pulse must contain high frequencies. If we pass the short pulses of *b* of Fig. *13.1* through a filter which passes low frequencies only, the short input pulses will give rise to longer, smoother output pulses. Suppose we pass the short pulses through a highly idealized filter such that all frequency components from O to B pass through without loss and with the same time lag, or delay, and all components of higher frequency are eliminated. Then the output of the filter into which the short pulses are fed will contain only frequencies lying between O and B.

What sort of output will a single one of the short pulses produce? This can be calculated, and the computed shape is sketched in *c* of Fig. *13.1*. For a pulse spacing $1/2B$ and an ideal filter of band width B, the third short input pulse will produce a rounded output pulse which is centered at a position, 3, corresponding to the position of the short pulse producing it, and which is zero at the positions 1, 2, 4, 5 etc., corresponding to the other short pulses spaced $1/2B$ apart. Similarly, the short pulse 4 will produce a rounded pulse centered at 4 and zero at 1, 2, 3, 5, etc. Thus, all the short pulses together will produce a combined output signal whose amplitude at position 1 is given entirely by the amplitude of short pulse 1, whose amplitude at 2 is given only by the amplitude of the short pulse 2, etc., and which is of a generally smooth character.

How good a reproduction of the original signal is this smooth output? Clearly, it is an exact reproduction of the original signal at each pulse position, 1, 2, 3, etc., for the amplitudes at these points are proportional only to the amplitudes of the short pulses 1, 2, 3, and these in turn were obtained from the original signal. It can be shown mathematically that the reproduction of the signal is in fact perfect provided that the original signal contains no frequencies higher than B! We remember that we send $2B$ short pulses per second, and we use a filter of band width B in reproducing the signal. Thus, we certainly couldn't reproduce a signal with a band width greater than B. Mathematical analysis shows that we can reproduce perfectly a signal with a band width B or less.

Suppose we want to send many signals of band width B on a channel which has an overall band width greater than B. First, we construct a series of short pulses spaced $1/2B$ apart for each channel. Then we interleave these sets of pulses in time. FIG. 13.2 shows

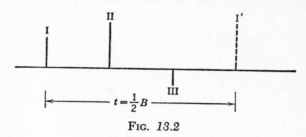

FIG. 13.2

short pulses from three channels, I, II and III, so interleaved. Thus, we have a composite signal representing three channels, each of band width B. Pulse I represents the voltage on channel I at a particular time; II that on channel II; III that on channel III; and I' that on channel I again, a period $1/2B$ later than I.

The short pulses of the combined signal in FIG. 13.2 contain very high frequencies. However, we can pass them all through a filter of band width $3B$. In the resulting output signal the signal due to I is zero at II and III; that due to II is zero at I and III, and so on. Thus, the signals due to the short pulses are by no means scrambled together, for if we measure the amplitude of the smoothed-out signal at I we find out the exact amplitude of the short pulse I, etc.

How much total band width have we used to send three bands each of band width B? We have used a band width of $3B$, just as we would have had to do in the case of frequency division.

The method and apparatus used to send three channels of band width B over a single channel of band width $3B$ is very different in the cases of frequency division and of time division, as is shown by the comparison in FIG. 13.3. In a of FIG. 13.3 we have the components of a frequency-division system. Channel II is shifted in frequency from the band O to B to the band B to $2B$ by a frequency shifter, $f.s.$ Channel III is shifted from $O–B$ to $2B–3B$. The three signals are combined and sent over a single channel of band $O–3B$. Then the three component channels $O–B$, $B–2B$, $2B–3B$ are separated by filters, F. Channel I is recovered directly and channels II and III are recovered by frequency shifting.

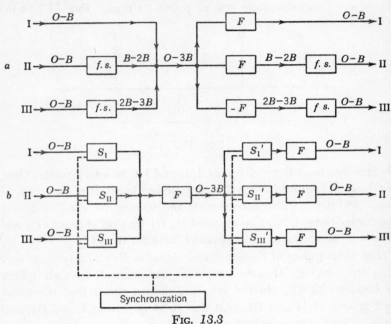

Fig. 13.3

In doing the same overall job by time division, as shown in b of Fig. 13.3, channels I, II, III are sampled by samplers S_I, S_{II}, S_{III} to produce short pulses representing their amplitudes at slightly different times. The interleaved samples are passed through a filter to reduce the band width to $3B$ and are sent over a common channel. At the receiver, the amplitudes of the samples are recovered by sampling the common wave at just the right times by samplers S_I', S_{II}', S_{III}'. The recovered samples, which correspond to the original transmitted samples, are passed through filters which pass frequencies in the band $O–B$, and the original channels are recovered.

Dashed lines and the box labeled *synchronization* in *b* of Fig. *13.3* represent a feature of time-division systems which is not needed in frequency-division systems. Sampler S_{II} must operate at a time just $1/6B$ later than sampler S_I, and sampler S_{III} must operate just at a time $1/6B$ later than S_{II}. Also, receiving sampler S_I' must operate at just the right time with respect to transmitting sampler S_I; that is, just when the part of the signal representing the amplitude sent out by S_I reaches S_I'. Synchronization is accomplished at the transmitter or at the receiver by operating the samplers by means of a common driving device. Synchronization between transmitter and receiver is accomplished by sending special, recognizable pulses over the common channel, along with the signal.

Our idealized time-division and frequency-division systems require just the same band width to send the same number of channels. What about noise? Suppose that in receiving the combined signal the receiver introduces a certain amount of noise. In separating the channels this noise is split up differently in the time-division and frequency-division systems, but it is split three ways in each case. If the intensity of the noise is constant with frequency, so that there is the same amount of noise power for each unit band width, in each case the total amount of noise in each recovered channel, I, II, or III, will be the same. Ideal time-division and frequency-division systems require the same band widths, and they are equally susceptible to noise.

In discussing noise and band width in connection with frequency division and time division, we have of course done so in a highly idealized way. Actually, to transmit three channels of band width B by frequency division requires a band width of greater than $3B$, because actual filters are imperfect and cannot sharply distinguish between frequencies which lie close together; some *guard band* must be allowed between different frequency channels. Similarly, in time division the ideal shapes of pulses which we have discussed cannot be attained exactly, and to avoid mixing up of samples, shorter pulses must be sent over the common channel; this takes more band width than that ideally required.

When we seek a realistic answer to our original question of which is better, frequency division or time division, we get various answers for various technical reasons. Frequency division is used in telephony to transmit many voice signals over one pair of wires, or one coaxial cable, or on microwave channel, for good but complicated reasons. Television is essentially a time-division transmission of many picture elements. Time division is used to transmit several voice channels over one microwave channel in many microwave military equipments and in some civilian microwave radio-relay systems. The reasons for choosing between frequency division and time division are much too complicated to discuss here.

We have seen, however, that the fundamental limitations on *ideal* frequency division and time division systems are the same; and these limitations show that band width is a very persistent quality. As FIG. *13.3* indicates, when we combine signals in very different ways and send them over a common channel, the ideal minimum band width which we need is the sum of the band widths of all the individual channels which we send simultaneously.

We might ask whether this is all the band width we ever need to send a signal in a perfectly operating system. If we cast our mind back to Chapter VIII, we easily see that the answer is no. When we modulate the amplitude of a radio-frequency wave of frequency f with a voice signal containing frequencies lying in the range $O-B$, we produce a radio-frequency wave of frequencies lying between $f - B$ and $f + B$, that is, a signal spanning a band $2B$ wide. Amplitude modulation is not an ideal system of transmission, even when the apparatus is ideal and works perfectly.

What about frequency modulation? Suppose that we use FM to send an audio signal with frequencies lying in the band $O-B$. If in frequency-modulating the radio-frequency wave we swing the frequency back and forth just a little, it can be shown that the band width of the frequency-modulated signal is $2B$, just as in the case of AM. Suppose, however, that we make the modulating audio signal louder, so that the frequency is swung further back and forth. This will of course make the received audio signal louder. It will also increase the band width of the frequency-modulated signal which must be transmitted and received. The *index of modulation* is defined as the ratio of the amount of frequency swing above or below the average frequency to the band width B of the signal to be transmitted. When the index is high, the band width needed is about twice the index times the band width B of the audio signal to be transmitted.

If we double the index of modulation, we double the voltage of the received audio signal, and hence we increase its power by a factor 2 squared, or four times. This tends to make the ratio of signal power to noise greater. This is not clear gain, however. If we double the index, we double the band width of the radio signal, and we have to double the band width of the FM radio receiver. As noise power is proportional to band width, this doubles the noise that the receiver adds to the received radio signal. The net effect is that for a given transmitter power, the final ratio of signal to noise in the received audio signal is proportional to the index of modulation, and hence to the radio-frequency band width used.

With a given transmitter power, we cannot, however, increase the band width indefinitely. For one thing, if we did keep on increasing the band width, we would finally get so much noise that the noise would swamp out the radio-frequency signal. This can be observed in FM reception when the signal from a distant station fades; in listening one hears at one moment quite a clear signal, and then, abruptly, nothing but noise as the fading radio signal becomes weaker than the noise.

There is, of course, an even more important limitation on the band width one can use than that imposed by noise. The Federal Communications Commission parcels out band width for various purposes. It has only so much to parcel out, and it will not give unlimited amounts for any one purpose. The channel width assigned to one FM station is 150,000 cycles. The highest audio frequency the station will ever send will be below 20,000 cycles.

It was the late Edwin H. Armstrong who in 1936 first demonstrated the use of broad-band frequency modulation in reducing noise. The result astounded and confounded radio engineers. Because noise increases with band width, they had always thought that the way to reduce noise in the finally received signal was to limit band width as much as possible everywhere in the transmission system. Armstrong, however, showed that in an FM system one could reduce the noise in the received audio signal by increasing the radio-frequency band width. Clearly, in an overall transmission system the relation between band width and noise was not as simple as engineers had assumed.

Frequency modulation is only one of many systems in which the overall effect of noise can be reduced by increasing the band width. In fact, in some systems of transmission the effect of noise added in transmission can be virtually eliminated. These systems use signals which are of essentially the same type as telegraph signals.

For instance, consider the signal shown in Fig. *13.4*, which consists of a series of pulses at regular times 1, 2, . . . 8. At these times

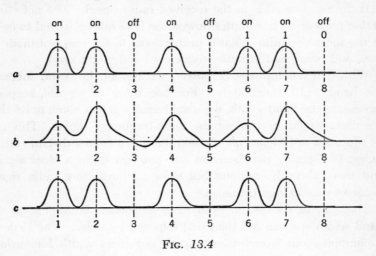

FIG. *13.4*

the signal must be either *on* or *off;* it can assume no intermediate values. Such a signal, reading *on, on, off, on, off, on, on, off* is shown in *a* of Fig. *13.4*. It is more convenient to write *1* instead of *on* for a pulse and *0* instead of *off* for the absence of a pulse. Thus, the signal of *a* of Fig. *13.4* may be represented 11010110.

Suppose we add a certain amount of random noise to the signal of *a* of Fig. *13.4*. This will raise the amplitude at some *pulse positions* (the times 1, 2, . . . 8) and lower it at others. Thus, the pulses plus noise may look as shown in *b* of Fig. *13.4*. If, as in the case of *b* of Fig. *13.4*, the noise is not great enough to obliterate the difference between an *off* and an *on,* we can tell whether an *on* or an *off*, a 1 or a 0, was meant, despite the distortion in the pulse pattern caused by the addition of noise. Even with a small amount of noise, a noise peak will sometimes (but very infrequently) cause an error in interpretation. We can make an electronic gadget called a *regenerator* which will examine the signal of *b* of FIG. *13.4* at each of the times 1, 2, . . . 8 and decide whether or not there is a pulse present. Then the regenerator can send out a new, noise-free signal, a clean, uniform pulse if a noisy pulse was present, and no pulse if no pulse was present among the noise. Such a regenerated signal is shown in *c* of FIG. *13.4;* it is indistinguishable from the original signal, *a.* When our signal can have only certain discrete values, as *off* or *on,* we can almost completely eliminate the effects of noise if the noise is not too large.

In the example, we have done this at the expense of sending not a continuous range of amplitudes but only *on* or *off;* 1 or 0. What is such a signal good for, anyway? For one thing, we could send the letters of the alphabet by means of such signals. We could send pulses in groups of 5 and let different patterns represent different letters. We could, for instance, use the following *code:*

Letter	Code (or pulse pattern)	Letter	Code (or pulse pattern)
a	00001	n	01110
b	00010	o	01111
c	00011	p	10000
d	00100	q	10001
e	00101	r	10010
f	00110	s	10011
g	00111	t	10100
h	01000	u	10101
i	01001	v	10110
j	01010	w	10111
k	01011	x	11000
l	01100	y	11001
m	01101	z	11010

In this case, the three groups of pulses, 1, 2, 3 of FIG. *13.5* would spell *cat.*

What about voice signals as used in telephony, however? We

can send them by using groups of pulses, too! We have seen, for instance, that if we are to send a voice signal with a 4,000-cycle band width, we can do this by sampling the amplitude of the signal

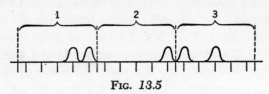

FIG. 13.5

8,000 times a second and sending the amplitudes of these samples to the receiver. For instance, *a* of FIG. 13.6 shows a part of a voice signal whose amplitude lies between 0 and 7. At appropriate sam-

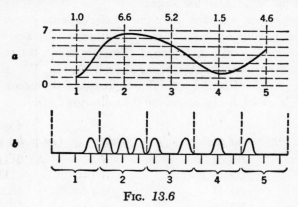

FIG. 13.6

pling times 1, 2, . . . 5 the amplitudes (written above) are 1.0, 6.6, etc. Suppose we take as an approximation the amplitude to the nearest units and represent it by the following code:

Amplitude	Code
0	000
1	001
2	010
3	011
4	100
5	101
6	110
7	111

If we now allow three pulse positions per sample, we can encode to the nearest digit the amplitudes of the samples of *a* of FIG. *13.6* as follows:

Sample Number	True Amplitude	Approximate Amplitude	Code
1	1.0	1	001
2	6.6	7	111
3	5.2	5	101
4	1.6	2	010
5	4.0	4	100

Thus, the coded version of the signal of *a* of FIG. *13.6* is shown in *b* of FIG. *13.6*. We can receive this coded version with almost perfect accuracy despite a considerable amount of noise. At the receiver, we can reconstruct perfectly the signal represented by the code. But the code itself is a little inaccurate. We may have made an error of as much as $\pm\frac{1}{2}$ unit of amplitude in choosing the code to fit the amplitude as nearly as possible.

The sort of transmission we have just described is called *pulse-code modulation;* the name may be abbreviated PCM. To send a signal of band width B by PCM we sample the signal $2B$ times a second and *encode* the amplitude of each sample as a series of n pulses. Thus, we have to transmit $2nB$ pulses per second in sending the signal, and the ideal minimum band width required for such transmission is nB, or n times the band width of the signal to be sent.

In choosing an amplitude to fit the sample, we have our choice of 2^n amplitudes, for there are 2^n different combinations of n ons or offs, taken n at a time. Because these 2^n amplitudes do not fit exactly the signal we want to transmit, the encoding process itself is responsible for a sort of noise called *quantizing* noise, which is the error between the actual signal amplitude and the nearest amplitude provided by the code. Power varies as the square of amplitude. The amplitude of the largest signal we can represent is 2^n times as great as the difference between adjacent amplitudes, and this difference is proportional to the amplitude of the quantizing noise. Hence, we can get some idea of the signal-to-noise power ratio by squaring the number of amplitudes, obtaining $(2^n)^2 = 2^{2n}$.

The table below gives some values of 2^{2n} for various numbers n of pulses per sample:

n (*number of pulses per sample; band width required is nB*)	2^{2n} (*the signal-to-noise power ratio is proportional to 2^{2n}*)
2	16
4	256
6	4,100
8	65,500
10	1,050,000
12	16,800,000

We see that the signal-to-noise ratio increases extremely rapidly with the increase in band width, much more rapidly than for FM. And PCM is almost completely immune to moderate noise in the receiver, although the system itself introduces the quantizing noise

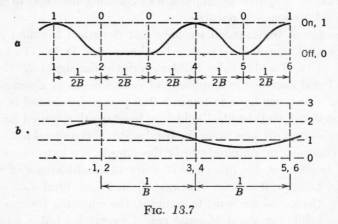

FIG. 13.7

we have discussed. If we use eight or ten pulses per sample; that is, eight or ten times the signal band width B, we can reproduce the signal with virtually no noise. Actually, for voice transmission, very acceptable reproduction is attained using six or seven pulses per sample, and these are typical numbers for PCM equipment.

In order to make our discussion of coded transmission complete, we might ask, can one *reduce* the band width needed to transmit a signal? A few years ago, if you had asked this of an engineer, he would have unhesitatingly said *no*, almost without thinking. By thinking just a little, we can see that this is indeed possible.

Suppose, for instance, that we want to send the two-valued, on-off signal of band width B, shown in *a* of Fig. *13.7.* The signal consists of a distinguishable *on* or *off*, 1 or 0, *pulse* or *no pulse* each $1/2B$ seconds. Ordinarily, we would simply transmit this signal as it is, by sending $2B$ zeros or ones, no-pulses or pulses, each second.

We can, however, describe the signal accurately by sending only B pulses per second, provided that we allow not two different kinds of pulses (amplitudes 0 and 1) but four different kinds of pulses (amplitudes 0, 1, 2, 3). We group the simple 0–1 pulses we wish to send into pairs and let one of the more complicated four-amplitude pulses describe a pair of the simpler two-amplitude pulses. Thus, we have to send only one complicated pulse for each pair of simple pulses we wish to describe.

We can let four-amplitude pulses represent pairs of two-amplitude pulses according to the following code:

	Pair of 2 on-off pulses	
		Amplitude of four-amplitude pulse
Amplitude of first two-amplitude pulse of pair	*Amplitude of second two-amplitude pulse of pair*	*representing pair of two-amplitude pulse*
0	0	0
0	1	1
1	0	2
1	1	3

The six pulses of *a* of Fig. *13.7,* and the corresponding codes, are given below:

Numbers of pulses constituting pair	*Amplitudes of pulses constituting pair*	*Amplitude of pulse representing pair*
1, 2	10	2
3, 4	01	1
5, 6	01	1

The four-value pulses corresponding to the six two-value pulses are shown in *b* of Fig. *13.7.* Because we have to send elements of the four-value pulses only half as frequently as we had to send the two-value pulses, we need only half as much band width. Thus, it *is* possible to reduce the band width needed to send a signal, but to do so it is necessary to construct a signal of more distinguishable values of amplitude than the original signal had. This makes the signal of reduced band width much more susceptible to noise than was the original signal.

Everything in this chapter confirms our earlier impression that band width is extremely important in connection with signals. If we have to send some number, N, of channels, each of band width B, we can shift the frequencies of these channels, stacking them one above the other in frequency, and so make a composite signal representing all the channels. This is called frequency division. In an ideal system, the band width required is NB, that is, it is the sum of the band widths of the individual channels. Practically, we require a little more band width.

Faced with the same problem of sending N channels each of band width B, we can send them by time division instead of by frequency division. To do this we first *completely* describe each channel by sampling the signal $2B$ times a second and by constructing a series of short pulses or samples which describe the amplitudes of the signal at these times. We then interleave the pulses for various channels and send them as a composite signal. The minimum band width which will allow us to send these N sets of pulses, constituting $2NB$ pulses per second, is again a band width NB, just as in the frequency-division case.

If we introduce the same amount of noise in the common combined signal of a frequency-division or time-division system, the total noises in the received channels will be the same on both systems.

Some methods of transmission are wasteful; to send a signal of band width B by amplitude modulation we must use a band width $2B$.

Some methods of transmission use a large band width to send a signal, but gain something in doing so. High-index FM uses a large band width, but the noise in the received audio signal is less than it would be if we had sent the signal by AM.

Coded signals, consisting of regularly spaced pulses which are either off or on, are particularly interesting, since they can be received and interpreted with negligible error in the presence of moderate amounts of noise. One can send the letters of the alphabet by means of such pulses, but one can also send audio signals by this means; this is called pulse-code modulation, or PCM. The received signal is unaffected by moderate amounts of noise introduced in transmission; but the system is not without error, for the code cannot describe the amplitude to be transmitted completely accurately. This error is called *quantizing noise.* Quantizing noise decreases extremely rapidly as the band width used is increased so as to increase the number of pulses in each code group and hence the number of quantizing levels.

Finally, by coding it is possible actually to reduce the band width needed to send a signal, but this means we have to transmit a signal which is more susceptible to noise than was the original signal.

Band width is important, but noise is also important. The two are in some way tied together. The exact sort of association between them, and much more besides, is the subject of *communication theory,* or *information theory,* which is the subject of the next chapter.

CHAPTER XIV

Communication Theory

As FAR as I can see, the terms *communication theory* and *information theory* are synonymous. I prefer the former, because it seems to me to imply less. Under one title or the other more nonsense has been written about communication theory than about any other technical subject since the advent of relativity and quantum theory. Everyone knows meanings of the words *communication, information,* and *theory*. When people hear that there is a theory about communication they immediately want to apply it to solve their problems. The problems may lie in philosophy, in linguistics, in psychiatry, in psychology, in chemistry, or in physics. The new theory may or may not be applicable to them. Whether or no, men will speak at conferences and men will write papers. Sometimes the gist of the talk or the text is that communication theory should be applied in some field. Sometimes the claim is that it has been successfully applied. Sometimes the lofty strain is merely that communication theory is wonderful.

I know a competent engineer who, having been appointed to speak summarizing a particular conference, could in honesty only say at its end that he hadn't understood a great deal of what had been said. A competent mathematician who attended the same conference reported that many speakers wore rapt expressions and gazed out above the audience as they talked, apparently receiving from on high some inspiration which had not been communicated to him. I myself have read some papers on communication theory which were bewildering and some which were just plain confused.

It is doubly difficult to make sense of the field of communication theory, because it is difficult at this point to tell what does make sense or is the beginning of something that will in time make sense, and what is just wishful thinking. All I can hope to do here is to state some of the very simplest concepts and results of communication theory, and to try to relate them to some commonplaces of the world. Perhaps in doing so I shall indulge in my own particular form of nonsense, but I will try to warn the reader when I find myself on tricky ground.

We have seen that a transmission system is a tool used to transmit signals from one point to another. The signals we transmit are in a sense tools too, or perhaps patterns; they enable us to reconstruct at some distant point a replica of a sound or of a scene. In communication, then, we built apparatus which transmits patterns or descriptions of things that we wish to reproduce. Some of these patterns appear to be more complicated than others. We can send roughly 1,000 telephone signals over the same microwave channel that can accommodate only one television signal. In this case, the distinction seems clearly to be that a television signal consists of a band of frequencies 1,000 times as broad as that of a voice signal. True as this may be, it cannot completely describe the difference. We have seen in Chapter XIII that we can send a voice signal by high-index FM; in this case, the radio signal covers a band of frequencies much broader than the 4,000 cycles used in ordinary telephony. By using this broad band, the received signal can be reconstructed with less noise. We have also seen in Chapter XIII that in one way at least the band width needed to transmit a signal can be halved.

In the early days, signals were more or less taken for granted as facts of nature. They had certain band widths; they required a certain fidelity of reproduction, and these requirements were to be met by rather direct means. With the advent of broad-band frequency modulation, engineers were somewhat shaken. During and after World War II, several men began to speculate rather deeply on the nature of signals. What is it that communication systems are asked to send? How can we characterize and measure it, so that we can make valid, quantitative comparisons between diverse sorts of signals? In 1948 Norbert Wiener published a book, *Cybernetics,* which had a good deal to say about communication theory. In the same year, Claude Shannon, another mathematician, published a paper, "A Mathematical Theory of Communication," which had even more to say. Shannon's paper, in fact, launched communication theory well on the way it has since taken.

Shannon found a way of characterizing signals by means of a quantity he called *the amount of information*. Sometimes merely the word *information* is used as a name for this quantity. The use of the word *information* in this sense is using an old word to express a very particular meaning, just as in physics *force* has a very particular meaning, completely excluding its meaning in such phrases as *force of circumstance*, or *forceful delivery*, and as, in engineering, *stress* has a particular narrow meaning which excludes the meanings of the word in *he was under great stress* or *great mental stress*. So, in information theory we must regard *information* as meaning no more than what we define it to mean. If we insist, for instance, that information so used must have or imply meaning, we are trying to carry into communication theory something of the useful but loose connotations of everyday language. In communication theory, *amount of information*, or more loosely, *information*, is a particular, quantitative technical term.

In communication theory, information can perhaps be best explained as choice or uncertainty. To understand this, let us consider a very simple case of communication. For instance, if you want to send a birthday greeting by telegraph, you may be offered a choice of sending one of a number of rather flowery messages, perhaps one from a list of sixteen. Thus, in this form of communication the sender has a certain definite limited choice as to what message he will send. If you receive such a birthday telegram, there is some uncertainty as to what it will say, but not much. If it was chosen from a list of sixteen standard messages, it must be one among the sixteen. The received message must enable the recipient to decide which among the sixteen was chosen by the sender.

In order for the sender to indicate to the recipient which message he has chosen, he must use some sort of signal. One particular form of signal might be a series of pulses or absences of pulses, such as we have discussed in Chapter XIII. We can think of such pulses or absences of pulses as representing a series of elementary choices or decisions between two alternatives. Such choices or decisions may be in various cases *pulse* or *no pulse, yes* or *no, heads* or *tails, right* or *left.* All are merely choices or decisions between two alternatives, and one can be represented by means of any other. By means of a sequence of such elementary choices one can choose among a larger number of alternatives. When the choices are made known to the recipient of the message, he can decide which alternative was chosen.

For instance, let us number the sixteen messages of which we spoke 0 to 15 and see how we can choose among these. We can follow a sort of tree of branching paths, as shown in FIG. *14.1.* At

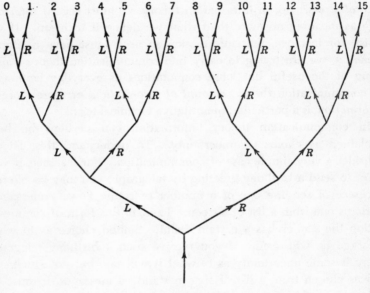

FIG. *14.1*

the top are the message numbers. The sender can choose, or the recipient of the message can arrive at, any one of these by taking at each branch point the *R* (right) or *L* (left) branch. To arrive at message 9, for instance, the elementary choices or decisions are *RLLR.* If we let 1 stand for *R* and 0 stand for *L,* we can describe the series of choices (on the part of the sender) which choose the one message out of sixteen by the sequence 1001. For the recipient of the message, these four elementary decisions decide which message among sixteen was intended.

Thus, the number 9 can be represented by a sequence of R's and L's, a sequence of ones and zeros, by the code 1001. Here we have arrived at this sequence by making four *elementary choices, R or L*. Such elementary choices are called *bits* of information; they are the fundamental units of information by means of which any message can be specified.

The word *bit* comes from *binary digit*. While we have approached the use of 0 or 1 from the point of view of information theory, these digits have long been used in a system for representing numbers. This system is called the *binary system* in contrast to the system we commonly use, the *decimal system*.

In the decimal system of representing numbers, the place of a digit in a number tells the value of the digit. When we write 275 we mean $275 = 2 \times 100 + 7 \times 10 + 5 \times 1 = 2 \times 10^2 + 7 \times 10 + 5 \times 1$. The digit furthest to the right stands for that number times unity, the digit second from the right stands for that number times ten, the digit third from the right stands for that number times ten squared (ten times ten), and so on. In binary notation, 101 means $101 = 1 \times 4 + 0 \times 2 + 1 \times 1 = 1 \times 2^2 + 0 \times 2 + 1 \times 1 = 5$. The digit third from the right stands for that number times two squared, and so on. Some typical binary numbers and their decimal equivalents are:

Binary	Decimal
1	1
10	2
100	4
1,000	8
10,000	16
10,100	20
1,001	9

Many electronic computers perform their computations in the binary system. The binary system is chosen because the binary digits, 1 and 0, can be represented by a switch which is open or closed, or by a pulse which is present or absent, while the representation of a decimal digit is more complicated.

We have considered a ridiculously simple case in which the message is chosen as one among sixteen. An actual message may be a five-minute talk or a half-hour television program. How many different sequences of sounds five minutes long can you distinguish by means of the telephone? The number is fantastically large, but it is not infinite. The number of sequences of pictures which can be sent in thirty minutes by television is still larger, but it is not infinite either. Any particular message of either of these sets of messages could be described by a sufficient number of bits, of elementary pieces of information, of yeses or noes.

Communication systems provide us with channels for sending messages. Shannon has derived a fundamental law for the maximum number of bits of information which can be sent over such a channel in one second. He finds that this number of bits per second depends on the band width, B, the signal power, P_s, and the power, P_n, of the noise which gets into the channel in one way or another. When the noise is Johnson noise or other noise having the same statistical properties, the capacity, C, of the channel for transmitting information, measured in bits per second is

$$C = B \log_2 \left(1 + \frac{P_s}{P_n}\right) \text{ bits per second}$$

Shannon's proof says that by *sufficiently ingenious means* and by using *complicated enough equipment* we could send information over the channel up to this rate with errors occurring as infrequently as we might desire, but that if we tried to send more bits per second over the channel we would necessarily make errors; that is, the man or device receiving the message could not receive all the bits, all the yeses or noes, correctly, and so could not correctly decide exactly what message was intended by the sender.

The mathematical quantity $\log_2 (1 + P_s/P_n)$ is called the *logarithm to the base 2* of $(1 + P_s/P_n)$. It is easiest to explain the meaning of this logarithm by some examples involving $\log_2 x$, where x is some one of the numbers listed at the top of the next page.

x	$\log_2 x$
2	1
4	2
8	3

We see that for multiples of 2 (even numbers)

$$x = 2^{(\log_2 x)}$$

Or, the logarithm to the base 2 of the number x is the number of times 2 must be multiplied by itself to give x.

Mathematically, we can define $\log_2 x$ for values of x other than powers of 2. Some examples are given below:

x	$\log_2 x$
1	0
9	3.2
9,999	13.3

Let us ask, as an example of Shannon's law, how many bits per second can be sent over a television channel if the band width is 4,000,000 cycles per second and the ratio of signal power to noise power is 10,000? The answer turns out to be approximately $C = 54,000,000$ bits/second.

In Chapter XIII we discussed two communication systems—high-index FM and PCM—which use large band width but which, to some extent, overcome noise. Shannon's law tells us what is theoretically possible along these lines. Consider the communication system indicated in Fig. *14.2*. Here we start out with some

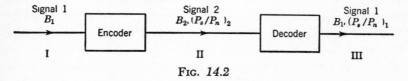

FIG. *14.2*

signal, 1, of band width B_1; it might be a TV signal, for instance. We wish to transmit this signal from point I to some point III, and we wish it to arrive with a signal-to-noise ratio of $(P_s/P_n)_1$. However, we will transmit it over some channel, II, perhaps a microwave link, which has some other band width, B_2, and some other signal-to-noise ratio $(P_s/P_n)_2$. Shannon's law says that this will be just possible if

$$B_2 \log_2 [1 + (P_s/P_n)_2] = B_1 \log_2 [1 + (P_s/P_n)_1]$$

It will certainly be possible if we make B_2 or $(P_s/P_n)_2$ greater than called for by this relation.

In order to represent and transmit signal 1 by means of some other signal, signal 2, we make use of some device which we will call by the general name, *encoder*. At the far end of the transmission channel II we make use of a *decoder* to recover the signal in its original form (plus any noise which may have been added in transmission or encoding). High-index FM and PCM, which we discussed in Chapter XIII, are examples of transmission in which we change the nature of the signal, or encode it, increasing its band width so that even with a small transmitter power we obtain a good signal-to-noise ratio when the signal is finally "decoded" to its original form.

Neither FM nor PCM lives up to Shannon's law. In FM, final signal-to-noise ratio $(P_s/P_n)_1$ for a given ratio $(P_s/P_n)_2$ in the transmission path II does not increase nearly as rapidly with band width as it should ideally, according to Shannon. In the case of PCM, the signal-to-noise ratio $(P_s/P_n)_1$ increases in the right way with band width in the channel II, but the signal-to-noise ratio in the transmission channel II must be around fourteen times as great as ideal. One of the chief activities of workers in the field of information theory is to seek more nearly ideal ways of encoding signals. Will this result in great changes in the way messages are transmitted in the future? Not necessarily. Although PCM is more efficient than FM, FM is generally used in preference, because the apparatus needed is simpler and because FM is in some ways more adaptable to a variety of conditions. In the same way, PCM might be simpler than some more nearly ideal system.

In Chapter XIII a means of reducing the band width was mentioned. Is this a very practical idea? We see that if we double the band width of the channel we double the channel capacity, but when we increase the transmitter power, the channel capacity increases only very slowly with an increase in the signal-to-noise ratio, P_s/P_n. This is illustrated in the table below:

P_s/P_n (signal-to-noise ratio)	$\log_2 (1 + P_s/P_n)$ (channel capacity is proportional to this quantity)
1	1
10	3.5
100	6.7
1,000	10.0
10,000	13.3

We see that especially for large signal-to-noise ratios, increasing the transmitter power, P_s, increases the information rate only slightly. Thus, very large increases of transmitter power are required if we are to reduce the required band width appreciably while sending information at a constant rate. Usually, one increases band width in order to reduce the required power, as in high-index FM, rather than increasing the power in order to reduce the band width.

So far we have taken the source of the signal rather for granted, but we really should include it explicitly in the communication system. When we do so, the diagram of a typical communication system is as shown in FIG. *14.3*. At the left we have a *signal*

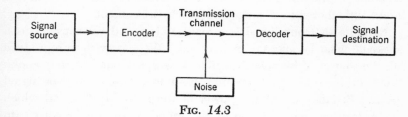

FIG. *14.3*

source. This may be a man speaking into a telephone, a scene which a television camera picks up, a girl operating a teletypewriter. We next have an *encoder,* which translates the signal into some form suitable for electrical transmission. In the case of voice transmission, this encoder might, in a particular instance, include a microphone, a device for turning the electrical signal from the microphone into PCM, and a radio transmitter for sending the PCM signal to the receiver. In transmission, a certain amount of noise is added to the signal; this noise may actually be added in the radio receiver. After it reaches the radio receiver, the signal is decoded by a decoder and returned to its original form. In the case of a voice signal the decoder might include the radio receiver, a device for changing PCM into the original form of electrical signal delivered by the microphone, and a loudspeaker for changing this electrical signal to sound. Finally, as part of the overall communication system we have the signal destination, which may be the ear of the hearer or the eye of the beholder.

So far we have dealt with the capability of a channel to transmit information: the channel capacity, C, which is measured in bits per second. If the channel capacity is adequate to transmit the information generated by the signal source, the actual rate of transmission must be governed by the rate at which the signal source produces information and by the rate at which the signal destination can accept information. How are we to measure these rates? We usually know the band width of the signal, and we usually know the signal-to-noise ratio required at the signal destination. Can we use Shannon's formula,

$$C = B \log_2 (1 + P_s/P_n)$$

to compute the information rate of the signal source? We can not, and a little thought will make it clear why we can not.

Suppose that our signal is a man talking, and we consider as a message what he may say in 1 second. We may wish to reproduce all the sounds of his speech which lie within a band of frequencies 4,000 cycles wide, and we may wish to attain a ratio of signal power, P_s (the part of the power of the reproduced sound which is an accurate reproduction of the sound of the man's voice), to noise power, P_n (any other power present in the reproduced sound), of 10,000. If we use a band width of 4,000 cycles and a signal-to-noise ratio of 10,000, we easily calculate that the number of bits needed to describe all of the distinct messages we could identify by means of a signal 1 second long as

$$4,000 \log_2 (1 + 10,000/1) = 53,000 \text{ bits}$$

Are all the messages described by this number of bits possible messages which we might receive from a speaker? Clearly they are not, for our system would transmit and reproduce *any* sound with a band width of 4,000 cycles and a signal-to-noise ratio of 10,000; the roar of a lion, the babble of a brook, the sound of an orchestra, as well as the sound of a voice uttering intelligible speech. Actually, the number of spoken messages a second long is much smaller, and it could be specified by far fewer than 53,000 bits, or binary digits.

Let us now consider the signal destination, which is in this case the listener. Actually, it would be inefficient to transmit even all of the sounds that a man utters in English speech, for the human ear cannot distinguish some sounds from others. For instance, FIG. *14.4* shows the variation of amplitude with time for two

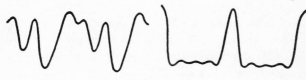

FIG. *14.4*

different electrical signals. Each is made up of the same frequency components, but the component sine waves of different frequencies are shifted relative to one another in the two signals. No one can deny that these two signals are different, and yet as sound waves they would sound the same to the human ear.

Even before the advent of information theory, back in 1939, Homer Dudley demonstrated a device called the vocoder, which took advantage of the limited nature of the voice to produce sounds and of the ear to distinguish sounds, in order to transmit speech over a channel of very limited information rate.

The vocoder relies on the fact that the human voice produces essentially two sorts of sounds; a buzz from the vocal cords and a hiss from the passage of air past the tongue, as in saying *s, ch, sh, th*. Accordingly, Dudley provided in the receiving part of his vocoder a source of hiss sound, a source of buzz sound, and controls for turning these on and off and for changing the pitch of the buzz sound.

These controls are not enough however. As we speak, the lips and tongue modulate or filter the buzz and hiss sounds so that some frequency components are strengthened relative to others. It is this filtering action which is responsible for the distinctive sounds of the various vowels and consonants. Accordingly, Dudley provided at the transmitting end of the vocoder devices containing electrical filters to detect the presence in the speaker's voice of certain ranges of frequencies and to send out indications of the presence of these ranges of frequency and their strengths.

Thus, in sending a signal, the vocoder detects whether a buzz or a hiss is present, and the pitch of the buzz if a buzz is present. It also detects what bands of frequencies of the buzz or hiss are emphasized and how strongly they are emphasized. It sends this information to the reproducing part of the vocoder, where a hiss or a buzz of appropriate pitch is generated, and the appropriate ranges of frequencies are emphasized to appropriate volumes. The result is an intelligible recreation of the original speech!

The recreated speech is not a result of transmitting and reproducing the exact variations with time of the electrical signal from the microphone which picks up the speech. In fact, the wave form of the recreated speech might bear little resemblance to that of the speech to be transmitted. But the recreated speech sounds like the original speech; not exactly so, but recognizably so. And it can be transmitted, using a total band width of 800 cycles instead of 4,000 cycles! Apparently, the information rate of speech is not more than a fifth the information rate of a channel which will transmit not only speech but any other sound as well!

Most signal sources can generate in each second far fewer distinct messages than we might at first think. The vocoder demonstrates this in the case of speech. It is true also in the case of television. For instance, in television thirty distinct pictures are transmitted each second. The television transmitter and channel could send an entirely different picture each time, yet, by and large, successive pictures are much the same. The actual information needed to tell what the next picture will be is less than the system is capable of transmitting, and so the system is in this respect inefficient. Likewise, as the electron beam of the pickup tube scans from one picture element to the next, the change of brightness is apt to be small, and on the average not much information is needed to specify the difference in brightness between one picture element and the next. Yet the television system is capable of transmitting a picture in which each picture element is wildly different from that preceding it. This capability is never called on in transmitting actual pictures, and so the television system is inefficient in providing more capabilities, more channel capacity, than is needed to transmit actual pictures.

We have a measure of the capacity of a channel to transmit information; this is the channel capacity, C, measured in bits per second. It is easily calculated in terms of the band width and signal-to-noise ratio of the channel. With actual signals, such as FM and PCM, we fall short of transmitting this much information.

A signal source also has a number of bits per second attached to it; this is the *average* rate at which the signal source generates information. This rate, which is also measured in bits per second, is the information rate of the signal source. It is also called the *entropy rate* of the signal source. It is a measure of the amount of choice the signal source has in generating a message a second long. It is a measure of the amount of uncertainty the signal destination has as to which among messages one second long a particular message may be. Usually, the information or entropy rate of a signal source is much smaller than one might at first think. It is difficult to evaluate it, however, for signals are very complicated.

Once we know enough about a signal to evaluate its information rate, we ought to be able so to encode the signal for transmission that we could send it over a channel with a channel capacity, C, no greater than the information rate of the source. Sometimes, as in the case of the vocoder, we can go a long way in this direction. Usually, however, the process is complicated and the results may be far from perfect.

Usually, in fact, it is cheaper to encode the signal by some very simple means and to use a great excess of channel capacity to transmit it rather than to provide the complicated encoding and decoding means needed to send the signal with reduced channel capacity. That is the chief reason why devices such as vocoders are not actually used in telephony. Band width is cheaper than vocoders.

Communication engineers are studying voice signals and television signals to see how they can be sent more economically. Such studies are complicated and hard to explain. Instead, in the next chapter we will consider a particularly simple sort of signal— English text.

CHAPTER XV

The Unexpected

COMMUNICATION theory deals with the unexpected, the unpredictable. The channel capacity needed to transmit a message in a given time depends on how uncertain the message destination is as to what the message may be, on how unpredictable the message is. This unpredictability depends on the source of the message, on how unpredictable the message source is, on how much freedom or choice it exhibits in producing messages.

The measure of unexpectedness in a message source is called *entropy*. The word *entropy* is also the name of a mathematically related quantity used in thermodynamics and statistical mechanics. I will say just a few words about this. In thermodynamics, entropy is a measure of the disorganization of a physical system. Disorganization may be interpreted as meaning how little the observer knows about the system. Some physicists have related the entropy of communication theory to the entropy of physical systems. If an observer learns something about a physical system, its entropy is decreased, since for him it has become less disorganized. When an observer knows more about a system, he can obtain work from it. Conversely, these physicists state that it takes work, real physical work, to obtain information about the state of a system— that is, to decrease its entropy. If this were not so, we might be able to build perpetual motion machines, and one thought up by James Clerk Maxwell, which depends on an imaginary imp called *Maxwell's demon*, who is able to sort out molecules with high thermal velocities from those with low thermal velocities, might actually work. Communication theory is invoked to show that Maxwell's demon actually couldn't possibly work at a profit.

The average reader need not be concerned if he fails to understand the paragraph above. I would be unable myself to prove that what it states is true. I believe, however, that it represents fairly accurately what physicists have to say about the relation between entropy in communication theory and entropy in physics. This is a big subject, which we just can't go into here, and the reader will have to get what satisfaction he can from what I have said.

Here we will be concerned only with the entropy of message sources. This unpredictability or freedom is difficult to measure and perhaps a little difficult to understand. We have seen that there is a good deal of predictability in television; one picture or *frame* is sent each thirtieth of a second, and succeeding frames usually bear a close resemblance to one another and are hence to some extent predictable. Voice signals, too, are reasonably predictable. A man's voice does not make just any sound; it utters sequences made up of a comparatively few phonetic elements, so we know that the next sound uttered will be chosen from among a few alternatives, and will not be, for instance, a chord, or the sound of an oboe or a piccolo.

Evaluating the unpredictability or entropy of a message source lies at the very heart of communication theory as applied to all message sources. It would be unwise to study this sort of evaluation in the case of complicated and continuously varying signals such as voice and television. It is simpler and clearer to consider *discrete* signals, signals of successive symbols, each symbol drawn from a *finite set*. Such a set may be the letters of the English alphabet, including the space between words—a symbol represented by a blank, the absence of a letter. Another discrete set of symbols consists of the binary digits 0 and 1. Let us first consider this simplest of all sets of symbols and then go on to the alphabetical symbols of English text.

Entropy is measured in bits, in *yes*-or-*no* choices. We might speak of entropy in bits per message, or bits per second. Here, however, we will speak of entropy as the average number of bits per symbol, as the average choice, measured as a binary number, which the message source has in producing the next symbol.

The simplest case we can consider is that in which the message source is perfectly free to choose a 0 or 1 as the next symbol in a message consisting of a sequence of these two symbols. Suppose, for instance, that 0 represented heads and 1 represented tails in a particular series of honest flips of an honest coin, and suppose we wished to convey this sequence of heads and tails to someone. What the next flip will reveal is entirely unpredictable; we can only convey the information by sending a 0 or a 1, representing a heads or tails, for each flip of the coin. The message will be a sequence of zeros and ones, and its entropy will be 1 bit per symbol. The message might look like this:

0 1 1 0 0 1 1 1 0 0 1 0 1 1 0

Suppose, however, that our message source consisted of the rolls of an honest die and that all we wanted to know was when the die turned up one and when it turned up something else. We might represent this by a sequence consisting of 0 for every time the die turned up 1 and 1 for every time any other side turned up. The sequence describing the series of rolls might look as follows:

1 1 1 1 0 1 1 1 1 1 0 1 0 1

This sequence is clearly not entirely unpredictable. It is a pretty safe bet that the next digit will be 1 rather than 0. The entropy must be less than one bit per symbol, and we ought to be able to encode the sequence in some other form which would take less than one bit per symbol to send. We can profitably encode a sequence of the sort given above in the following way:

Let us send a sequence of three-digit binary numbers telling how many ones we encounter after each zero in the original message before reaching a zero or the end of the message. Thus we will let binary code groups represent the number of ones following a given zero and before the next zero according to the following table:

Binary Code Group	Number of ones following a zero and before the next zero
000	0
001	1
010	2
011	3
100	4
101	5
110	6
111	7 plus the number corresponding to the following code group

Thus, a sequence of no 1's following a 0 and before the next 0 will be represented by the code group 000; a sequence of six 1's by 110, a sequence of seven 1's by 111 000 (the groups of three binary digits have been separated for clarity), a group of ten 1's by 111 011, a group of twenty 1's by 111 111 110, and so on.

The representation of the particular message given a little earlier will then be

$$100 \ 110 \ 001 \ 001$$

The sequences of three characters are separated merely to show they represent different sequences of ones. They would be sent one after the other without spaces in transmitting the message.

By encoding this particular message in this manner we have cut down the number of zeros and ones required to represent it from fifteen to twelve. If this were the average saving, we would know that the entropy was not greater than $1\frac{2}{15}$, or $\frac{4}{5}$, bits per symbol. As a matter of fact, Shannon's work shows that it is less than this. He shows that if a message source chooses or produces symbols so that the symbol chosen does not depend on what symbols occurred earlier, the entropy, I, per symbol is

$$I = -\Sigma p_n \log_2 p_n$$

The Σ sign (which is the Greek capital *sigma*) means to add up for all different values of n. p_n is the probability that the nth symbol will be chosen. In our case we have a probability of ⅙ that 0 will appear next and a probability of ⅚ that 1 will appear next. The entropy per symbol is

$$I = -[\tfrac{1}{6}\log_2(\tfrac{1}{6}) + \tfrac{5}{6}\log_2(\tfrac{5}{6})]$$

$$I = -[\tfrac{1}{6}(-2.59) + \tfrac{5}{6}(-.263)]$$

$$I = .651$$

Thus, if we encoded a message concerning the throws of a die with the best possible code, it should take on the average (.651) (15), or less than ten binary digits to represent each fifteen digits of the original message. Our code reduced a particular fifteen-symbol message to twelve symbols. This may be partly happenstance, but it is partly because we did not use a perfectly efficient code. In this simple case it would be possible to find a more efficient code, but in most realistic cases it is very difficult to find a highly efficient code even when we know the entropy of the message source, and it is very hard to get even a good estimate of the entropy of the message source.

Let us now consider the case of English text. Certainly, the next letter in a written message does not appear at random with a probability of ½₇ for each letter and for a space. If this were true,

XFOML RXKHRJFFJUM

would be English text. In this sequence the symbols were chosen randomly with equal probabilities for all symbols, including the space. To do this each letter of the alphabet and the space was assigned a different number, and then letters and spaces were written down corresponding to successive numbers in a table of random numbers.

Even if we choose the symbols independently according to their probability of occurring in English text, *e* frequently, *z* seldom, and so on, we still don't get English text. The following passage was chosen in this manner:

LL NBNESBYA TH EEI

The truth is that a man writing English is not very free in choosing the letter he will set down next. *U* inevitably follows *q*.

Vowels and consonants are grouped in certain patterns. In fact, cryptographers have compiled tables which give the probability of occurrence of certain *digrams* and *trigrams,* that is, groups of two and three sequential letters. Some of these digrams and trigrams occur much more frequently than others. Some digrams and trigrams such as *qq* and *eee* never occur except in such instances as this; the probability of their occurrence is very nearly zero.

Actually, of the many sequences of letters which we could write down, very, very few ever occur in English. It is for this reason that cryptographers are able to decipher English even after it has been horribly scrambled. The strong pattern of English text survives any amount of scrambling. It is also why English text is easy to predict.

For instance, Shannon made an experiment in which a man was shown English text up to a certain point and asked to guess the next letter (or space). Then he was shown the actual letter and asked to guess the next letter, and so on. Part of the result is given below. The actual text is shown in the upper line. The correct guesses are shown below by dashes; the letters he got wrong and had to be told are written in:

THE ROOM WAS NOT VERY LIGHT A SMALL
----ROO------NOT-V-----I------SM---

In the overall text of 129 letters, a total of 89 letters, or 69 per cent, was guessed correctly.

By making more elaborate experiments and by means of mathematical calculations, Shannon has estimated that the entropy of English text is only about one binary digit per symbol. That is, in writing English text as I am now doing, on the average I have just about two alternatives as to what the next symbol (letter or space) will be. Sometimes, as in the middle of some words, I have no alternative; at the end of a word I have more alternatives, and at the end of a sentence I have many. The average of one bit per symbol is an average over all of these cases.

This means that in transmitting English text by telegraph it should be possible so to encode the text that the message could be transmitted using only as many zeros and ones, or pulses and absences of pulses, as there are letters and spaces in the original text. However, to attain perfect encoding of English text would require the taking of fantastic amounts of data and the use of impossibly complex equipment.

Even if we could encode English text so very efficiently, we might not wish to do so in transmitting messages. In perfectly encoded English text, every message that could be transmitted would represent some message in English, just as every sequence of digits represents a number. No provision would be made for transmitting gibberish. Thus, if a mistake were made in transmission of the coded message, the erroneous signal which was received would not be interpreted as a mangled English message. There would be no provision, no assigned code or sequence of symbols, for transmitting mangled English. Instead, an erroneous code would be interpreted as some other English message, perhaps entirely different from the one it was intended to transmit. This could cause great confusion.

English is *redundant* in the sense that it uses more, or more complex, characters than are needed to represent the number of messages which may actually occur (the number of sequences of letters that are English and not gibberish). If we change a digit in a number we get a different number, but if we change a letter or even a few letters in a written message we get a mutilated but recognizable message rather than some other message. If we took the mangled message literally, it would be gibberish, not English. This is a valuable property of written English. It enables us to decipher bad handwriting, for instance. The analogous redundancy in spoken English enables us to catch the meaning of imperfectly heard remarks and to understand people who speak ungrammatically or with foreign accents.

The redundancy of English also enables us to write down things which in a statistical sense are not English, even if they are understandable. James Joyce's *Ulysses* is one example. The texts of children's readers offer another, as:

> "We will go" said John.
> "Yes, yes" said all the boys,

"We will go and find it."
So all the boys went.
All the boys went to find it.
They did not find it.

The most elementary sort of statistical tests would show that such sequences of words are very different from English as it is commonly spoken or written. They form a related language made up of English words; we might call this language *primer pidgin*.

So far we have considered the nature of actual meaningful English text. We have seen that such text is made up of only a few of the many possible combinations of the letters of the alphabet. In English text, some combinations of letters occur more frequently than other combinations, as *th* occurs more frequently than *qu*, and *qu* more frequently than *qq*, which never occurs except in such cases as this. Finally, words occur in certain orders, for only some sequences of words make English, while others make gibberish, or at best, Joyce or primer pidgin. This all makes English highly predictable and allows a man writing or speaking English only a small choice as to what the next letter or sound will be. It also makes it possible to understand English despite a reasonable amount of mutilation.

We can, if we wish, approach this matter from a little different direction. If there are certain statistical rules for the association of letters and words in English, can we construct English mechanically following these rules? Shannon made some experiments along these lines.

One can start by constructing sequences of letters or words according to a table of random numbers, or by an equivalent process. Shannon has done this, and I present several examples:

1. Zero-order approximation (symbols independent and equiprobable. The symbols include the letters of the English alphabet and the space):

X FOML RXKHRJFFJUJ ZLPWCFWKCYJ
FFJEYVKCQSGHYD QPAAMKBZAACIBZLHJQD

2. First-order approximation (symbols independent but with frequencies in English text):

> OCRO HLI RGWR NMIELWIS EU
> LL NBNESEBYA TH EEI ALHENHTTPA
> OOBTTVA NAH BLR

3. Second-order approximation (digram structure as in English):

> ON IE ANTSOUTINYS ARE T
> INCTORE ST BE S DEAMY
> ACHIN D ILONASIVE TUCOOWE AT
> TEASONARE FUSO TIZIN ANDY
> TOBE SEACE CTISBE

4. Third-order approximation (trigram structure as in English):

> IS NO LAT WHEY CRATICT
> FROURE BIRS GROCID PONDENOME
> OR DEMONSTURES OF THE
> REPTAGIN IS REGROACTIONA OF
> CRE

5. Second-order word approximation (one word chosen with the correct probability of following the preceding word):

> THE HEAD AND IN FRONTAL
> ATTACK ON AN ENGLISH WRITER
> THAT THE CHARACTER OF THIS POINT
> IS THEREFORE ANOTHER METHOD FOR THE
> LETTERS THAT THE TIME OF WHO EVER TOLD
> THE PROBLEM FOR AN UNEXPECTED.

Numbers 1–4 were made using tables of letters, letter frequencies, digram frequencies, and trigram frequencies together with a table of random numbers. Number 5 was made by choosing a word in a novel, leafing through the pages until the word was found again, and writing down the word that followed it in the new context, looking for that added word in a new context, and so on.

The progression toward English in going from 1 to 5 is clearly recognizable. The examples illustrate that a mechanical process obeying the statistical rules of English can produce something resembling English text. The thing which surprised me most about these examples was, however, something quite different. It was the charm of some of the words and the tantalizing quality of the "passage" in number 5.

Suppose that you, the reader, were asked to make up a number of "words" which were to be plausible, pronounceable and not obvious combinations of existing words. I think that you would find this most difficult. Habit is a much more characteristic human trait than is originality. We are all bound by the chains of custom. We see, however, that a mathematician has provided a means for avoiding the limitations of habit, by making up "words" according to a random statistical procedure which could be followed by a computing machine.

For me, at least, many of the words have great charm. I find DEAMY pleasant (from dream?), PONDENOME strikes me as solemn, INCTORE as somewhat less so. ILONASIVE has a dubious connotation. I should hate to be called ILONASIVE in these troubled days. TIZIN sounds foreign. I would not like to be characterized as GROCID (because of gross, groceries, and gravid?).

Let the reader amuse himself by conscientiously trying out his reactions; I believe that he will have some. Yet they are all his. Nothing was intended by the words. They are the product of chance working through a rather narrow channel, of chance circumscribed by the statistics of English text. There is no feeling of an author to be conveyed. That which is found is like the pattern of sound in dripping water, the face on the rock, the scene portrayed by stains on the wall; all is in the mind of the beholder. Such chance products as these words give an unalloyed opportunity for creative appreciation. The enjoyment comes from within. It is the enjoyer's own, and this, I should think, would make it all the more valuable to him.

It would seem odd if mathematics had nothing to contribute to the arts. The idea is so obvious that many have tried to evoke art from mathematics. An eminent mathematician, Birkhoff, wrote a book on esthetic measure. To me, personally, the work seems doubtfully founded in that it looks at pieces of porcelain and scraps of paper rather than at the human beings who appreciate them. As far as creation goes we need not argue about the methods proposed. The author gives an example to illustrate the application of the rules derived in writing a poem. We see at once that a second-rate poet is as an artist far ahead of a very eminent mathematician. A later author, Joseph Schillinger, claims a share of the merit of *Porgy and Bess* for his mathematical system of composition. A skeptic might argue that a composer of genius can make a good thing of anything. Certainly when mathematics is used as a sort of guide or crutch it is hard to apportion credit between mathematics and its user.

I think that in the past those who tried to use mathematics in artistic creation have expected too much. They strove for *Paradise Lost* rather than good nonsense jingles. Moreover, I think that they tried to use mathematics for just exactly the wrong purpose. They tried to use mathematics to put order into art rather than to take it out.

While order is necessary to art, mediocre art is troubled by too much order. The bad poet repeatedly rhymes love with dove. We know the next word, the next cliché, before we encounter it. The same thing holds true for bad music and bad painting. There is no surprise, nothing fresh. The artist is chained and directed by stale habits. More order could not help him, but a little unpredictability might.

While human beings are strongly unoriginal, generally predictable, mathematics or machines can provide total originality. There is nothing predictable about a series of flips of a coin, about a series of random digits. There is nothing very interesting, either. These sequences are too surprising, too random, too unpredictable.

We have seen, however, that some order can be added to a random process, as in the examples 3–5 quoted above. The element of surprise is still there, but the use of some of the statistics of the English language, the choice of sequential letters or words according to their probability of occurring together in English, has added a pattern which we can recognize and appreciate.

As I have said, I was charmed by DEAMY and impressed at least by PONDENOME, INCTORE, ILONASIVE, TIZIN and GROCID. Further, I felt a strange concern for the plight of the English writer in example 5, the second-order word approximation. These words and this passage have for me at least an element of art, whether deliberate or not. Perhaps the element is small. Perhaps it is not even new, for Captain Lemuel Gulliver saw at the Grand Academy of Lagado a word frame consisting of lettered blocks mounted on shafts, which a professor turned at random in seeking new wisdom. Nonetheless, I wanted to pursue the matter further.

The most promising avenue seemed to lie in putting words together according to the statistics of English. Unfortunately, there are no tables of the probabilities of words occurring sequentially in twos, threes, fours, and so on. Thus, the construction of random "prose" in which, on a short-range basis, words follow one another in a probable order cannot be done entirely mechanically. However, Shannon found a way around this difficulty. The statistics of the English language exist in our brains, fixed there through years of practice, and we can easily avail ourselves of these statistics through using human beings.

One can proceed as follows: First write down three words (the number is arbitrary) of a sentence in a column at the top of a short slip of paper. Show these words to someone and ask him to make up a sentence in which the words occur and to add the word in the sentence which follows the three he has been shown. Then turn down the top word so that it cannot be seen and ask the same of another individual, and so on. In this process the choice of a given word is dependent on but not determined by the preceding three words. The following example was obtained by this process.

"When morning broke after an orgy of wild abandon he said her head shook vertically aligned in a sequence of words follows what."

This begins well, and the fifteen words following the initial three have a clear meaning. Afterwards there is a wandering of the mind, as in some cases of schizophrenia. But whose is the meaning, and whose mind wanders? The meaning exists only for the reader. Each of the twenty-one writers who contributed to this particular passage knew only four words, and each thought of them in a different context.

Presumably, written English is coherent over long stretches, when it is, because of some overriding purpose in the writer's mind. When this fails, we find merely a series of words associated reasonably over a short range, as in the case of a schizophrenic person, or perhaps over a longer range, as in the case of Uncle Anselmo in Hudson's *The Purple Land*. And one may well wonder how often the tongue runs on, started by an initial impulse, to glide aimlessly along a flow of probable words.

We can add some long-range order in the construction of passages as described above simply by writing a "subject" or "title" at the bottom of the slip, where each man who adds a word can see it. In some of the passages quoted below no title was used. When a title was used, it is given at the head of the passage. In producing the passages it seemed unwise to pester an endless number of dubiously sympathetic individuals, so a large number of slips were circulated among six individuals and English-like text was produced wholesale.

(1) This was the first. The second time it happened without his approval. Nevertheless it cannot be done. It could hardly have been the only living veteran of the foreign power had stated that never more could happen. Consequently, people seldom try it.

(2) John now disported a fine new hat. I paid plenty for the food. When cooked asparagus has a delicious flavor suggesting apples. If anyone wants my wife or any other physicist would not believe my own eyes. I would believe my own word.

(3) That was a relief whenever you let your mind go free who knows if that pork chop I took with my cup of tea after was quite good with the heat I couldn't smell anything off it I'm sure that queer looking man in the

(4) I forget whether he went on and on. Finally he stipulated that this must stop immediately after this. The last time I saw him when she lived. It happened one frosty look of trees waving gracefully against the wall. You never can

(5) McMILLAN'S THEOREM

McMillan's theorem states that whenever electrons diffuse in vacua. Conversely impurities of a cathode. No substitution of variables in the equation relating these quantities. Functions relating hypergeometric series with confluent terms converging to limits uniformly expanding rationally to represent any function.

(6) MURDER STORY

When I killed her I stabbed Paul between his powerful jaws clamped tightly together. Screaming loudly despite fatal consequences in the struggle for life began ebbing as he coughed hollowly spitting blood from his ears.

(7) SALARIES

Money isn't everything. However, we need considerably more incentive to produce efficiently. On the other hand, too little and too late to suggest a raise without reason for remuneration obviously less than they need although they really are extremely meager.

(8) HOUSE CLEANING

First empty the furniture of the master bedroom and bath. Toilets are to be washed after polishing doorknobs the rest of the room. Washing windows semiannually is to be taken by small aids such as husbands are prone to omit soap powder.

(9) EPIMINONDAS

Epiminondas was one who was powerful especially on land and sea. He was the leader of great fleet maneuvers and open sea battles against Pelopidas but had been struck on the head during the second Punic war because of the wreck of an armored frigate.

I believe that few people will read the material without some interest or amusement. Is this not enough justification in calling it a contribution of mathematics to the arts?

While interest and enjoyment are clearly the contribution of the reader, the reader will be interested and will enjoy only if the text is (1) recognizable in part at least as a possible sequence of words, (2) original. Thus, consider "It happened one frosty look of trees waving gracefully against the wall." We realize that someone might say this, or, even, might want to say it. However, a person's habits are so strong as to make him unlikely to say it. Starting with the first three words, anyone would almost inevitably have said something different and more common. The simple process by which the sentence was constructed has no such inhibitions. As a matter of fact, some people, including madmen and distinguished artists, don't have many. In case the reader has not suspected already, numbers 3 and 9 are not statistical English. Number 3 is from James Joyce's *Ulysses* and number 9 from the writings of a schizophrenic patient.

Perhaps the best way to explore this subject further is to apply similar means in a different field of art. In the field of visual art one finds himself anticipated by the kaleidoscope, which combines a random arrangement of colored fragments into a sixfold geometric pattern—a simple example of much the sort of thing we have been considering. We may remember, too, that many years ago Marcel Duchamp allowed a number of threads to fall on pieces of cloth and then framed and preserved them. Our example shall be from the field of music. It was produced by M. E. Shannon and the writer.

In order to construct music by a stochastic process, a catalogue of allowed chords on roots 1–6 in the key of C was made. Actually, it was necessary to make a catalogue of root-1 chords only; the others could be derived. By the throwing of three especially made dice and by the use of a table of random numbers, one chord was chosen to follow another. The only rule of connection was that two succeeding chords have a common tone in the same voice. Each composition consisted of eight measures of four quarter notes each. In order to give some pattern, measures 5 and 6 repeat measures 1 and 2. In addition, it was specified that chords 1, 16, and 32 have root 1 and that chords 15 and 31 have either root 4 or root 5.

Three statistical pieces were rapidly constructed according to these rules. Each took perhaps half a day. They are reproduced here so that the curious may play them.

I asked an experienced pianist to play these three for me several times. After a few repetitions, he came to add a certain amount of phrasing and expression which he felt natural. Thus, he made a *performer's* contribution to these works of art. Certainly one cannot object that he was violating the intentions of the composer.

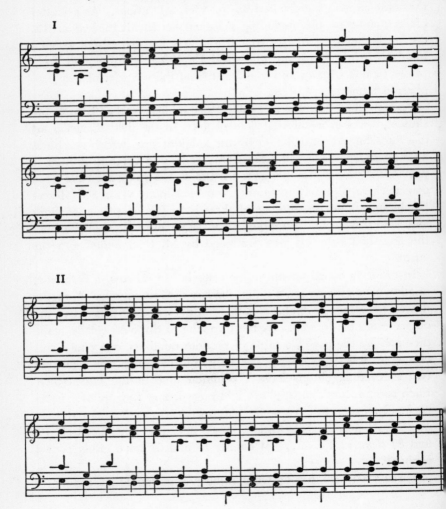

III

What about the listener's contribution? I found the pieces a little meaningless at first, but after I had heard them several times and could recognize them they became more "comprehensible." Acting in the capacity of a music critic, I find them pleasing rather than deep. They are less dull than poor hymns but are considerably inferior to Bach.

From their common characteristics the pieces are clearly products of the same composer. Some identifying features are that voices tend either to stick to one note repeatedly or to jump wildly. Too, many "laws" of harmony—no parallel fifths, no doubling of the leading tone, and so on are flagrantly ignored.

No doubt, by use of more complicated rules stochastic music could be produced which would violate fewer of the rules of harmony. But would this result in a gain or a loss? If the process has value, does this not in some degree come from its lack of prejudice and predictability? Statistical music should be urged toward respectability only with caution.

How seriously is all this to be taken? I think that the crude material presented shows that short pieces of amusing and enjoyable text and music can be produced by processes which are essentially statistical in their character. The interest of this text and music is clearly dependent both on familiarity and on surprise. The processes could be refined. It is not beyond conjecture that a machine could write murder mysteries, every one different, at the punch of a button, with *hard-boiled, sex, deduction,* and other styles and features adjusted to the user's individual taste. It is quite beyond possible attainment, however.

My experience has, however, raised an issue beyond that of the stochastic generation of art. Apparently, if I try I am capable of liking almost anything that is surprising if only it has some order or recognizable feature. Too, I am not entirely alone in this. I wonder, how much of the appreciation of some of the more drastic of "modern" writing, music, and painting is a combination of a knowledge of the artist's style and tricks and a determined effort to enjoy? How can one tell?

CHAPTER XVI

Relativity and Quantum Mechanics

IN THE earlier chapters we started with some basic laws of physics concerning motion, electric and magnetic fields, waves, and noise. We saw these at work in particular devices such as transmission lines, resonators, antennas, and vacuum tubes. We saw how such component devices can be put together into systems to accomplish certain overall purposes. Finally, in communication theory we considered something of the basic philosophy of communication systems; what their purpose is, how they can accomplish it, and how well they can accomplish it. As is common with philosophy, in the end this discussion wandered rather far afield.

We have traced one particular path through the field of electronics. Starting in much the same way, we might have discussed control systems, or computers, or telephone switching systems rather than the communication systems we have discussed. This would have involved going into the broad field of digital art, including Boolian algebra and other parts of mathematics which deal with and systematize off-on processes of great complexity. These matters I have scarcely mentioned. I have also excluded something which I regretted very much leaving out; the whole field of feedback, which is a part of all automatic regulation and of many amplifiers used in communication. It is out of feedback, together with communication theory and some other parts of statistics, that Norbert Wiener created that important, popular and glamorous field, cybernetics.

Much had to be left out to make a book which is not too long and, I hope, not too hard to read. It seems to me, however, that two things which can't be left out are relativity and quantum mechanics. The reader would have a right to feel cheated if nothing were said about these subjects. He has inevitably read something about both. He knows that they are relatively new and are truer than older parts of physics. How do they change the things that have been said in earlier chapters?

Here I do not propose to discuss philosophical questions which have been raised concerning relativity and quantum mechanics. Relativity and quantum mechanics consist of certain mathematical expressions with directions for applying them in calculating the behavior of natural phenomena or man-made devices. With these equations and rules go a certain amount of interpretation, of useful words and useful general ideas. Associated with relativity and quantum mechanics is, so to speak, a constructive frame of mind for people who want to advance these arts.

Finally, somehow tacked onto relativity and quantum mechanics, are speculations and questions such as the following: Is not relativity contrary to common sense, or to the teachings of philosophy? Is there not a corresponding relativity in morals, or in religion, or in politics? Does quantum mechanics, involving as it does an uncertainty principle, establish the existence of free will? Many people, some of them scientists, have written at great length about matters of this sort. The more I think about such questions, the less I understand what they mean. Perhaps I lack the proper frame of mind.

In the last century, and well into this, there were hot arguments concerning the ether, an all-pervading susbtance assumed to exist in order to transmit waves of light. What must the ether be like so that Maxwell's equations may be true? Can we conceive of waves traveling without an ether; of waves with nothing waving? Clearly, people felt strongly about this matter. Today the feelings are as dead as the people who had them. Different generations have different emotions. Today, people argue hotly about the "meaning" and interpretation of relativity and quantum mechanics. All I know is that they work.

Let us consider relativity first, since it attained popular fame the earlier of the two. In electronics, when do we have to take relativity into account? The answer is, whenever particles go very fast, whenever, in fact, their velocities are appreciable compared with the speed of light. For instance, according to relativity, the velocity, v, of an electron accelerated by a voltage, V—that is, an electron with an energy of V electron volts, is

$$v = c \sqrt{1 - \frac{1}{\left(1 + \dfrac{eV}{m_o c^2}\right)^2}}$$

Here c stands for the velocity of light, and e/m_o is the charge-to-mass ratio of the electron, taken as a positive quantity. According to Newton's laws of motion, we would have

$$v = \sqrt{\frac{2eV}{m_o}}$$

The relativistic expression above gives an answer negligibly different from that of the Newtonian expression when the voltage, V, is small. In Fig. 16.1 the ratio of the velocity to the velocity of

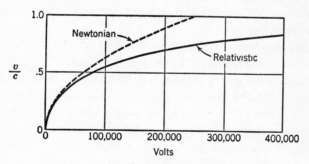

FIG. 16.1

light, v/c, is plotted from the true relativistic expression. On the same plot the Newtonian expression for the velocity is plotted as a dashed line. We see that below 10,000 volts the Newtonian expression is very accurate; above 100,000 volts, it is very inaccurate.

Are we really to believe the relativistic expression for velocity rather than the Newtonian expression? We surely are! Out at Stanford University physicists have built a *linear accelerator* which is 260 feet long, to accelerate electrons to an energy of a billion volts. Essentially, a linear accelerator consists of many resonators similar to those which we discussed in Chapter VI in connection with klystrons. FIG. *16.2* shows a series of such resonators. Across the gap of each resonator there is a powerful sinusoidal voltage. In the Stanford accelerator, voltages across the resonators are pro-

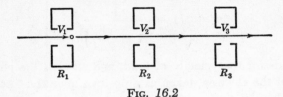

FIG. *16.2*

duced by the output of nineteen powerful klystrons, each giving a pulsed power of seventeen million watts at a wave length of 10 centimeters. Each of the voltages, V_1, V_2, V_3, etc. of successive resonators reaches its peak just as a given electron or, rather, a given group of electrons, passes through that resonator. Thus, for example, the energy in the group of electrons is increased by the peak voltage, V_n, across the nth resonator as the group passes through the nth resonator.

In order for the accelerator to work at all, the electrons must arrive at a given resonator at just the right time. Thus, in order to design the accelerator it is necessary to know the relation between the velocity and the energy of an electron. According to the true, relativistic law, the electrons travel with a speed less than but very little different from that of light in all but a short section near the beginning of the accelerator. This makes the design simple. It would be much more difficult to cope with an electron velocity that changed appreciably with the energy.

If the voltages across the resonators do not speed the electrons up appreciably, how can they increase their energies? According to Newton's laws, the kinetic energy of a particle of mass m_o is

$$\tfrac{1}{2}m_o v^2$$

According to relativity, the total energy of a particle of mass m is

$$mc^2$$

Here c is again the velocity of light.

Why is m_o written in one expression and m in the other? In relativity we distinguish between the *rest mass*, m_o, and the mass m. The rest mass, m_o, is the mass exhibited at low velocities; it is a characteristic of an electron or an atom; it is something which is preserved as the particle is accelerated. The rest mass, m_o, is related to the actual mass, m, which the particle has when traveling with a velocity v by

$$m = \frac{m_o}{\sqrt{1 - \left(\dfrac{v}{c}\right)^2}}$$

When a particle is at rest, its total energy is

$$m_o c^2$$

When the particle is set in motion with a velocity v, its mass increases. Its kinetic energy is the difference between mc^2 and $m_o c^2$; that is, the kinetic energy is

$$m_0 c^2 \left(\frac{1}{\sqrt{1 - \left(\dfrac{v}{c}\right)^2}} - 1 \right)$$

For very small ratios of v/c this becomes indistinguishable from the Newtonian expression for kinetic energy.

Thus, in most of the linear accelerators, the electrons aren't made to go appreciably faster; they are first speeded up nearly to the velocity of light, and thereafter the added energy given to them changes their speed only a very little, but in doing so makes them more and more massive. And the relations given must be essentially correct, or the machine wouldn't work!

There are other high-voltage machines for which the Newtonian laws of motion are inaccurate. For instance, in the very klystrons which drive the Stanford linear accelerator, the electrons of the beam are accelerated by 300,000 volts. These klystrons had to be designed using relativistic equations of electron motion.

The cyclotron offers another example of the importance of relativity in high-voltage machines. Cyclotrons are used to accelerate ions, which are much more massive than electrons. Thus, for a given energy in electron volts, ions don't go as fast as electrons would, and relativistic effects set in only at higher voltages. None-theless, as we try to give ions more and more energy with cyclo-trons, relativity becomes important.

We saw in Chapter IV how the cyclotron works. Particles moving in a uniform magnetic field travel in circles, going around once in a time, T, such that the mass times the acceleration, which is $m_o 2\pi v/T$, is equal to the force due to the magnetic field, which is $q\mu Hv$. Thus,

$$T = 2\pi \frac{m_o}{q}$$

Here m_o is the mass of the particle and q is its charge.

According to relativity, the force should be equal not to the rest mass times the acceleration but to the rate of change of momentum with time, where momentum is the actual mass times the velocity—that is, momentum is

$$\frac{m_o v}{\sqrt{1 - \left(\frac{v}{c}\right)^2}}$$

In the above expression, v in $(v/c)^2$ is taken to be the magnitude of the velocity v; the momentum is a vector pointed in the direction of the velocity, v.

If we speed a particle up, as in a linear accelerator, we have to take into account changes in v where it appears in the quantity $(v/c)^2$, and this complicates matters. In the case of a circular orbit, however, $(v/c)^2$ is constant. We can get the relativistic equation for the period simply by using m in place of m_o, thus:

$$T = \frac{2\pi m_o}{q\mu H \sqrt{1 - \left(\frac{v}{c}\right)^2}}$$

We see that the time it takes an ion to circle around within the dees of a cyclotron increases as the velocity of the ion is raised by the voltage applied to the dees. This sets a limit to the amount of energy that can be given to an ion by a simple cyclotron. However, by lowering the frequency of the voltage applied to the dees as the particles are accelerated, greater energies can be attained at the expense of having the particles, as the frequency is lowered, accelerated intermittently rather than continuously. The frequency-modulated cyclotron at the University of California accelerates ions to over a third of a billion volts.

The reader will find what I have said so far very different from other popular accounts of special relativity. This is because I have considered first the importance of relativity in connection with particular practical problems. There is a great deal more to be said about relativity. For instance, suppose we imagine two systems consisting of observers and sets of mechanical and electrical equipment. Suppose that we imagine these to move in straight lines with respect to one another, at a constant relative velocity. Special relativity, which is the sort we have dealt with, together with Maxwell's equations, provides physical laws which are of exactly the same form for both sets of observers and for both systems. We can apply these laws without saying what the "absolute" velocity of either system is. Newton's laws of motion together with Maxwell's equations lead to contradictions and absurdities in such a case.

As a part of the fact that the relativistic equations of motion and Maxwell's equations are the same for any system, regardless of its velocity with respect to anything else, the special theory of relativity tells us that any observer will obtain the same value for the velocity of light or other electromagnetic waves, regardless of his motion with respect to the source of the light. This is in accord with what experiments we can make. Special relativity also says that in order for the equations of motion to be the same in each of a number of systems in the relative motion, an object moving rapidly with respect to an observer must appear to shrink or shorten in the direction of motion. This is not observed directly, but is in accord with experiment. It is also required that a clock moving swiftly with respect to an observer appear to him to run slower. This effect has been observed. Ives observed that excited ions of gas radiate light of a lower frequency when they are moving rapidly than when they are standing still. Certain unstable particles such as mesons, which would rapidly transform themselves into something else if they were at rest, last for a much longer time when they are traveling at a velocity close to that of light.

We may ask, however, if, when A and B are in relative motion, A's clock seems to go slow to B, while B's clock seems to go slow to A, what will happen if A and B rush away from one another and then rush back, stop, and compare clocks? This is called the clock paradox. It has been discussed at great length, and I gather that it has been satisfactorily resolved. Presumably, if one understood *general relativity,* which deals with accelerated motion, gravitation, and the world at large, he could explain this and many other matters. The trouble with general relativity is that it is very unfamiliar or difficult and most physicists feel that it does not promise to solve the problems which they consider to be most challenging and interesting. Thus, the most able physicists work on nuclear physics and on some aspects of quantum mechanics, and general relativity is comparatively neglected.

The Newtonian laws of motion of Chapter II of this book are approximations. They are inaccurate when we deal with very fast motions. They also prove to be inaccurate when we examine physical phenomena in very minute, submicroscopic detail. Our justification for having used the simple laws of Newton is practical; these laws predict the paths of electrons through vacuum tubes with satisfactory accuracy.

To explain very fine details of electron motion, we must use quantum mechanics rather than Newtonian mechanics. Just as the equations of relativity give answers indistinguishable from the Newtonian equations for low velocities, so the equations of quantum mechanics give answers indistinguishable from those of Newtonian mechanics for most phenomena involving large distances and long times. We have seen in Chapter V, however, how quantum effects show up in the electron microscope, so as to limit the smallness of the objects which we can clearly distinguish. Quantum effects are apparent in other large-scale devices as well.

For instance, suppose, as in Fig. *16.3,* that we shoot a very narrow beam of 50,000-volt electrons at the surface of a crystal, that is, a substance in which the atoms are arranged in a regular pattern. The crystal may be perhaps 2 feet away. The beam strikes its surface at a grazing angle, is reflected, and falls on a photographic plate, perhaps 2 feet further on. The electrons which are reflected from the crystal and fall on the photographic plate will not all fall on just one spot. Instead, they will fall in a geometrical pattern

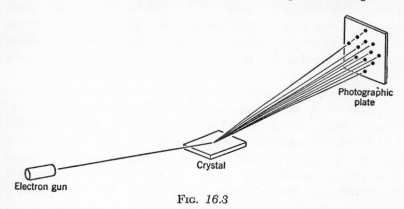

Fig. *16.3*

consisting of many dots in concentric circles. If the material on which the electrons fall consists of many small crystals rather than one large crystal, the pattern consists of concentric rings instead of dots. Such *electron diffraction* patterns are very useful in determining the nature of materials, both in working out the atomic structure of known materials and in determining the presence of unknown materials.

These dots of the electron diffraction pattern are just what we would get if we illuminated the regularly spaced atoms of the crystal with waves of very short length and if each atom scattered the waves. At some points on the photographic plate, waves scattered by all the regularly spaced atoms would add up in phase; at other points the waves from different atoms would cancel.

Clearly, if we examine the motions of electrons in sufficiently fine detail, we find that these motions are in accord with the phenomena we associate with waves. This does not necessarily mean that we should think of the electrons themselves as waves rather than as particles. If in the electron diffraction apparatus of Fig. *16.3* we replaced the photographic plate by a fluorescent screen, and if we shot the electrons at it at an average rate of only a few a second, we would see tiny flashes of light from the fluorescent screen as the electrons struck. Thus, each electron could be seen to strike the screen at a definite point. The probability of an electron striking the screen varies from point to point on the screen, being high at some points and almost zero at other points. Thus, when many electrons have reached the screen (or a photographic plate at the same place), some portions of the screen or plate have been heavily bombarded and other portions have been struck by very few electrons.

The equations which describe electron motion deal with waves. The solutions to these equations do not tell us the particular location of a particular electron at a particular time. They tell us the probability of finding an electron at a given position with a given momentum, or the probability of an electron arriving at a given time with a given energy. The waves which are the solutions of the quantum-mechanical equations describing electron motion are very far removed from our experience. Waves on the ocean represent the actual motion of a physical substance, water. Electromagnetic waves are merely the appearance of the electric and magnetic fields which constitute the waves at successive positions along the path of the wave. It seems optional and rather out of fashion to demand in connection with electromagnetic waves an ether which will wave as the wave travels, just as the water waves as a billow passes.

In wave mechanics, we are faced with waves which seem to merely be a way of representing a solution of certain mathematical equations which tell us all we can predict concerning the motion of an electron—the probability that it will reach a certain point with a certain momentum, for instance. Some physicists try to look behind these waves, seeking some mechanism which will "explain" them, some picture which will be more akin to other familiar phenomena. It appears, however, that most physicists have been more bent on refining the wave equations of quantum mechanics. De Broglie, who was the first to associate waves with the motion of matter, did not deduce equations complete enough to be very useful. Later, Schrödinger found a fairly complete equation which took physics a long, long way. Later still, more accurate equations of Klein and Gordon and finally of Dirac put wave mechanics in accord with special relativity. Refinements have followed, and it appears that there may be room for more.

The truly astonishing thing about wave mechanics is its success, its accuracy. We should note, I suppose, that Heisenberg's uncertainty principle, which is inherent in the equations of wave mechanics, says that we cannot determine both the energy and the time of arrival of an electron with unlimited precision. In wave mechanics, energy determines frequency, and Heisenberg's principle is related to the fact that a very short pulse must contain components of many frequencies. However, within the limits imposed by the uncertainty principle, wave mechanics shows itself completely in accord with observed phenomena.

Given the existence of the proton and the electron, wave mechanics tells us that there must be a system made up of the two, and that this system must have certain predictable properties. The system is the hydrogen atom. By means of wave mechanics one can calculate all the complicated spectra of the hydrogen atom, the various colors of light which are emitted when hydrogen is electrically excited in a tube much like a neon sign and the various frequencies at which hydrogen will absorb or emit radio waves. It is harder to calculate the properties of more complicated atoms which are made up of many protons, neutrons, and electrons, but whenever a calculation can be made in sufficient detail the result is in agreement with experiment.

Wave mechanics is of great practical importance in many ways. It is particularly important to electronics because it gives us a way of understanding the behavior of crystalline solids, in which atoms are arrayed regularly in patterns. It was only with the coming of wave mechanics that we were able to understand solids in a basic way: to make useful calculations about what holds crystals together, about the magnetism of iron and other materials, about how electrons leave hot cathodes, and about how electrons travel through solid materials. All this is the province of *solid-state physics*, a field of great complexity, of many problems which are still unsolved because of the mathematical difficulty of getting even approximate answers to the extremely complicated wave equations for crystals, a field of growing importance.

One extremely important outgrowth of work in solid-state physics is the transistor, which is the only versatile amplifier to appear since the birth of the vacuum tube almost fifty years ago. The transistor ordinarily makes use of a tiny piece of one of two solid elements, germanium or silicon. This particle of germanium or silicon may be no larger than the point of a pencil. To it, three (or sometimes more) electrical connections are made. The resulting device has many of the properties of a triode vacuum tube. It is superior in some ways, however. There is no need to expend electric power heating a cathode. Some transistors will act as amplifiers when powered by only a hundred-thousandth of a watt. Yet, if operated at a greater voltage and current, a transistor can deliver enough power to operate the speaker of a portable radio, as those who happen to own transistor radios well know. The transistor has tremendous potentialities in light, portable equipment and in extremely complicated equipment such as electronic computers, which call for so many amplifiers that both the bulk and the power drain may be excessive if vacuum tubes are used.

In order to understand at all how transistors work we must understand something of the motion of electrons through crystals. This motion is governed by wave mechanics, which we have been discussing.

In order to find out how an electron may move through a crystal we must solve an equation of a wave nature. The frequency of the wave involved depends on the energy of the electron. The wave length and velocity, if any, depend on the nature of the crystal through which the electron travels.

Consider a crystal such as pure germanium or silicon. For certain energies—that is, certain frequencies—the equations show that sinusoidal waves can travel through the perfectly regular lattice formed by the atoms of the crystal. Wave mechanics tells us that when this is so, electrons having these energies can travel perfectly freely through the solid crystal, without being stopped or deflected by the regular array of silicon or germanium atoms.

Astonishing as this may seem, it appears to be true. We should remember that microwaves can travel freely through a regular array of small metal disks which form an artificial dielectric used as a lens in a microwave antenna. As calculations concerning the motion of electrons deal with waves, it should perhaps seem natural that electrons have a similar ability to travel among the regularly arranged atoms of a crystalline substance.

In actual germanium or silicon, the electrons do not travel on indefinitely without being stopped or deflected, because the crystal lattice is not perfectly regular. The lattice is distorted by certain foreign substances. Even more important, it is continually vibrating with that motion of heat which we have discussed in Chapter IX in connection with Brownian motion and Johnson noise. For these reasons, an electron will be deflected in its motion through the crystal after having passed some thousands of atoms, but it moves very freely nonetheless.

That is, it moves freely if it has the right energy. What must this energy be? For a perfect crystal of a finite size, there are many energies which an electron may have and travel freely; these energies are called *energy levels*. In simple crystals, each energy level represents a two-way highway by means of which an electron can get from one side of the crystal to the other side, traveling with a particular velocity in either direction.

It is conventional to represent the energy levels of a crystal graphically as horizontal lines, with energy in electron volts plotted

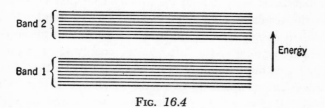

FIG. 16.4

vertically, as shown in FIG. 16.4. The energy levels are found clustered together in *energy bands,* as indicated in the figure. The number of energy levels in an energy band is proportional to the number of atoms in the crystal. Hence, for large crystals the energy levels are very close together and very numerous. In Fig. *16.4* the bands labeled band 1 and band 2 are only two among many energy bands having higher and lower energies.

As I have said, energy levels may be regarded as two-way highways for electrons; they show the energies electrons can have and travel through the crystal. There may be no electrons in an energy level. No more than two electrons having opposite *spins* can travel in one direction in an energy level. Two pairs of two electrons having opposite spins can travel in opposite directions in one energy level. The energy level is then completely filled with electrons, two going each way. In a perfect crystal, some energy levels are occupied by electrons belonging to the atoms of the crystal and some are empty. In insulators, such as perfectly pure silicon or germanium held at a low temperature, the energy bands lying below a certain energy are completely filled and the energy bands lying above a certain energy are completely empty, as indicated in Fig. *16.5*.

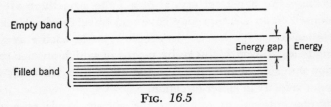

FIG. *16.5*

Obviously, no electric current can flow as the result of an empty energy band. It turns out to be equally true that no current can flow as the result of a completely filled energy band. In a completely filled energy band there is an electron going to the right for every electron going to the left. Every energy level is a two-way highway for no more than two pairs of electrons at a time, and every energy level is occupied by two pairs of electrons, one pair going each way. If a very strong electric field were applied to the material, an electron might jump from the highest filled band to the lowest empty band and so become free to move, but this requires an extremely large electric field.

Such materials as germanium and silicon actually can conduct electricity because of the presence of certain impurities. Such impurities can act in one of two ways. The presence of small amounts of one group of elements, including phosphorus, antimony and arsenic, adds electrons to the empty levels. When there is no electric field applied, these settle down four to a level, two traveling to the right and two to the left. However, if a small electric field is applied so as to force electrons toward the right, some electrons jump into vacant levels of a shade higher energy and travel to the right.

Another group of substances, including boron, aluminum, and gallium, make silicon or germanium conducting by taking away electrons from a filled energy band, so that the band is not filled but is only almost filled instead. As before, in the absence of an electric field the electrons are paired in the lowest energy levels of the band, an electron traveling to the right for each electron traveling to the left. When an electric field is applied, some electrons will jump to one of the few vacant levels and travel in the direction in which the electric field urges them to go.

If we could see the motion of electrons in this case of the almost-filled energy band, we would see among the filled levels a few vacancies or holes where electrons, if they were present, could be traveling to the right or left. Perhaps surprisingly, when the mathematics of the almost-filled energy band are worked out they show a behavior much like that we would expect from positive charges traveling through the crystal, and much of the physical behavior is like that we ordinarily associate with the motion of positive charges. Thus, there is a real reason to think of the conduction as due to *holes* in the almost-filled band, holes which act much as positive charges would.

Materials such as phosphorus, antimony, or arsenic which, when present in germanium or silicon, add electrons to an empty band are called *n-type impurities* or *donors* because of the negative electrons they add. Silicon or germanium containing *n*-type impurities is called *n*-type silicon or germanium.

Materials such as boron, aluminum, or gallium, which, when present in germanium or silicon, remove electrons from filled bands and create holes which behave like positive charges, holes which are free to move, are called *p-type impurities,* or *acceptors* and germanium or silicon containing *p*-type impurities is called *p*-type germanium or silicon.

When two types of impurities are present in the same silicon or germanium, that of which there is most predominates, and the silicon or germanium is *n* type or *p* type accordingly.

Single crystals of germanium or silicon are produced by pulling the material up from molten material in a crucible. The material solidifies in the form of a rod. Suppose that the material in the crucible is *n* type because *n* type impurities predominate. Suppose that a crystalline rod has been partly formed by pulling from the molten material. Suppose that at this point enough *p*-type impurity is added to the molten material so as to predominate over the *n*-type impurity. Then, as the rest of the crystal is formed, it will be *p* type, not *n* type. There will be a *p-n junction* between the two types of material.

What are the properties of such a junction? Such a junction acts as a rectifier. That is, current can flow across the *p-n* junction in one direction only. The filled band of the *p*-type material has a few holes in it; these can flow into the corresponding completely filled band of the *n*-type material (really, electrons move from the completely filled band of the *n*-type material into the holes in the corresponding band of the *p*-type material). Electrons can flow from the almost empty band of the *n*-type material into the corresponding but completely empty band of the *p*-type material. This

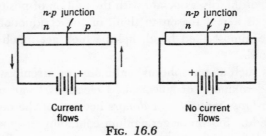

Fig. *16.6*

is illustrated at the left in Fig. *16.6*. When the *p*-type material is connected to the positive pole of a battery and the *n*-type to the negative pole, an electric current can and does flow through the material and across the junction.

What happens if the negative pole of the battery is connected to the p-type material and the positive pole is connected to the n-type material, as in the right of Fig. *16.6?* No current flows. The electric field is such as to urge holes from the filled band of the n-type material to the corresponding almost-filled band of the p-type material, but there are no holes in the n-type material to move. The field is also such as to urge electrons to move from the empty band of the p-type material to the corresponding almost empty band in the n-type material, but there are no electrons in the empty band of the p-type material to move. No current, or almost no current, flows.

Germanium and silicon rectifiers consisting of p-n junctions are extremely valuable devices. They are used in computers, they are used as non-linear devices for such functions as frequency changing in superheterodyne receivers, and they are used for many other purposes. The transistor, which uses junctions to make an amplifier, is even more valuable. Fig. *16.7* shows one particular type of

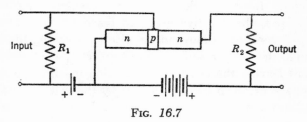

FIG. *16.7*

transistor, called the *junction transistor.* This consists of a section of n-type material, a very thin section of p-type material, and another section of n-type material, connected as shown.

The right-hand section of n-type material is held quite positive with respect to the p-type material. Thus, no current can flow from the p-type material, which acts an as input electrode, to the n-type material, which acts as an output electrode.

The p-type material is just a little positive with respect to the left-hand section of n-type material so as to cause a flow of electrons from the n-type material into the p-type material, and a flow of a few holes from the p-type material to the n-type material as well. If there is more n-type impurity in the n-type material than there is p-type impurity in the p-type material, the current flow will be mainly electrons from the n type to the p type rather than holes from the p type to the n type.

What happens to these electrons which enter the p-type region? They might travel along the thin direction of the layer and into the input circuit, but the right-hand portion of n-type material is much closer, and it is positive and attracts them. Thus, almost all of the electrons which enter the p-layer from the left-hand section of n-type material go directly to the positive right-hand section of n-type material and flow through the output resistor R_2.

Thus, the input voltage between the p-type material and the left-hand section of n-type material controls the current of electrons which leaves the left n section, but it is the right n section that collects these electrons. The n-p-n transistor acts much like a triode vacuum tube. The left n section corresponds to the cathode which emits electrons, and is called the *emitter,* the p layer acts like the control grid, and the right n section acts like the anode and is called the *collector.* In the triode the electrons which leave the hot cathode all pass the negative grid and reach the positive anode. In the n-p-n transistor, almost all the electrons leaving the n layer pass through the p layer and reach the collector. But the current of electrons leaving the emitter is controlled much more strongly by the voltage of the p layer than it is by the voltage of the collector, and so the n-p-n transistor is a very effective amplifier.

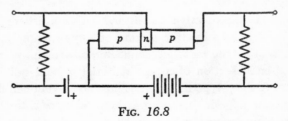

FIG. 16.8

One can also make p-n-p transistors, in which a thin n layer sandwiched between two p layers controls a current of holes from the p-type emitter. In this case the collector must be held negative in order to collect holes rather than electrons. Such a transistor is illustrated in FIG. 16.8.

This discussion by no means exhausts the story of transistors. Indeed, it barely starts it. Nothing has been said of *tetrode transistors*, which can be used as oscillators at frequencies above 1,000 megacycles, or of *p-n-i-p* transistors, which can also be used at high frequencies. Nothing has been said of the many fine points and the many practical difficulties of transistor art. To do so would take a very big book indeed, and not one part of a chapter.

Rather, if anything more is to be said, it should be about the importance of the transistor to the future of electronics. The overall story is that the transistor will not amplify at a frequency of 50,000 megacycles, as traveling-wave tubes can; so far it can act as an amplifier up to frequencies of a few hundred megacycles and as an oscillator somewhat above 1,000 megacycles. The transistor cannot give powers of tens of millions of watts, as the klystron can. The virtue of the transistor is that it is small and that it doesn't take much power.

This is graphically illustrated by the Bell Laboratories' transistor digital computer, Tradic. This computer can do sixty thousand additions or subtractions or three thousand multiplications or divisions in a second. It may go through as many as 250 steps in solving a problem. It can handle simultaneously thirteen sixteen-digit numbers. Tradic contains nearly 800 transistors together with nearly 11,000 germanium diodes, yet it occupies a space of less than 3 cubic feet, and requires a power of less than 100 watts to operate. Tradic was built for use in military aircraft. A comparable vacuum-tube computer would be impractically larger and would take a power of at least 2,000 watts.

The electronic art owes a great debt to W. H. Brattain and J. Bardeen, who invented the type of transistor first made public, and to W. Shockley, who instituted and directed the program of research in solid-state physics which led to the invention of the transistor, and who himself invented the junction transistor.

CHAPTER XVII

The Future

I AM very suspicious of prognosticators, because they are so often wrong. I remember that we were told after World War II that prices would go down after price controls were removed. My favorite example, however, is that of Upton Sinclair, who, shortly before World War I, speculated that William Randolph Hearst might be elected president and lead the United States peacefully into socialism, provided that international troubles did not change the course of events.

How ridiculous this is! Yet, if a bad guess, it was much less ridiculous in its day than it seems now. In those days socialists were elected to office. And in those days William Randolph Hearst was a young man with political ambitions and liberal if not too definite views. At least, Sinclair did have the good sense to foresee that a foreign catastrophe might change completely the complexion of our internal politics. In 1918 many prewar attitudes had been swept away completely. Today socialism seems as outdated as the streetcar.

I quoted this example just to show how ridiculous it can be to try to make predictions, and especially when one is an enthusiast, as I am about electronics and about communications. Why can't one make satisfactory predictions? It is partly because new and unforeseeable things are continually being discovered and partly because so many different things influence the widespread application of technology in our society.

Let us first note how easy it is to go astray in the application of technology even when it is not entirely new. For instance, I think that before World War I one might have prophesied a greatly improved automobile, but never the present-day use of automobiles, or present-day motor transport. The roads of that era wouldn't allow it, and I am sure that the idea of our modern networks of roads would have seemed completely fantastic in those days. Rather, had one tried to predict the future of transportation, he might have looked toward major advances in a field that has proved almost static, that of railroads, or to improvements in streetcars, which actually have almost disappeared.

New inventions, too, make the calling of the prophet a dubious one. Before or even well after the invention of the airplane, it would have seemed rash to look forward to a day (the present) when more passengers would cross the Atlantic by air than by sea. The telegraph is no longer our chief resource for fast, sure public communication; it has been largely displaced by a later invention, the telephone. Yet, the mails persist in the face of telegraphy, telephony, and facsimile transmission, although they are perhaps used largely as a cheap advertising medium. Can we foresee a future when the physical transportation of printed or written information will wither to negligible proportions? I suppose this might come to pass, but the answer to the question is that we really cannot foresee anything.

Finally, there are, besides inventions in the sense of the telephone and the airplane, fundamental discoveries about the physical constitution of the universe which shape our life in ways that cannot possibly be foreseen. The example which is in everyone's mind is, of course, atomic energy. This is truly something new under the sun. In a few short years we passed from being a powerful but almost invulnerable nation to being a powerful but extremely vulnerable nation. Some of us are beginning to understand this, and prophets of atomic doom are assailing our general complacency.

The atom bomb and the hydrogen bomb have competition, however. In a world devastated by nuclear energy, nuclear physics would have proved to be the most important technical feature of the age. Suppose, though, that nuclear war does not come? Some other sort of scientific advance might then dominate the world. Solid-state physics is ready with a host of devices, such as transistors and magnetic cores, which promise to make all sorts of electronic control, computation, and communication far cheaper and more widespread than they are now. It has even furnished us with the solar battery, and sun power might well prove more important than nuclear power in a peacetime economy. Or will new medical and biological discoveries be the dominant feature of the coming age? Will the extermination of pests, the conquest of regional diseases, the cheap production of new foods be the chiefest features of the age to come?

We may as well make up our minds that we cannot answer questions such as these. We can be ready to expect change, we can try to influence it rationally as it comes, and we can learn to accept it as we sense what the change is to be. It may be possible in some primitive societies to equip a child with rules for all the social situations he will have to cope with during his life, but the idea is ridiculous in our society. A man's profession or trade may completely vanish during his lifetime. The things that do not disappear change radically. Imagine trying to run a typical 1915 business enterprise in 1955! A 1915 scientific or engineering education would be equally out of place in a 1955 university. Further, where we are going from here no one can know. What is clear is that we must learn to put up with it.

The earlier chapters of this book have presented an orderly picture of the electronic art. This is not an untrue picture, but it is an incomplete picture. It is a picture showing the broad features of the known electronic art. What has been said will not change or become untrue when we learn more, but it will be added to, and to the man of the future it will look different. In this sense, science is something like geography. Spain did not vanish when America was discovered. Physically, it is still the same size. Yet, to a man of today it *looks* smaller than it did in the time of Columbus.

I am continually amazed in my own technical life to see how things change from year to year, both by the addition of new knowledge and by our re-evaluation of the old in the light of the new. Every now and then I get in a fuddy-duddy frame of mind and begin to believe that a field is closed, fully understood and evaluated. Promptly I find that I was all wrong. A few days before I wrote these particular words my ideas about the production and use of electron beams were upset when an ingenious experimenter in another laboratory discovered that a simple hollow beam focused by a magnetic field can be unstable and break up into a series of strands.

This is an example of the unexpected in a comparatively well-explored and well-cultivated field. Even more unexpected and exciting things happen as new fields are opened up. Now that we have had the transistor, magnetic cores, ferroelectronics, and the solar battery from solid-state physics, molecular physics promises to do its share in revolutionizing electronics. The electrical resonance of the ammonia molecule will surely give us the most accurate time standard in the world. Moreover, in the work of Townes and Gordon it promises to go beyond that and provide a microwave amplifier which will add virtually no noise to the signal. Beyond this, who can tell what physics will add to electronics, or from what part of physics the addition will come?

I have tried to make it clear that it is unsafe to trust any prophecies concerning the future of electronics other than the general prophecy of change. I hope I have made it clear that I feel in no position to tell anyone what will happen in the future. Yet, I am sure that some would still like to hear something about various matters that are frequently discussed, and, with a sure feeling that there is much wrong about what I say, I propose to discuss some of these.

In looking toward the future of communications we must take into account certain very fundamental matters which have been explored in this book. One of these is that of band width and frequency. Past experience has shown a continually increasing use of electrical communication and a continual increase in the band width required. We have gone from telegraphy, which requires a band width of a few tens of cycles per second, to voice communication, which requires a few thousands of cycles band width, and on to television, which requires a few million cycles.

In transmitting an increasing number of signals with increasing band widths we have gone to higher and higher frequencies. Starting with telegraph-frequency and voice-frequency signals, in wire transmission we have gone on to open-wire and cable-carrier systems which use frequencies of tens of thousands of cycles and to coaxial cable systems which use frequencies of millions of cycles. In radio, we went from long-wave radio at frequencies of tens of kilocycles on to short-wave radio at frequencies of tens of megacycles. We now have microwave radio relay at around 4,000 megacycles, and we shall soon be using frequencies of 6,000 and 11,000 megacycles.

This is by no means the end. Workers are already busily exploring the possibility of sending television and telephone signals across the country in 2-inch pipes, using frequencies around 50,000 megacycles. Who knows where the limit will be? What we can be sure of is that men will go on trying to find frequency space to provide for an ever-expanding communication art. Part of their effort will go into using broader bands of frequencies, and into using higher frequencies in order to attain these broader bands.

There is, however, another and quite different force at work in electronics. One way to get more communication is to make many similar communication links, to use many pairs of wires, for instance, but to do this more cheaply through the use of new components. The newest and most promising components come to us from solid-state physics. With quantum mechanics there has come an understanding of the behavior of solids which has led to a number of tiny gadgets, gadgets which perform functions important in communication. Formerly, these functions could be carried out only by vacuum tubes or relays, which are much bulkier and more expensive, and which use up more power.

The most publicized solid-state gadget is the transistor. The transistor can act as an amplifier, at small or moderate power levels, up to frequencies of hundreds of megacycles. The chief advantages of the transistor are its small size and the fact that it requires very little power to operate. In a portable radio, for instance, the batteries are smaller and they last longer.

Some people expected the transistor to replace almost all vacuum tubes overnight. Actually, there is not much point in putting transistors in devices designed to make use of vacuum tubes. In some ways, the performance of vacuum tubes is better than that of transistors. In some devices power drain may be of secondary importance, and in these cases it may be better to use vacuum tubes. The transistor is not just a replacement for or a substitute for vacuum tubes. It is a new beast. It will bring change rather than mere improvement. It will make new sorts of things possible, and among them, things of the nature of Dick Tracy's wrist radio, for instance.

Less publicized than transistors are *ferrite cores*, little circles of a magnetic ceramic called a *ferrite*. Since we have not considered digital operations, it would be hard to explain the importance of these devices. We can only say that they are useful in computing operations. They provide very cheap, compact, reliable means for carrying out operations that deal with on-off pulses such as we use in representing numbers or letters in electronic devices. Ferroelectric materials offer similar possibilities.

Quartz and barium-titanate delay lines can be used in computing machines and other devices, to remember sequences of pulses for short times, or for long times if the pulses are amplified and sent through the lines again and again.

In addition to these solid-state components, we have or may expect other important components and techniques from the art now in progress: special-purpose vacuum tubes, flat and small picture tubes for television, and improved magnetic recording for TV and sound. Other possible advances in components and techniques will be mentioned as we go along.

What can we make by putting together the present electronic art with things which we may expect to have in the near future? What human needs exist, or what may human beings be made to feel that they need? Of such needs, which ones can we fill?

Among the first things we think of is more picture transmission. What about transatlantic TV, for instance? It seems unlikely that a transatlantic television channel would pay for itself, but if people believed that one would, they would surely try to provide it.

Short waves do not provide a signal of high enough quality for TV, and there is not enough band width available. Line-of-sight microwave signals cannot be used until a day when the space station or artificial satellite provides us with a repeater site which can be seen from both sides of the Atlantic. That day seems far off, especially if the cost of putting up the satellite has to be borne by TV revenues. However, if a satellite were built for some other purpose it could provide transoceanic TV as a cheap by-product. Coaxial cable at the ocean's bottom might achieve television band width in some years, but it is hard to tell whether it would be economically justifiable. Perhaps we will have millimeter wave-guides under the ocean some day, but that is surely far in the future. Radio relay along a continual chain of planes flying the Atlantic has been suggested, but this seems crude and not too satisfactory.

If we examine the globe carefully we see that we can draw a path from here to Europe which is mostly over land. To do this one goes up Labrador, across to Greenland, from Greenland to Iceland, thence to the Faroes, and on to England. The longest jump is about 500 miles, from Labrador to Greenland; by going on to Baffin Island we could cut the longest jump down to around 250 miles.

Recent work has shown that when large powers and large antennas are used, signals in the frequency range of 500 to 1,000 megacycles can be transmitted far beyond the horizon, to a distance of several hundred miles. The signals are deflected or scattered by non-uniformities in the part of the earth's atmosphere which is high enough to be seen from both the transmitter and receiver. It is possible that such scatter propagation could provide a TV link to Europe along the roundabout path described above. Certainly the cost would be great.

The reader will readily conclude that I know neither when we will have transatlantic TV nor how it will be achieved. I am sure that we could get it in a few years by one of a number of means if we were willing to pay for it. Perhaps it will rather come as a matter of course during the gradual improvement of transatlantic communication. The construction of the first transatlantic telephone cable, which is now under way, is a step in this general direction, and it may lead to other orderly steps.

There is more to the future of television than merely sending the same programs farther and farther. In all movies and stories of the future, you see a person as you talk to him by telephone. Will our telephone of the future be equipped for picture transmission?

Why should one want picture transmission with telephony, any-way? Some would reply that they want to see the party at the other end. This is probably a better argument than to say that they want to see how well Dad is, or whether that man from the Ajax Company is telling the truth. Maybe people will want to see others enough to bring about picture transmission with tele-phone, and to pay what it costs.

There are other reasons for picture transmission, of course. Remember trying to give directions for going to some place by phone? How much easier it would have been if you could have drawn a map! Engineers have difficulties in explaining matters to one another, and editors and advertising men must have trouble, too. Perhaps there is, or could be, a real need for pictures to go with telephones. What stands in the way?

Right now you could, if you wished, rent a TV circuit for your own use. However, the band width required for TV is about 1,000 times that for telephone. While the cost might not be greater by quite this factor, it would be so large that you would be disinclined to pay for it. Too, even if you paid for the circuit it would not connect you to a large body of subscribers, as your telephone does.

The present cost of television transmission gives an unduly dis-couraging impression, for we may expect television transmission to get cheaper as time goes on. In the field of local transmission, the Bell Laboratories have demonstrated a transistor amplifier .15 inches in diameter and 1.5 inches long which goes with a coaxial cable only a tenth of an inch in diameter. Too, for long-distance transmission, engineers are working toward wave-guide transmis-sion of broad-band signals through a 2-inch copper pipe. Among various attacks, some or several are bound to prove better than what we have now.

The cost of TV transmission may go down, but it seems that such broad-band transmission will still be much more costly than voice transmission. Does this necessarily rule out the possibility of picture transmission in connection with telephony? Not at all!

In the first place, it may be that a picture of less resolution than a commercial TV picture would be satisfactory to a telephone user. Ideally, a commercial TV picture is made up of about 250,000 picture elements. However, a 1-inch-by-1¼-inch cut of a man's head in a newspaper has only about 2,500 picture elements. Perhaps this is too rough a likeness, but something in between might do. It may be possible to cut down the band width required in other ways. Perhaps picture transmission with telephony will become fairly common in our day. Or perhaps it will not!

In the meantime, there is a growing use of TV for other purposes than the broadcasting of programs. A New York bank has already made use of a private TV system in letting one centrally located set of records serve all its branches. Manufacturers and distributors have made considerable use of TV in introducing new products and new models. To do this, they gather audiences of salesmen in theaters or other halls which are equipped with large-screen television and at one time explain and show the product to men in many parts of the country.

Further, doctors have experimented with color TV, not only for viewing surgical operations, but for examining diseased tissues under a microscope. It is possible that in the future busy specialists will not have to travel hundreds or thousands of miles to see patients and render their opinions.

I believe that something of this sort may be the first new widespread use of TV. Every day, busy men shuttle here and there by plane and train to attend conferences. How inefficient this is! People have tried to hold conferences by phone, but that is very confusing. Often one can't identify the speakers, and one can't show charts or documents. It may be that in the near future someone will work out a conference TV system which will obviate a great deal of travel.

So much for pictures. What about other matters? One which naturally comes to mind is portable telephones. At present, in some cities you can have a telephone in your car, although the charge is a good deal higher than that for a phone in your home.

There are two important aspects to mobile telephony. The technical problem is perhaps the minor one of the two. It may well be that transistors and new techniques will give us a mobile telephone service which is substantially cheaper than that which we have now. It might conceivably be cheap enough to be attractive to a large group of automobile owners. However, this in itself would not mean that you could have a telephone in your car. For the problem of mobile telephony is only partly a technical problem. It is also a problem of the use of the radio spectrum.

At present, the total band width assigned for mobile telephone service, including marine and highway service as well as urban service, is about 1.4 megacycles, which is only about a quarter of one TV channel. This reflects the disposition which the American people, acting through the Federal Communications Commission, have made of the radio spectrum. To put a phone in each car, or in a large fraction of cars, would take a much broader band of frequencies, perhaps equal to many TV channels. This band of frequencies would have to be withdrawn from various military services, or from TV itself. Perhaps we want many TV channels more than we want telephones in our cars.

What about telephones in our pockets? This isn't completely unreasonable, though it would require a lot of technical advances as well as new assignments of frequencies. However, in some cities you can get something that goes part way. That is a paging service. You can rent a little box which is just a tiny radio receiver. If you listen to it, you hear a string of telephone numbers read off. If you hear your own, you go to the nearest phone and call in for the message.

This is a crude paging service, considering the possibilities offered by modern electronics. In fact, the Bell Telephone Company of Pennsylvania has scheduled for trial in the Allentown-Bethlehem area a much more sophisticated paging device. This is a pocket-size radio receiver which emits an audible tone when and only when a particular subscriber from among as many as 3,000 is signaled. The subscriber can then call his office or the number of some assigned operator.

If we are optimists, we can believe that in the future, when techniques have been pushed a little beyond those presently available, we may each have a gadget which will buzz when a distinct radio signal, one among millions, is sent out. Perhaps some sort of automatic machinery at the telephone office may handle the whole matter of paging us when we don't answer our phone. Who knows? I for one do not.

Picture transmission and mobile and personal telephony or signaling offer fascinating possibilities of future development. So does another field which might easily be overlooked by an outsider. That is the field of communication between machines and between men and machines.

While Bell Laboratories' *Audrey* shows that a machine can under favorable circumstances recognize spoken numbers, even a complicated machine does this only fallibly. For a machine, the recognition of spoken words is a difficult trick. The natural language of machines is a digital one; it consists of pulses or absences of pulses rather than spoken words or written letters. The pulses may represent numbers, or words, or even sounds or pictures, but the machine deals with the pulses themselves. It is even very difficult for a machine to read ordinary printed or typed words, although less difficult than for a machine to recognize spoken words.

The natural mode of communication with or between machines is by means of pulsed electrical signals. Pulses may be transmitted from point to point, or they may be recorded on and reproduced from punched tapes or cards or magnetic tapes. With such signals and records machines deal efficiently and easily.

Machines are already in touch with one another within our land. This is perhaps best exemplified in automatic telephone switching, and especially in distance dialing—that is, in the automatic switching of long-distance calls. A substantial number of long-distance calls are dialed directly by the local operator. In a few communities the subscribers can dial long-distance calls. When a long-distance number is dialed, switching machinery may ask the aid of, query, and direct machines at intermediate points clear across the country in seeking free lines and establishing a talking path.

There is other communication between machines in our land. A number of companies have announced networks interconnecting computing and business machinery. Type for news magazines is set remotely by teletypewriter connections. Elaborate teletypewriter nets are used in the flight control of airlines. In such highly integrated systems, an address typed at the head of a message automatically directs it to one or many points which it should reach. Similar systems control the production of cars at assembly plants. Information from dealers goes to a central coordinating office, where Joe Jones's specification for a red car with such and such accessories becomes part of a detailed list. This list is transmitted by teletypewriter to key points at an assembly plant, and it assures that the next day, at the right time, a set of parts will converge on the assembly line and make just what Mr. Jones wants. A similar service controls the inventory of assembly plants and the shipments of parts to them so accurately that such plants can operate with only one or two days backlog of parts.

Such operations do and will increasingly involve not only the transmission of digital information, but the use of elaborate computing machinery to sort data, to collate it, to make computations concerning it. Above all, however, they involve the reduction of symbolic data such as numbers and letters to some form which can be easily recognized and processed electronically.

It may well be that any prediction about the future of electrical communication based on communication between human beings by means of spoken words or pictures will prove far afield. It may be that communication between machines will so favor the discrete symbolical signal as to bring a telegraphic type of message back into prominence. Perhaps we shall record what we have to say on punched cards or magnetic tapes rather than speak it or type it, so that we can use our messages to control directly computers or automatic factories, or so that we can use machines to sort, process, or reproduce what we have set down.

Whatever aspect of the future we consider, we will all know about it tomorrow more than the most astute can predict today. Perhaps those who are well informed in a field are better prophets than are outsiders, but there is much evidence against even this. I do feel sure that the future will be different, and I hope that it will be better. All of my experience tells me that the way to make it so is to work hard on present problems, with an eye always open for the unexpected.

Appendix

Remarks on the M.K.S. (meter-kilogram-second) system of measurement and on the equations in this book.

THE equations in this book have been written so that they hold true using M.K.S. units. In this system of units, length is measured in meters, mass in kilograms, and time in seconds. The following discussion goes a little beyond questions raised in the various chapters, but the additional material may be of interest to technically inclined readers.

1 meter = 3.281 feet; 1 foot = .3048 meters
1 kilometer = 1,000 meters
1 meter = 100 centimeters
1 centimeter = 10 millimeters
1 meter = 10^{10} Angstrom units (abbreviated A)
1 meter = 10^6 microns

All physical quantities have descriptive names called *dimensions*. A mass may be 30 kilograms. Here *kilogram* is the name or dimension associated with mass. Velocity, for instance, is measured in meters per second. When we give the magnitude of a particular velocity, v, as 100 meters per second we write

$$v = 100 \frac{\text{(meter)}}{\text{(second)}}$$

It is the practice to use the singular (*meter*) instead of the plural (*meters*) to avoid confusion in the case of more complicated quantities to be discussed later.

The kilogram is a unit of mass; that is, of quantity of matter, not of force.

1 kilogram = 2.205 pounds; 1 pound = .4536 kilograms
1 kilogram = 1,000 grams

The unit of force used in the equation

$$f = ma \quad \text{newton}$$

is the *newton*.

Gravitational attraction exerts a force on a mass. At the surface of the earth the acceleration of gravity is 9.81 meters per second per second; this is written

$$9.81 \, \frac{(\text{meter})}{(\text{second})^2}$$

$$\left(32.2 \, \frac{(\text{feet})}{(\text{second})^2} \right)$$

Thus, at the earth's surface, the force, f, of gravity acting on a mass of one kilogram is 9.81 newtons, and the acceleration of any falling mass is 9.81 meters per second per second.

Newton's law of gravitation may be written

$$f = \frac{gm_1m_2}{r^2} \quad \text{newton}$$

The gravitational constant, g, is

$$g = 6.67 \times 10^{-11} \, \frac{(\text{newton}) \, (\text{meter})^2}{(\text{kilogram})^2}$$

The M.K.S. unit of work or energy is the *joule*. A force of one newton pushing an object a distance of one meter does a work of one joule. The M.K.S. unit of power is the *watt*. When a work of one joule is done in one second, the power is one watt.

1 kilowatt = 1,000 watts
1 kilowatt = 1.34 horsepower

Electrical power, P, in watts is given by the product of the current, I, in amperes and the voltage, V, in volts.

$$P = IV \quad \text{watt}$$

When a convection current of I amperes flows for 1 second, the electric charge transferred is 1 *coulomb*. The charge, q, of an electron is

$$q = -1.602 \times 10^{-19} \quad \text{coulomb}$$

The mass, m, of an electron is

$$m = 9.11 \times 10^{-31} \quad \text{kilogram}$$

Electric field, E, is measured in volts per meter. Electric flux, ϕ, is measured in coulombs (by Gauss's law, electric flux is directly related to charge). Magnetic intensity, H, is measured in amperes per meter, and magnetic flux, ψ, is measured in *webers*. The constants, ϵ and μ, used in relating ϕ to E and ψ to H are

$$\epsilon = 8.85 \times 10^{-14} \quad \frac{\text{(coulomb)}}{\text{(volt) (meter)}^2}$$

$$\mu = 1.257 \times 10^{-6} \quad \frac{\text{(weber)}}{\text{(ampere) (meter)}}$$

As we saw in Chapter V, the velocity of light, c, is

$$c = \frac{1}{\sqrt{\mu\epsilon}} = 3 \times 10^8 \frac{\text{(meter)}}{\text{(second)}}$$

A capacitor which has a charge of Q coulombs when the voltage across it is V volts has a *capacitance*, C, measured in *farads*.

$$C = \frac{Q}{V} \quad \text{farad}$$

We see that the dimension *farad* is the same as $(coulomb)/(volt)$. The inductance of a coil is measured in henries. The dimension *henry* is the same as $(weber)/(meter)$.

Boltzmann's constant, used in Chapter IX in connection with Johnson noise, is

$$k = 1.380 \times 10^{-23} \frac{\text{(joule)}}{\text{(degree)}}$$

INDEX